Restoring America's Wildlife
1937-1987

The First 50 Years of the
Federal Aid in Wildlife Restoration (Pittman-Robertson) Act

Prepared in Cooperation With
The Wildlife Agencies of the States and Territories

Editorial and Production:
Harmon Kallman, Chief Editor
C. Phillip Agee, Associate Editor
W. Reid Goforth, Assistant Editor
J. P. Linduska, Assistant Editor
Steven R. Hillebrand, Art Director
Nan Rollison, Photography Editor
William J. Savannah, Printing Consultant
W. Thomas Nebel, Printing Consultant
Shirley A. Exum, Administrative Officer
Gerald Gallo, Graphic Consultant

United States Department of the Interior
Fish and Wildlife Service
1987

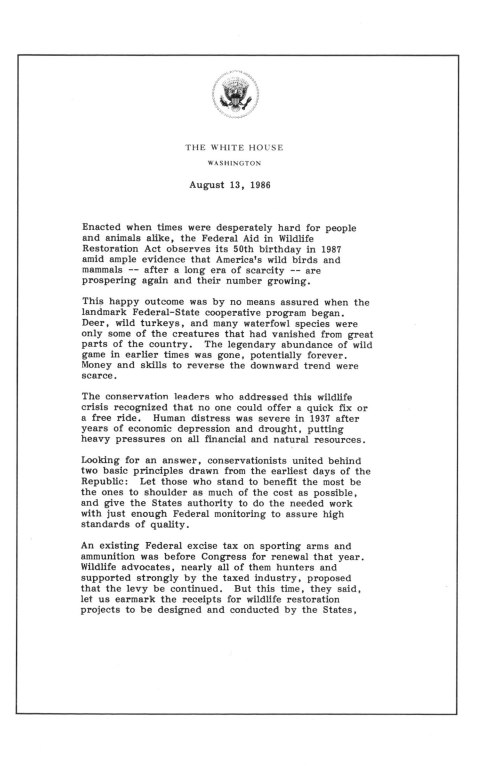

THE WHITE HOUSE

WASHINGTON

August 13, 1986

Enacted when times were desperately hard for people
and animals alike, the Federal Aid in Wildlife
Restoration Act observes its 50th birthday in 1987
amid ample evidence that America's wild birds and
mammals -- after a long era of scarcity -- are
prospering again and their number growing.

This happy outcome was by no means assured when the
landmark Federal-State cooperative program began.
Deer, wild turkeys, and many waterfowl species were
only some of the creatures that had vanished from great
parts of the country. The legendary abundance of wild
game in earlier times was gone, potentially forever.
Money and skills to reverse the downward trend were
scarce.

The conservation leaders who addressed this wildlife
crisis recognized that no one could offer a quick fix or
a free ride. Human distress was severe in 1937 after
years of economic depression and drought, putting
heavy pressures on all financial and natural resources.

Looking for an answer, conservationists united behind
two basic principles drawn from the earliest days of the
Republic: Let those who stand to benefit the most be
the ones to shoulder as much of the cost as possible,
and give the States authority to do the needed work
with just enough Federal monitoring to assure high
standards of quality.

An existing Federal excise tax on sporting arms and
ammunition was before Congress for renewal that year.
Wildlife advocates, nearly all of them hunters and
supported strongly by the taxed industry, proposed
that the levy be continued. But this time, they said,
let us earmark the receipts for wildlife restoration
projects to be designed and conducted by the States,

instead of turning the money back into the Treasury general fund, as in past years -- and let the States share the costs of wildlife restoration projects, using funds from their hunting license fees.

Enthusiasm was bipartisan and nationwide. Fittingly, the Act's chief sponsors were a Senator from Nevada, Key Pittman, and a Representative from Virginia, A. Willis Robertson. The Pittman-Robertson Act, as it came to be called, sped through Congress and was signed into law by President Franklin Roosevelt on September 2, 1937.

From a modest beginning, the Pittman-Robertson program has grown with the economy and the human population of our country. By now it has channeled nearly $1.7 billion in Federal excise tax receipts, augmented by some $600 million from the States, into activities to restore wildlife.

The projects include State acquisition of acreage needed to bring wildlife back, research into wildlife requirements and problems, active management of habitats, and development of scientific ways to enable wildlife and people to share our land in harmony. The program has strengthened State governments and built wildlife management into a respected profession. For the past 15 years it also has been training some 700,000 hunters annually in safety and sportsmanship, substantially lowering the hunting accident rate and promoting sound conservation ethics. It has stimulated the economy of rural communities all across the land and given healthful outdoor recreation to many millions.

But most of all, Pittman-Robertson has restored to abundance many of America's most beloved wild mammals and birds which are so much a part of our national heritage. And the beneficiaries include not only the game species but also many which are not hunted, from songbirds to bald eagles, from sea otters to prairie dogs.

All this has been accomplished without resorting to general tax revenues. Those who pay the freight are those who purchase firearms, ammunition, and in recent years, archery equipment. Millions of Americans who never have purchased bows or sporting arms have shared in the enjoyment of wildlife that has come back as a result of those special levies.

Pittman-Robertson's 50th anniversary is an ideal time to take stock of what this remarkable program has accomplished, what still needs to be done, and what the future seems to hold for our wildlife in a period of rapid change. It also is an appropriate time to salute the thousands of concerned Americans who have made substantial contributions of time and money to the success of this national effort.

These are important achievements that give all of us yet another reason to take pride in America. They demonstrate that people can respect and replenish our living resources so that those resources may endure and be shared on this blessed planet, so rich in all forms of life, with present and future generations.

Ronald Reagan

A Message from the Secretary of the Interior

There is reason to believe that an objective, nationwide poll of hunters, archers, skeet and target shooters, and other Americans who enjoy the sports of marksmanship, would disclose that many of them know a little, but not very much, about the Federal Aid in Wildlife Restoration (Pittman-Robertson) Act.

And that is ironic, because their excise tax dollars—collected from sales of firearms, ammunition, and archery equipment—have built the world's finest program of restoring wildlife populations after a long, apparently irreversible decline.

The scientific rebuilding of America's wildlife heritage has succeeded so well and so quietly that most citizens have not noticed what a dramatic change it has brought within the span of their memory.

The Pittman-Robertson program is decentralized, operated by the States and U.S. commonwealths and territories. It has done its work in silent woods and fields and waters, in research laboratories and modest offices, far from the scenes where the news of the day is made. That is probably why most of us, living in cities, towns and suburbs as we do, have not heard about the achievements of this nationwide effort.

Yet the thrills of hearing wild geese call overhead, of seeing deer step out of a trailside wood, of witnessing wild turkeys burst from a nearby thicket, are experiences nearly anybody can enjoy close to home today, thanks largely to Pittman-Robertson. Such opportunities were rare indeed for a majority of Americans in 1937, the year when conservationists of vision persuaded Congress to adopt this self-financing system. All our lives are richer for it, hunters and non-hunters alike, and Pittman-Robertson has advanced the frontiers of biological science in ways we still can hardly appreciate.

In this 50th anniversary year, the Interior Department's U.S. Fish and Wildlife Service has brought forth a report on the program's record for public officials and private citizens to consider. Experts from State and Federal agencies and the academic community have contributed enthusiastically to its preparation. They are dedicated people who know and care about America's wildlife; they have given generously of their time and labor to share their knowledge with us, recognizing the importance of public understanding. I take renewed pride in America as I reflect on this book and all that it represents. May it stimulate the attention and vigorous public discussion it so well deserves.

Donald Paul Hodel

A Message from the Director of the Fish and Wildlife Service

In a way, as a wildlife professional with long experience at the State level, I grew up together with Pittman-Robertson from enthusiastic youthfulness to seasoned maturity. Neither of us can afford to become complacent; there is still a lot to be learned, and a great deal of work to be done.

Federal Aid in Wildlife Restoration has taught us Americans many encouraging things about our country and ourselves. We know now that we have more control over our future than some people dared to believe back in 1937 when this law was passed. There is much we can do to ensure a future for our heritage of wildlife, from the way we manage the land to the way we behave as hunters or fishers or watchers. And because it is inevitable that people will influence the health and size of wildlife populations, we have a responsibility to be good managers. It is a responsibility we cannot walk away from. Nature, unassisted, will not do our job for us.

Consider what surely would have happened to many species if there had been no Pittman-Robertson Act and no science of wildlife management during these 50 years, when our country's human population almost doubled and millions of acres of habitat disappeared under intensive development. These birds and mammals were already depleted in numbers as a result of previous human abuse, indifference, and ignorance. They had no chance to recover without careful human action to restore their places to feed, rest, and breed. And habitat restoration, in turn, depended on finding out where a species thrives, and why. Therefore, a wide array of knowledge and techniques had to be developed to restore some semblance of harmony between wildlife and people.

How this knowledge was gained and how these techniques were developed, all within a few decades, is a remarkable tale. Primitive notions and methods have given way to responsible stewardship, often employing space-age technology. Almost no scientific knowledge existed about some of our most common wild species as recently as 20 or 25 years ago, but we are now on track and making up for lost time. The consistent funding provided by the Pittman-Robertson excise tax on shooting equipment and supplies has made all this possible. More knowledge and skill will be needed in the years to come, as people and wildlife continue to compete for living space. While we salute Pittman-Robertson's 50th birthday, we would be wise to reflect that the work begun so well in 1937 is not finished and never will be.

Frank Dunkle

Acknowledgments

The editors wish to express special thanks to the following:

Remington Arms, a division of the Dupont Corporation, for its calendar illustrations.

Artist **Tom Beecham,** who painted and sketched the illustrations, and who gave us his encouragement and highly useful advice.

Calendar Promotions, Inc., whose personnel cheerfully helped us to obtain reproducibles of the Remington/Beecham artwork, and released them specifically for use in this book.

The **J.N. "Ding" Darling Foundation,** for granting permission to reprint the cartoons reproduced in this book, and for special efforts by Trustee **Jeanette M. Redman.**

J. R. Fielding and Phil Million, U.S. Fish and Wildlife Service, for perceiving the need for this book and working tirelessly to make it a reality.

Warren C. Wilcox, U.S. Fish and Wildlife Service, and the good people of the **National Wild Turkey Federation, Inc.,** for exceptional assistance in the preparation of maps used herein.

The **Wildlife Management Institute,** for many contributions, courtesies, and helpful acts beginning with the book's earliest planning on through to completion.

Each State and Territorial wildlife agency, for contributions of photographs and text, and for consistent moral support throughout.

Reviewers

The following wildlife professionals generously donated their time and effort to technical review of chapters in this book:

Evolution of a Landmark Law, John S. Gottschalk, Karl F. Stutzman

How P-R Works, Donald V. Friberg, George F. Pushee

Success Story: Wild Turkey, Lovett E. Williams, Jr., James E. Miller

Success Story: White-tailed Deer, Wayne R. Porath, Gerald L. Storm

Substituting Facts for Myths, Thomas S. Baskett, George V. Burger

Restoring a Land Base, George F. Pushee, Dale N. Martin

Managing Habitats, Dale N. Martin, Thomas R. Williams

Wood Duck/Coastal Plain, Frank C. Bellrose, John P. Rogers

Black Bear/Eastern Highlands, Gary L. Alt, Michael R. Pelton

Prairie-Chicken/Midwest, Kenneth F. Higgins, Arnold D. Kruse

Pronghorn/Great Plains, Bart W. O'Gara, James D. Yoakum

Elk/Rocky Mountains, James M. Peek, Alan G. Christensen

Desert Bighorn/Intermountain Plateaus, Steve Gallizioli, Lanny O. Wilson

Caribou/Alaska, William H. Martin, Raymond D. Cameron

Wildlife Benefits and Economic Values, John Charbonneau, Michael J. Hay, Robert K. Davis

Restoring Nongame Wildlife, James L. Ruos, Gary Taylor, Marshall Howe

The Challenge of Islands, J. Michael Scott, Robert J. Shallenberger

P-R and Professionalism, Theodore A. Bookhout, Jack H. Berryman

Mule Deer, James M. Peek, Paul R. Krausman

Giant Canada Goose, Arthur Hawkins, Harvey Nelson

Beaver, Robert S. Cook, James E. Miller

Bobcat, James D. Yoakum, Marshall White, S. Douglas Miller

Sea Otter, Karl B. Schneider

Bobwhite Quail, Daniel Q. Thompson, Sydney Johnson

Ring-necked Pheasant, Raymond L. Linder, Richard H. Bishop

Chukar Partridge, Harold Harper, Robert J. Fischer

Gray and Fox Squirrels, Charles M. Nixon, Donald M. Christisen

Wildlife Tomorrow, Durward L. Allen

For sale by the Superintendent of Documents
U.S. Government Printing Office
Washington, D.C. 20402

Library of Congress Catalog Card Number:
86–600–588

Table of Contents

The game warden and the game preserve represented the state of the art in wildlife management during the early decades of this century. Professional wildlife biologists entered the scene significantly only after Pittman-Robertson Act became law.

Evolution of a Landmark Law

by Lonnie L. Williamson

There was a lot of wildlife in America when the first European settlers came. Reports from that era depict an Atlantic coastline replete with shorebirds, falcons, waterfowl and such. The eastern deciduous forests were alive with white-tailed deer, wood bison, wild turkey, black bear, ruffed grouse, passenger pigeon, cougar, timber wolf and other animals.

To the west, grasslands held huge herds of bison, elk, pronghorn and mule deer. There were prairie-chickens, plovers, eagles, ferrets, waterfowl and more sharing the endless vistas of waving natural grasses dotted with water-filled potholes scoured by glaciers of long ago.

Farther west, the Rocky Mountains and coastal ranges harbored grizzly bears, bighorn sheep, white-winged doves, mountain goats, elk, mountain lion and a host of other species. The Pacific shoreline was a world of seabirds, seals, sea otters and all the rest.

But something went wrong as civilization crept across the land. Wildlife was in the way. Much of it began to disappear with immigrating humanity, felled forests, plowed prairies, overgrazed deserts and market hunting. Wild creatures were no match for the unchecked invasion by ax, plowshare, livestock and gun.

The 20th Century arrived with wildlife flat on its back, badly in need of a lift. The wildlife conservation movement already was underway in the U.S. by 1900, but it was woefully inadequate. The Bureau of Biological Survey was operating in the Agriculture Department, but that agency, which would later become the U.S. Fish and Wildlife Service in the Interior Department, was concerned primarily with wildlife's relationships to agriculture. Several groups such as the Boone and Crockett Club were at work, and many local game-protection societies had been established. However, wildlife's problems were bigger than them all. Yet these dedicated few managed to get the country's first Federal wildlife law enacted. The Lacey Act of 1900 made it a Federal offense to transport wildlife across state lines if the animals were taken in violation of State law.

Dire predictions about the future of America's wildlife were common in those days. Conservationist Madison Grant wrote in 1904: "It may be confidently asserted that twenty-five years hence, the rinderpest (a viral disease) and repeating rifle will have destroyed most, if not all the larger African fauna . . . and game in India and North America in a wild state will almost have ceased to exist." Ernest Thompson Seton reported in 1909 that ". . . all the 'old-timers' agreed that there are no Antelope in the country now." Preservationist William T. Hornaday predicted an early demise for game species, saying: "It seems as if all the killable game of North America, except rabbits, is now being crushed to death between

Mr. Williamson is Secretary of the Wildlife Management Institute and Editor-at-Large for Outdoor Life Magazine. The Institute, created in 1911 by the sporting arms and ammunition industry, has been a leader in establishing and improving the Federal Aid in Wildlife Restoration program.

1

the upper millstone of industries and trade, and the conglomerate lower mill-stone made up by the killers of wildlife."

Indeed, wildlife's future may not have been bright back then, but State, Federal and privately funded conservationists decided to have a go at some solutions anyway.

New organizations appeared to join the fight. Predecessors to today's National Audubon Society, Wildlife Management Institute and Izaak Walton League were organized. State wildlife agencies were formed. The conservation movement gathered steam and things began to happen.

State wildlife laws were codified in many States. The 1913 Weeks-McLean Act, which placed migratory birds under Federal custody, was enacted. The Migratory Bird Treaty with Great Britain (for Canada) was signed in 1916, and the Migratory Bird Treaty Act in 1918. These major mileposts were followed by eight years of struggle that resulted in the Migratory Bird Conservation Act of 1929, which authorized the National Wildlife Refuge System. Wildlife began doing better. Then came a relapse.

The Dirty Thirties

Drought, panic and poverty spread across much of America as the 1930s arrived. Bone-dry winds and economic depression combined to break institutions, families and spirits. The dust storms and unemployment whipped wildlife habitat destruction and poaching to a peak. People were hungry, ammunition was inexpensive, and game provided high-quality protein. Waterfowl hit all-time lows. Other wildlife populations began to falter also. Gains that had been made in wildlife restoration since the century's turn began to erode. Wildlife conservation leaders were very concerned.

Aldo Leopold, pushing for adoption of an American game policy in 1930, warned: "The game stock, for one thing is losing by delay. We are still losing stock, range, and even species." The U.S. Senate Special Committee on Conservation of Wildlife Resources warned a year later about "convincing and undisputed evidence of a rapid disappearance of wild life," and "a corresponding increase in the number of hunters and fishermen amounting to 400 per cent in the last decade." The committee called for more and better wildlife management and research.

Dr. T. Gilbert Pearson, National Association of Audubon Societies, lamented: "Wild water-fowl in this country have recently passed through two very adverse breeding seasons and their numbers are less today then during the life time of any one present. Drainage has taken from them at least one hundred million acres of lake, pond and marshland, thus reducing their breeding and feeding ranges. Hunters increase every year. More wardens are needed to prevent illegal shooting which is rampant in many sections. Sanctuary areas for wild-fowl are pitifully small when compared with the vast needs that exist. Where is the necessary money to come from to correct this situation?"

Fortunately for wildlife, the nation's "conservation elite" was prominent in the 1930's. That distinguished corps were sportsmen, but they were not the average. They were leaders of business, industry and science. Most were well-off financially. Early on, the group had included Theodore Roosevelt, George Bird Grinnell, Charles Sheldon, John Burnham and others. During the 1930's, the likes of J. N. Darling, M. Hartley Dodge, Charles Horn, Carl Shoemaker, Aldo Leopold, Thomas Beck, Ira Gabrielson and Fredrick Walcott were members of conservation's special forces. They were good at their work, but also, they arrived on the scene when the Federal Government was in a most innovative

ANY OLD DUCK SLOUGH 25 YEARS AGO

THE SAME PLACE TODAY

Why It Seems About Time To Begin Talk Of Conservation

"Ding" Darling—cartoonist, hunter, and conservationist—mobilized public opinion for wildlife measures with dozens of visual essays like this, published in 1930. Note how he conveyed his environmental message by sketching in smokestacks and degraded marsh habitat.

mood and devising programs to beat the Depression. Consequently, they took advantage of the situation and helped foster the most fruitful decade of wildlife conservation ever.

In quick order, these conservation leaders and others spawned enactment of the Duck Stamp and Fish and Wildlife Coordination Acts in 1934, established the Cooperative Wildlife Research Unit Program in 1935, organized the first North American Wildlife and Natural Resources Conference in 1936, created the National Wildlife Federation that same year, and pushed the Federal Aid in Wildlife Restoration program to passage in 1937.

Pittman-Robertson

All of these accomplishments were significant, but one stands out from the rest. The Federal Aid in Wildlife Restoration program, or Pittman-Robertson (P-R) program, as it is called in honor of its legislative sponsors, has proven to be the single most productive wildlife undertaking on record. It has meant more for wildlife in more ways than any other effort. And it is a story of how cooperation gets things done, how States, the Federal Government, private conservation groups, and the sporting arms and ammunition industry joined hands to give Uncle Sam the best wildlife management scheme in the world.

The P-R program might be described as the blue-collar worker among Federal wildlife laws. It is not flashy like the Duck Stamp program, nor highfalutin like the Migratory Bird Treaties. It is apart from front-office politics, and out in the hinterlands building new homes for wildlife, educating hunters and constructing public shooting ranges. More than any other, it is a statute constantly producing tangible results.

Under the P-R banner, States have purchased nearly 4 million acres of critical habitat, and annually manage more than 50 million additional acres for wildlife. Most of the voluminous wildlife research that States have produced during the past 50 years was financed by P-R funds. Also, about 700,000 hunters are trained with P-R money each year. And numerous shooting ranges have been built under the program, providing safe facilities for hunter training and public use.

The results of all this are more wildlife for everyone, lower hunting accident rates, better-behaved hunters in the field and more well-run shooting ranges for public enjoyment. Not a bad yield to say the least.

An Idea Whose Time Had Come

The P-R program is rather straightforward, an idea that had to materialize. It is funded by an 11-percent manufacturers' excise tax on sporting rifles, shotguns, ammunition, and archery equipment used in hunting, and by a 10-percent manufacturers' excise tax on handguns. In fiscal year 1985, those tax receipts amounted to more than $120 million.

The U.S. Treasury Department collects the taxes and transfers the money to the U.S. Fish and Wildlife Service. Up to 8 percent of the funds may be retained by the Service for administrative expenses and the remainder is apportioned to State wildlife agencies. For each $3 of P-R funds received, the States add at least $1 of State money, making the program even stronger. Since its birth in 1937, the P-R program has pumped over $2 billion into building a future for the Nation's wildlife and its recreational use.

The first suggestion that excise taxes on guns and ammo might be good sources of financing for wildlife conservation appeared in the 1920's. At that time, Americans increasingly were flocking to sport hunting and other outdoor leisure activities. Victory in World War I and the subsequent economic boom had brought on good times. Industries, businesses and farms were humming. Work weeks were shorter, leisure time was longer. Workers fled to fields and forests each fall in pursuit of more happiness. There were an estimated 6 million licensed hunters in 1920, at least double the number of a decade earlier.

America's human population expanded rapidly during the 1920's, also contributing to the rise in hunter numbers. Birthrates mimicked the stock market and soared. Immigrants from Europe and elsewhere flowed through ports-of-entry like bathtub gin from a fruit jar. That double-barreled shot of people boosted the population to compete with wages for record growth. The time indeed was joyful, like an all-night dance. But farsighted conservationists knew that morning would come, and wildlife would have to pay the fiddler. As the Twenties roared, State and Federal wildlife administrators got their first visions of the big problem ahead. Habitat loss caused by population growth and economic development was recognized as the greatest threat to wildlife.

As new factories, roads, houses, towns and large farms peppered the landscape, habitat disappeared. Wetlands were especially hard hit. What to do! Purchasing lands for Federal refuges was decided upon as a practical way to build a future for waterfowl and other wildlife.

Uncle Sam already was in the refuge business, having established the first in 1892, when President Benjamin Harrison signed an executive order creating the Afognak Forest and Fish Culture Reserve in Alaska. Then President Theodore Roosevelt entered the scene and put refuges all over the map. He created Pelican Island Reserve in 1903, and quickly followed with 50 more in 17 States and 3 territories by the end of his first term in office. There were complaints from Congress and elsewhere, yet the undaunted Roosevelt bull-moosed ahead in typical fashion, and 36 more refuges appeared during his second term. However, TR's refuges were carved from the public domain, land already owned by the Federal Government. With this "use what you already have" approach, only a few areas, such as Malheur Lake and Lower Klamath in Oregon, turned out to be prime waterfowl habitat. Most were better suited and intended for colony-nesting birds and big game mammals. In fact, the best and most-threatened waterfowl areas were private lands, lands that had to be purchased before getting refuge status.

The leading convervationists of that time reasoned that places to hunt would dwindle as habitat became scarce. They thought it prudent to include areas in the refuge system that serve both wildlife and sportsmen. John B. Burnham, president of the American Game Protective Association, wrote in 1919: "If the young men of the next generation are to enjoy from the country's wild life anything like the benefits derived by the present outdoor man, we must be the one to shoulder the burden and see that our thoughtlessness or selfishness does not allow us to squander that which we hold in trust.

"Public shooting grounds must be established for the rank and file of the gunners who cannot afford to belong to exclusive clubs. This is the duty of the State, but the sportsmen must take the initiative. . . . In many places land of little value from a commercial standpoint furnishes the best hunting territory. Why shouldn't some tracts be set aside as public recreation grounds for all times to come? . . . With the public shooting grounds must come more reserves where the birds should have absolute protection, for as the country becomes more settled, shooting would become impossible without them . . . ."

Burnham's shooting grounds/refuge proposal was inspired by Tennessee's establishment of a successful hunting area across the Mississippi River from the

Big Lake National Wildlife Refuge in Arkansas. It was not a new concept by any means. Sportsmen's groups had discussed it for years as a good way to protect rapidly disappearing wetland areas, but no one offered a means to raise funds necessary to buy the land.

Federal Hunting Stamp?

George A. Lawyer, chief U.S. game warden, had been suggesting since shortly after World War I that a Federal hunting stamp was a feasible way to raise funds for wetland acquisition. Burnham learned of Lawyer's idea and agreed. He enlisted endorsements from E.W. Nelson, chief of the Bureau of Biological Survey, Henry S. Graves, chief of the U.S. Forest Service, and Aldo Leopold for a refuge/shooting grounds/hunting stamp proposal. Bills were introduced in 1921 by Senator Harry S. New (Indiana) and Congressman Dan R. Anthony (Kansas), and a long, rather heated debate began.

The New-Anthony bill drew broad support from numerous groups including the U.S. Department of Agriculture, International Association of Game, Fish and Conservation Commissioners, Boone and Crockett Club, American Fisheries Society, American Forestry Association, American Farm Bureau, National Audubon Society, and National Federation of Women's Clubs. But after passing the Senate, it was defeated in the House by a coalition of States' rights advocates.

The bill was reintroduced in 1923 and quickly cleared the House. But this time the Senate failed to act before adjourning. It reappeared during the next Congress, but immediately ran into a little buzzsaw by the name of William T. Hornaday of the New York Zoological Society. Hornaday had become anti-hunting in his latter years and sorely mistrusted the Bureau of Biological Survey and State wildlife agencies. He preached eloquently that wildlife already was doomed because the autoloading shotgun had been perfected, and that passage of the refuge/shooting grounds/hunting stamp bill would only hasten its demise. Hornaday built a coalition of big city newspaper editors, States' rights advocates and disgruntled waterfowl hunters opposed to the Federal stamp and defeated the bill once more.

As the 70th Congress opened, the bill was introduced for a fourth time. After more divisive debate between Hornaday's faction and conservation groups, the shooting grounds and hunting stamp provisions were dropped. And in February 1929, the Migratory Bird Conservation Act became law. However, it merely provided for a refuge system to be financed by congressional appropriations. The reliable funding source in the form of a Federal hunting stamp had been lost—but it would be captured half a decade later when the Migratory Bird Hunting Stamp Act was signed creating the Duck Stamp.

In 1925, as the refuge/shooting grounds/hunting stamp battle raged, the International Association of Game, Fish and Conservation Commissioners appointed a five-man committee to find an alternative to the unpopular hunting stamp. The idea was to devise another funding scheme and turn opponents of the stamp into supporters of the bill. John B. Burnham, T. Gilbert Pearson, George Selover (Izaak Walton League), David H. Madsen (Utah Fish and Game Department), and William C. Adams (Massachusetts Division of Fish and Game) were members of that committee. They recommended that the existing 10-percent excise tax on sporting arms and ammunition be diverted from general receipts and substituted for the hunting stamp to finance the pending refuge bill. It was a first-rate suggestion. Hunters and States' rights enthusiasts who opposed the stamp would switch camps and maybe the bill would pass. But it was not to be. Before appropriate action could be taken, Congress repealed all excise taxes.

Carl Shoemaker wrote the original bill, found sponsors for it, and bird-dogged the measure through Congress in less than three months.

Depression and drought hit the U.S. full bore in 1929. President Herbert Hoover and Congress struggled to right the crippled country, and reinstated excise taxes in 1932 to help pay the bills. President Franklin Roosevelt took the helm in 1933 and a new wave of conservationists moved to Washington, D.C., and picked-up the wildlife gauntlet. Among them were Jay N. "Ding" Darling and Carl D. Shoemaker.

Enter Darling and Shoemaker

Darling, a nationally syndicated political cartoonist, was lured from Iowa by FDR to be chief of the Bureau of Biological Survey. His stint in that position was brief (March 1934-November 1935), but his contributions were lasting. Among other things, he implemented the Duck Stamp Program, fathered the Cooperative Wildlife Research Unit Program, and helped organize the 1st North American Wildlife Conference and the National Wildlife Federation, all within 20 months. Obviously, Darling is remembered for a lot of things, not the least of which are his impassioned cartoons in support of wildlife conservation. But his Wildlife Research Units would be as enduring as his art. They would furnish the grist to make P-R work—a steady supply of qualified wildlife researchers, biologists and managers, as well as management techniques.

Darling envisioned a complement of 10 research units at land-grant colleges and universities around the Nation. Each unit would be financed jointly by the Federal Government, and the State wildlife agency and school involved. He and Aldo Leopold already had created a unit at Iowa State College, and they saw the need for more to supply trained technicians for the growing wildlife conservation effort. At an April 1934 meeting at the Waldorf-Astoria Hotel in New York City, Darling convinced representatives from the DuPont Company, Hercules Powder Company, and Remington Arms Company to underwrite the Unit Program until Federal funds were available. Darling evidently made a good pitch because those same companies made annual contributions to the Unit Program for the next 50 years through the industry-sponsored Wildlife Management Institute.

Carl Shoemaker might well be dubbed "father" of the P-R program. He wrote the original bill, found sponsors in the Senate and House, and shepherded the measure through Congress in less than three months.

Shoemaker began his career as a lawyer in Ohio. Apparently tiring of that profession, he moved to Oregon in 1912 and became owner and publisher of the Roseburg Evening News. His interest in conservation matters eventually led to his 1915 appointment as head of the Oregon Fish and Game Commission. He later became director of the Fish Commission when the game and fish divisions were separated.

Shoemaker came to Washington, D.C., frequently on special legislative projects for the State and learned his way around. In 1930, he was appointed special investigator for the newly created U.S. Senate Special Committee on Conservation of Wildlife Resources. He later became permanent secretary of that committee and remained at the post until the committee was disbanded in 1947.

National Wildlife Federation

While attending to his Senate duties, Shoemaker also worked diligently with Ding Darling and the American Wildlife Institute to organize the 1st North American Wildlife Conference, held in 1936. And at that meeting, he helped create the National Wildlife Federation.

Darling resigned from the Bureau of Biological Survey and became president of the Federation. Shoemaker was named secretary of the new organization, and was the glue that held the Federation together during those early, trying years. He maintained his office in the Senate, and opened a new one at the American Wildlife Institute from which he handled Federation affairs.

The 2nd North American Wildlife Conference was held in St. Louis, Missouri, in March 1937. The year-old Federation met at that conference. Shoemaker and other participants recalled the Burnham-Pearson excise tax proposal of more than a decade earlier. So they decided on a new effort to capture the 10-percent (later increased to 11 percent) manufacturers' excise tax on sporting arms and ammunition "for allocation to the States on some equitable formula." Thus, the young Federation's first major undertaking was to promote what soon became the P-R program.

Shoemaker returned to Washington, D.C., from St. Louis, went to his Senate office and began drafting the legislation. He went through 13 drafts before feeling that the proposal was "in shape to present to all the interested people . . ." In each draft, he incorporated "cogent and convincing" suggestions of conservation leaders. The one thing that did not change, however, was Shoemaker's formula for apportioning the funds to State wildlife agencies.

Shoemaker's Solution

Being recently from Oregon, a large State with relatively few people, and then living in the East, which had many smaller States with more people, Shoemaker realized that population would not be an equitable basis for the apportionment formula. "After probing the various possibilities," he wrote years later, "I decided that the number of paid license holders would be justifiable as one of the factors in the formula. This would protect the Western States with their smaller populations while using the area of the State as the other factor would equalize the advantage that the Eastern States had because of their much larger number of paid license holders."

Conservation groups, State wildlife agencies and the Bureau of Biological Survey endorsed Shoemaker's draft bill. Shoemaker traveled to New York and met with leaders of the firearms industry at a gathering of the Sporting Arms and Ammunition Manufacturers Institute (SAAMI). After the bill was explained section by section, T. E. Doremus (DuPont), Charles L. Horn (Federal Cartridge Company), and M. Hartley Dodge and C. K. Davis (Remington Arms Company) immediately gave it their full support. However, Horn did raise one objection to the proposed language. Shoemaker had provided that 10 percent of the tax collections each year be set aside to cover the Survey's cost of administering the program. Horn thought 10 percent was too much. The SAAMI meeting adjourned without the issue being resolved. But the industry members told Shoemaker to settle the difference with Horn, and that whatever was decided would be fine with them.

A few days later, Horn called Shoemaker and requested a meeting at the industrialist's suite in Chicago's Blackstone Hotel. The meeting was set for 11 a.m., preceding an important business luncheon that Horn had to attend at noon. Shoemaker was an amateur stamp collector and knew that Horn was a renowned philatelist, so he carried along two volumes of stamps to help get the conversation flowing amicably. The men met, and Shoemaker asked Horn's opinion of the collection. To Shoemaker's surprise, Horn spent the next 55 minutes studying the albums page by page. Noting that time was running out, Shoemaker suggested that they discuss the administration percentage. Horn closed the albums and said that 10 percent was excessive. Shoemaker held out briefly. Then seeing that Horn was getting impatient about his luncheon engagement, Shoemaker suggested 8 percent as a compromise. Horn agreed readily. The 8-percent limit for administration, which remains 50 years later, was set.

In 1960, however, Shoemaker wrote that "Mr. Horn was right." The most that had ever been used to administer the P-R program, he said, was about 5 percent of the annual collections, an admirable record.

With outside support for the bill nailed down, Shoemaker began looking for sponsors to introduce the measure in Congress. His first contact was Senator Charles L. McNary (Oregon) who signed on immediately. Then Senator Key

Representative (and later Senator) A. Willis Robertson of Virginia added 29 crucial words to Carl Shoemaker's bill, based on his own experience as a member of the Commonwealth's Game Commission.

Pittman (Nevada), chairman of the special committee on wildlife, added his name, stimulating several other Senators to follow.

Shoemaker turned his attention to the House for sponsorship. He called Congressman (later Senator) A. Willis Robertson (Virginia) and invited him to lunch in the Senate Dining Room. Robertson, who was chairman of the House Select Committee on Conservation of Wildlife Resources and previously chairman of the Virginia Game and Inland Fisheries Commission, accepted. At lunch, Shoemaker handed Robertson a copy of the bill to read. "I watched him nod his head as section after section passed before his eyes," Shoemaker wrote later. "When he had finished he asked me for a pencil and he interlined a very short clause in Section 1. He handed it back to me and I read what he had written between the lines. It was the most important addition that had been made by anyone. He said, 'With this amendment I have inserted I will gladly introduce the bill in the House.' What he had inserted made the bill foolproof. States could not tamper with or divert their own game protection funds and receive the Federal aid provided in the bill. What he wrote followed the enacting clause and read, '... and which shall include a prohibition against the diversion of license fees paid by hunters for any other purpose than the administration of said State fish and game department ...'"

Robertson's 29 Words

Robertson's experience on the Virginia Game and Inland Fisheries Commission had taught him that State legislatures were not above taking license receipts from wildlife agencies and using them for other State programs. It was a common occurrence in those days. But Robertson put a stop to it with 29 words from his pen. And those words have meant many millions of dollars for wildlife conservation over the past half century.

On June 20, 1937, Senator Pittman introduced Shoemaker's final draft in the Senate. Several days later, Congressman Robertson dropped an identical bill in the House hopper. The legislation proceeded through Congress with amazing dispatch. Without fanfare or even hearings, Pittman reported the bill out of his committee on July 7, shortly after Shoemaker had finished writing the committee report. It passed the Senate without delay and was sent to the House.

Rules in the U.S. House of Representatives at that time required that all bills dealing with Agriculture Department agencies, such as the Bureau of Biological Survey, be handled by the Agriculture Committee. Thus Robertson's Wildlife Committee did not have jurisdiction over the measure. Fortunately, responsibility for guiding the bill through committee fell to Congressman Scott Lucas (Illinois), an ardent duck hunter. But Lucas reportedly did not push the bill aggressively. So Shoemaker sent telegrams to all the garden clubs and women's groups in Illinois, urging them to contact Lucas on the matter. A few days later, Shoemaker happened to meet Lucas in the hall outside the Congressman's office. Shoemaker wrote of the meeting: "He (Lucas) threw up his hands and exclaimed: 'For God's sake, Carl, take the women off my back and I'll report the bill at once.'"

P-R Becomes Law

The bill was reported to the House and passed on August 17. It was sent back to the Senate for its concurrence with some technical amendments, and then forwarded to the White House. President Roosevelt signed the P-R Act on September 2, 1937.

Within 12 months, 43 of the 48 States had enacted laws prohibiting use of hunting-license revenues for any purpose other than to operate the wildlife agency. The other 5 States did likewise in time, and all States then were eligible to receive P-R funds.

Ira N. Gabrielson, Ding Darling's hand-picked successor, was chief of the Bureau of Biological Survey when the P-R Act became law. A vocal supporter of the P-R program, Gabrielson put his able assistant, Albert M. Day, in charge of implementing the new Federal Aid Act. Day immediately began meeting with groups of State wildlife agency directors to get their views on how the program should be implemented. He traveled to Albuquerque, New Mexico, Portland, Oregon, Pocatello, Idaho, Pierre, South Dakota, Boston, Massachusetts, Baltimore, Maryland, Jacksonville, Florida, and Omaha, Nebraska to discuss proposed policies and rules with State representatives.

When the International Association of Game, Fish and Conservation Commissioners held its 32nd convention on June 20 and 21, 1938, in Asheville,

North Carolina, Day announced three types of State projects that would be approved for Federal assistance under the P-R program: "1. The purchase of land for wildlife-rehabilitation purposes. 2. The development of land to make it more suitable for wild mammals and birds . . . 3. Research projects set up on a definite basis and directed to the solution of problems that stand in the way of wildlife restoration."

"Trained and Competent"

Gabrielson and Day, as well as many of the State program directors, recognized that the P-R Act regulations offered an excellent opportunity to strengthen State programs. Thus an important policy was added, which requires that management personnel hired by a State with P-R funds be trained and competent to perform their duties. That policy lifted State wildlife programs out of the political-appointee quagmire, allowing them to become respected, professionally-run operations. Perhaps more than anything else, it is responsible for the vast improvement in State wildlife agencies over the past 50 years.

Getting the new P-R program functioning as intended was no easy task. The arms and ammunition tax receipts were running about $3 million per year, but Congress refused to appropriate the full sum. The program received only $1 million in 1938, the first year of operation, and just $1.5 million the following year. Complicating the situation further, Congress decided again to repeal excise taxes. And they were eliminated—except the one on sporting arms and ammunition. Carl Shoemaker put together a coalition of conservation organizations, State agencies and arms manufacturers to keep that tax in force.

The rapid hiring and firing of State wildlife agency directors created additional problems for the young program. Al Day, who had become the first chief of the Federal Aid Division, reported in June 1939: "One of the chief difficulties we have encountered and one of the most discouraging things in the administration of the wildlife resources of this country has been the large turn-over in the administrative officers of the various State game departments. As a result of recent changes there are new administrators handling the fish and game affairs in twelve States. This has meant a turn-over of 25 percent since July 1, 1938, and has naturally retarded the progress of the cooperative wildlife restoration program. It has meant back-tracking, going over the same ground with new individuals, and in some cases the new administrators have reversed plans that had already been given preliminary approval."

Obviously, Day and his colleagues had some trying times in those early years. But with cooperation from most of the States, he got the P-R program under way.

First P-R Project

The first P-R project approved and funded was in the Weber River Delta of Utah. Botulism was killing large numbers of waterfowl in the area. Utah's Department of Fish and Game developed plans for a 5-mile dike that would impound freshwater from the river, prevent intrusions of saltwater from Great Salt Lake, and thereby reduce incidence of the disease. Utah submitted its plan to the Bureau of Biological Survey, which approved the project immediately. The dike was constructed in 1938, with $7,500 in P-R money and $2,500 in State funds.

In 1939, the Bureau of Biological Survey was moved to the Interior Department, meshed with the Bureau of Fisheries from the Commerce Department and renamed the Fish and Wildlife Service.

Senator Key Pittman of Nevada obtained Senate approval of the bill without even the formality of a committee hearing.

When World War II erupted, wildlife conservation in general and the P-R program in particular sagged as young men gave up their squirrel rifles and shotguns for M-1's and machine guns. But when the Armed Forces returned from that conflict, the number of licensed hunters in the country jumped from 9.8 million to 12 million almost overnight. These additional hunters purchased sporting arms and ammunition, and the P-R fund increased accordingly.

The growing tax receipts were not helping wildlife as they should have, however, because Congress continually refused to appropriate the full amount. According to Fish and Wildlife Service records, part of the problem was solved in 1947 when the Administration began requesting that all of the receipts collected each year be transferred to P-R. Congress complied, but a $13-million backlog of previously impounded P-R funds remained. The States needed that money desperately. Along with conservation groups, they complained vehemently. Out of the side of its mouth, the Fish and Wildlife Service kept whispering, "Yell louder."

The noise finally was too much for Congress. First, language was added to the FY 1951 Appropriations Act, giving P-R funds a "permanent-indefinite" appropriation status. From then on, *all* the sporting arms and ammunition tax collections would be *automatically* transferred to the Fish and Wildlife Service and apportioned to the States. Thus, neither the Administration nor Congress could hold P-R funds hostage without enacting an appropriations bill permitting it. This cleared the way for future tax collections. Then, Congressmen Lee Metcalf (Montana), Clifton Young (Nevada), Homer Angell (Oregon) and Melvin Price (Illinois) introduced bills in 1954 to force release of the $13 million in impounded P-R funds. A bill was enacted in 1955, and Interior Secretary Fred A. Seaton released the money in June 1956. A problem that had haunted the program from its inception was resolved.

P-R experienced numerous other inconveniences in its early years. In 1950, for example, legislation was introduced to repeal again the excise tax on arms and ammunition. Its enactment, of course, would have killed the P-R program. But supporters of that bill did not reckon on the opposition that ensued. Conservationists, sportsmen, State wildlife agencies and sporting arms manufacturers rallied around P-R and prevented enactment of the repealer.

When the P-R program was enacted in 1937, there were 6.8 million licensed hunters in the country. By 1969, the number had increased to 15.2 million, and wildlife habitat continued to decline under increasing pressure from a burgeoning human population and the resulting land developments. State wildlife agencies were hurting for funds and needed to stretch their budgets as far as possible. A good way to do that was by expanding the P-R program.

Hunter Education

Conservation leaders also realized that more hunters in forests and fields each fall increased the risk of accidents with firearms. They also were concerned about hunter misbehavior and its effects on public attitudes toward hunting. In 1969, all 50 States offered some form of hunter education. But there was an obvious need for overall improvements in those programs. Ira N. Gabrielson had retired in 1946 as director of the Fish and Wildlife Service to become president of the Wildlife Management Institute. Under his leadership, WMI began considering ways to enhance the P-R program for wildlife *and* hunter education purposes. The idea surfaced to expand P-R by capturing the existing 10-percent manufacturers' excise tax on handguns, and levying an 11-percent tax on archery gear and components of handloaded ammunition. The handgun tax, somehow, had escaped the periodic repeals of excise taxes, and had been on the books since 1932. WMI elicited support from the arms and ammunition people for redirecting the tax on handguns and establishing the tax on ammunition components. It offered a resolution supporting the effort which had been adopted in September 1967 by the International Association of Game, Fish and Conservation Commissioners.

Several bills dealing with the hundgun, archery gear and components taxes were drafted, but went nowhere. Finally, the decision was made to go after the taxes one at a time. Consequently, Congressman John D. Dingell (Michigan) introduced a bill in 1969 that would pluck handgun tax receipts from the General Treasury and add them to P-R. Dingell was chairman of the House Subcommittee on Fisheries and Wildlife Conservation. He expertly moved the bill through committees and past the House by unanimous vote.

Senators Hugh Scott (Pennsylvania) and Philip Hart (Michigan) introduced similar legislation on the Senate side in 1970. That bill, too, was steered through the legislative process with minimum delay, and the handgun tax was signed by President Nixon in October 1970.

Archers Sign On

Even before the handgun tax amendment had cleared the House or Senate, Congressman George Goodling (Pennsylvania) introduced a bill to levy an 11-percent manufacturers' excise tax on archery equipment to bolster the P-R program further. Goodling was the ranking minority member of Dingell's subcommittee, and his bill received prompt attention. But some of the archery gear manufacturers objected to the bill and were able to stall it until Congress adjourned. Goodling reintroduced the bill in 1971, and it was reported favorably by the Dingell subcommittee within a month. However, manufacturers' coolness to the proposal kept it bottled up in the House Ways and Means Committee. But Fred Bear, president of Bear Archery, came to the rescue.

A well-known sportsman and dedicated wildlife conservationist, Bear exerted his considerable influence to lessen the archery industry's opposition to Goodling's bill. He wrote Subcommittee Chairman Dingell: "In discussions and an exchange of letters with Mr. Dan Poole of the Wildlife Management Institute, we of Bear Archery feel that our industry should contribute to the Wildlife Restoration Fund. This we would like to do on the basis of the program outlined in my letter to Mr. Poole, a copy of which I enclose."

Bear also wrote letters to all members of the Archery Manufacturers' Organization and encouraged them to support the bill. Some responded favorably, and the bill passed the House without incident.

Senator Frank Moss (Utah) introduced an identical bill in the Senate, and it proceeded smoothly and was approved. Consequently, the archery gear tax amendment was signed by President Nixon during the closing hours of the 92nd Congress in October 1972 ... thanks in great part to the involvement and foresight of Fred Bear.

The ammunition components tax was not approved by Congress. However, there still is interest on Capitol Hill in levying such a tax to expand P-R even more.

The significance of the handgun and archery equipment tax amendments to wildlife and hunting extends far beyond the additional research and management funds provided. The amendments also sparked vastly improved hunter-education programs in State wildlife agencies by authorizing up to one-half of the

Jay Norwood "Ding" Darling, one of this century's most effective conservationists.

receipts from handguns and archery gear to be used for hunter education and shooting range construction and maintenance. The other half must be used for the traditional wildlife-restoration purposes. This funding has vastly improved hunter-education efforts in most States.

Formal hunter education is a relatively recent phenomenon among State wildlife agencies. In 1946, Kentucky initiated the first statewide firearms-safety course in the Nation. The program operated through State-run youth camps. Wildlife agency involvement in hunter education began in 1949 when the New York Department of Conservation, with help from the National Rifle Association of America, devised a firearms-safety course that all 14- and 15-year-olds had to take before obtaining a hunting license. The New York initiative has since spread throughout the U.S. All 50 States now offer hunter-education courses. In 36 States, certain hunters—primarily young people—are *required* to complete education courses.

The value of P-R-enhanced hunter-education programs is clear. New York, for example, has trimmed its fatal hunting accident rate by more than 70 percent and its nonfatal accident rate by almost 50 percent through its education program that now is funded by P-R. And saving lives is not the only advantage of improved hunter education. Better hunter behavior in the field and more shooting ranges are additional rewards. The entire shooting sports fraternity benefits.

During the early 1980's, another threat to the P-R program arose. The President's Task Force on Victims of Crime issued a 1982 report which recommended that the excise tax on handguns be diverted from P-R to a Crime Victim's Assistance Fund. Legislation was introduced to that effect in 1983. It would have cut financing for P-R by about one-third. Conservationists, State wildlife agencies, and arms ammunition manufacturers objected. So did Senators Malcolm Wallop (R-Wyoming) and Ted Stevens (R-Alaska), and Congressmen John Dingell (D-Michigan) and John Breaux (D-Louisiana). The actions of these distinguished legislators proved again that the support for P-R is bipartisan and nationwide.

Senator Wallop summed up a lot of Capitol Hill feeling about P-R in the May 26, 1983 Congressional Record: "Furthermore, Mr. President, I believe we have a commitment to sportsmen and women who pay the excise taxes that for 46 years have supported wildlife conservation through the Pittman-Robertson program. They and the manufacturers whose products are taxed are strong backers of the program. Years ago in fact, when it was decided that a number of excise taxes should be eliminated, hunters and the manufacturers urged Congress to retain the taxes on sporting arms and ammunition to continue the wildlife restoration efforts which they support. How often have you encountered that situation? This unselfish support of wildlife conservation by sporting arms purchasers and manufacturers is a credit to both. To divert the special funds they provide to other purposes, no matter how noble, would betray their valuable contribution to a public resource."

The crime victims bill passed eventually. But the provision that would have removed the handgun tax from P-R was deleted beforehand.

The P-R program has grown and changed with circumstances during the past 50 years. It had to. The U.S. human population has nearly doubled since 1937. There are almost three times as many licensed hunters in the country now as then. Thus, the pressures on wildlife habitat and wildlife are much, much greater. Yet, most species of wildlife are better off now than they were in 1937.

Something has gone right with wildlife in America. And that something includes the P-R program. It must continue to be protected, expanded and refined.

16

Reprinted courtesy of the J.N. (Ding) Darling Foundation

The choices were clearly defined by "Ding" Darling in another prophetic cartoon. His hard-hitting works were syndicated nationally by Des Moines Register and Tribune and also for a time appeared in Collier's Weekly, popular national magazine.

Like any governmental process, Pittman-Robertson Act administration involves plenty of nitty-gritty at times. But the objective – pleasures like this for millions of outdoors lovers – makes it all worthwhile.

How P-R Works

by Charles K. Phenicie

About 8:45 a.m. on a Tuesday late in April a gentleman carrying a briefcase enters a State office building and proceeds to an office on the fifth floor where he is greeted by a State fish and wildlife agency employee. They chat a few minutes, while the secretary makes some interoffice calls. At 9:00 a.m. the two men go to a conference room where 10 or 12 individuals are assembling. There are handshakes, friendly words are exchanged, and all take seats around an oblong table. As our gentleman arranges papers from his briefcase, he glances around the table and greets the group, "Good morning. I'm from the Fish and Wildlife Service, and I'm here to he'p you." When the laughter subsides, the group proceeds with the business at hand. The significance of this in-house joke will be seen as we observe the meeting and consider roles of the participants.

This man is indeed from the Fish and Wildlife Service. He is a wildlife biologist from the Division of Federal Aid of one of the Service's Regional Offices. The State employee who first greeted him is the State Federal Aid Coordinator, and the others in the meeting are the Game Division Director, Game Research Chief, project leaders, and others involved in the State's Pittman-Robertson (P-R) program.

Those present at this meeting represent the backbone of P-R program administration. Since the program involves 7 Service regional offices, 50 States, and 5 Territories, no meeting, organization, arrangements, or job classifications are typical of P-R administration nationwide from the Northern Mariana Islands to the Virgin Islands or from California to Maine. Administration is as varied as are the wildlife resources and the State and Territorial governments. Nevertheless, the functions and products of this meeting are typical.

The Federal biologist is the principal Regional Office contact with the State agencies regarding wildlife research, surveys, and management matters. There are normally other Federal specialists as well who handle land acquisition, development, and hunter education matters with the States.

His regular contact person in the State is normally the Federal Aid Coordinator, who accomplishes the State administrative matters for Federal grant-in-aid programs and who provides the link with the State's wildlife managers and field personnel. The Federal Aid Coordinator normally handles P-R and D-J (Dingell-Johnson or Sport Fish Restoration) grant programs and is frequently responsible for other Federal grant programs as well.

The papers on the table are largely P-R project proposals, prepared by State project leaders, and submitted to the Service's Regional Office by the State Federal Aid Coordinator for Federal approval. The Service biologist raises many questions about the need for certain work, the design of the plan-of-work, and the use the State will make of the results obtained.

"I assume you made a thorough literature review for your new black bear proposal, Jim, under project number W-96-R, but your project application

Mr. Phenicie headed the U.S. Fish and Wildlife Service's Division of Federal Aid for 10 years before retiring in 1985. Earlier, he had administered both the Pittman-Robertson and the Dingell-Johnson (Federal Aid in Sport Fisheries Restoration) programs for seven years in two USFWS regions, and managed Dingell-Johnson for five years for the Montana Fish and Game Department.

doesn't indicate its use in the project design. How will this utilize results from Michigan's research and work going on in Kentucky?" Jim expresses surprise at the Service biologist's interest in this, and the State Coordinator apologizes for his neglecting to advise Jim to include the information in the project application. Jim's brief explanation is satisfactory to all present.

Such harmony, however, does not typically last for long. The State Game Director or Game Research Chief may themselves severely question a project leader on a matter overlooked previously, but typically voices are raised at Federal interference in presumed State affairs. For example, as the Service biologist come to project W-15-R-22, he sighs deeply and begins: "Well, here we are again back to your annual pheasant surveys. You remember my comments a year ago regarding this project. Well, I guess it's up to you to change my mind. How long have these surveys been going on now?"

"You know good and well we've done them for 21 years," snaps the Game Director, "and we'll do them for 21 more. The Commission needs this information and we have to supply it to them."

"Yes, Bill," responds the Fed, "I'm well aware of that, but we're way past the point where I can certify that this project is substantial as it is designed. There may well be some survey data you need to manage and regulate pheasants, but certainly not at the cost estimated for this project. The use and benefits are simply not here. In the last five years the Commission has set the pheasant regulations before they had your data. What I said a year ago still stands. Either you lay out your pheasant problems and design a survey project to furnish data to address those problems, or I'll have to recommend against approving the project. If your Commission really needs the data for public relations purposes, they may just have to use State dollars without Federal reimbursement."

Friendly Tension

Now don't you ever believe this matter ends here. This is a good place for us to bow out of the meeting, however. Sometimes the Feds win some and sometimes the States. In spite of heat generated, Federal-State relations remain remarkably amicable, perhaps because both parties have a common goal, to restore, maintain and enhance wildlife resources.

At the beginning of this meeting there was laughter when the Service biologist said, "I'm from the Fish and Wildlife Service and I'm here to he'p you." There are basic State/Federal conflicts and overlaps in roles which often cause problems and which make the Fed a true pain-in-the-neck. Several of these roles, however, are the basic strength of the Federal Aid in Wildlife Restoration program which has carried it through these 50 years, making it a model among Federal grant programs. Because of the P-R program's successes, its provisions were largely incorporated in the early 1950's by Congress into the Federal Aid in Sport Fish Restoration Act and were continued with the Wallop-Breaux amendment in 1984 which expanded the fisheries grant program some three-fold.

Basically, Congress passed the P-R Act to provide funds to States for wildlife restoration projects, but, in addition, it also legislated certain controls and conditions which have been carried out through the 50-year period. To these, other requirements have been added by Congress and by Presidential executive order, not applying to P-R specifically, but to all Federal grant programs collectively. Thus, to get P-R dollars, States, both willingly and reluctantly, must do certain things. To see why the Fed is considered a helpful, friendly pain-in-the-neck by many State people, a few of these things States must do to get P-R dollars are summarized under the following four headings.

Maintain Eligibility

Only State wildlife agencies of the 50 States, the Commonwealths of Puerto Rico and the Northern Mariana Islands, Guam, Virgin Islands, and American Samoa may be eligible for wildlife grants. Only the 50 States are eligible for hunter education grants. Before it can become eligible, each State or Territory must, in the words of the 1937 Act, have "assented to the provisions of this (the P-R) Act and shall have passed laws for the conservation of wildlife which shall include a prohibition against the diversion of license fees paid by hunters for any other purpose than the administration of said State fish and wildlife department." This dedication of State license fees by legislatures to fish and wildlife purposes is probably the most important and least publicized aspect of both the Wildlife and Sport Fisheries Restoration Acts.

For example, in 1984, P-R grants totaled $88,450,000, while the hunting license receipts which these grant funds ensure will be used for fish and wildlife purposes totaled $292,344,274. All States have legislation prohibiting diversion to other purposes, but every year some legislatures or other State officials consider how to circumvent this provision. It takes the combined efforts of State fish and wildlife and Service people to prevent this happening. Such Service intervention into State affairs is truly popular with fish and wildlife workers and managers.

By rules of the Secretary of the Interior, published in the *Federal Register,* three other matters can effect a State's continued eligibility to receive grants.

Whether in a city office building or deep in the woods, Federal and State wildlife people share a close, mutually supportive working relationship, thanks largely to cooperation estab-lished through Pittman-Robertson. Wildlife people who work for Federal land-managing agencies including the Forest Service are part of this community of interest.

First, if P-R funds are applied to any activity or purpose other than those approved by the Service Regional Director, such funds must be replaced or the State becomes ineligible to participate. Occasionally State/Federal conflicts result from this, but they are short lived. Second, real property (lands and permanent improvements) acquired or constructed with P-R funds must continue to serve the purpose for which it was acquired or constructed. If used for any other purpose, or if a use interferes with the approved purpose, that use must cease, or the real property must be replaced using non-Federal Aid funds. This rule has been applied often and is rigorously supported by wildlife professionals because it ensures long-term commitment of real property to wildlife purposes. Third, loss of control by the State fish and wildlife agency of capital assets acquired with license revenue, or income resulting from such assets, is treated the same as a diversion of the license revenue itself. This rule is relatively new and has not yet been invoked.

In 1981, the International Association of Fish and Wildlife Agencies canvassed each State fish and wildlife agency regarding State/Federal roles in Federal Aid in Wildlife Restoration programs. The State responses were furnished to the Service and were included in the Service report, "The Federal Aid Program and Alternative Methods of Administering It," April, 7, 1982. Eligibility determinations which are discussed above were rated "highly favorable" by the States. Not all administrative matters were treated so enthusiastically, as will be noted in the other sections.

State Responsibilities

States have a host of project and administrative responsibilities which are stipulated in various Federal laws and regulations. These are monitored by Service specialists and others as measures of program control. Only a sample of these is discussed here to provide some flavor to the heated interactions between the Service wildlife specialist and State people.

States are responsible for maintenance of all capital improvements acquired or constructed with P-R funds. Such maintenance costs are eligible for P-R reimbursement when included in an approved project. Service specialists monitor these to assure that project purposes are being accomplished. It is easy to imagine how such inspections cause heated discusions, particularly when work and funding priorities are at issue. One case involved a hunter education target range. An inspection in 1983 revealed that the range constructed with P-R funds was no longer available for use, since public access was denied. The State corrected the problem quickly.

States must maintain current and complete financial, property, and procurement records and have them available for audit. The States have demonstrated their desire to be properly accountable for funds and assets; however, they have expressed concern about the scope of audits and the numerous shifts of audit authority.

Beginning in the 1960's the audit roles and scope have been constantly moving targets. Audits previously preformed by Service auditors were shifted between two Interior Department offices, contracted to private auditing firms, and eventually assigned to the States themselves, with Interior's Office of the Inspector General having oversight authority. The audit scope has increased from grant audits to agency-wide audits, such as a State's Department of Natural Resources, testing financial systems of the entire agency. Limited audits, such as of the P-R program or a Division of Fish and Wildlife, are not accepted. The constant changes have been confusing; and, because they are readily available to

State personnel, the Service wildlife specialists have been largely burdened with the chore of explaining and justifying each change.

P-R Projects

The key to this subject is the following statement from the P-R Act: "Any State desiring to avail itself of the benefits of this Act shall, by its State fish and game department, submit programs or projects for wildlife restoration. . . ." This may be done by submitting to the Service Regional Director either "a comprehensive fish and wildlife resource management plan" for the Department or "full and detailed statements of any wildlife-restoration project proposed for the State." When the Regional Director determines that a plan or project is "substantial in character and design" (identifies objectives based on stated need; utilizes accepted principles, sound design and appropriate procedures; and is cost-effective), then he shall approve it. Only after approval may the State begin to carry out the described work, and only after State funds are expended can a State request reimbursement from P-R funds.

States may request reimbursement of up to 75 percent of eligible project costs from P-R funds with at least 25 percent being each State's share. Some States commonly elect a smaller P-R share in order to include a larger portion of the fish and wildlife department's eligible wildlife programs and people under the grant program. This indicates, with added emphasis, the favorable attitude of many State administrators to the discipline required by P-R in project selection, design, completion and reporting, and to the added protection given to assets and personnel.

The meeting described at the beginning of this chapter occurred in a State office in April. Its urgency was to assure substantial projects would be approved by the Regional Director prior to the beginning of the State's fiscal year, July 1. The wildlife specialist at the meeting was a principal Service person responsible for evaluating State P-R projects, assisting the State personnel if problems surfaced, and ultimately recommending approval or disapproval.

The P-R Act allows a considerable latitude to projects intended to benefit wildlife and users of wildlife and to provide hunter education. There are, however, some dos and don'ts which are provided to the States by the Service in the *Federal Aid Manual.* While don'ts sometimes creep inadvertently into projects, most questions normally arise over substantiality.

There is a Federal Aid axiom, "The States propose and the Feds dispose." The Federal Government has no role, unless asked to assist, in the development of State programs or projects. These are entirely State roles. The Federal role is to evaluate proposals for substantiality. Issues of substantiality are raised frequently to question the need for the activity or to clarify the intended use of the project. This can happen when a favorite idea of State commissioners or staff members is forced to fit somewhere in the program or when activities are continued beyond their productive life. The latter was the case with Bill's pheasant survey project, which has already been done for 21 years with doubtful resource benefits emerging in recent years. "Hobby research" can be another problem, but may be less common today than in the past. Problems frequently show up when ongoing projects are moved from those funded wholly by State dollars to the P-R program. These shifts often are made during State budget exercises when deadlines are short. P-R projects may result which lack clarity, or the activities being shifted may not receive close scrutiny either to justify continuance or to determine eligibility for P-R.

Compliance Requirements

When a State official signs and forwards a project proposal to the Regional Director, he certifies that his agency will comply with all applicable Federal laws, regulations, and policies. If the State agency is subsequently found in "noncompliance," any action or project that fails to meet the standards may be terminated or suspended, or the State may be declared ineligible to participate in the program.

For the first 25 years of P-R, compliance requirements were pretty much limited to those from the P-R Act or from other sources to assure fiscal integrity, general accountability, and acceptable performance. These were the good old days when P-R administration was a relatively simple affair.

Beginning largely in the 1960's, Congress, Presidents, and Federal agency heads, through laws, executive orders and regulations, began to use Federal grants as a carrot for grantees to accomplish other national goals, saying in effect, "If you want Federal dollars, you must agree to do these." Since all States are recipients of many different grants, State governments have a strong monetary incentive to comply. For this and other reasons, many States have laws and regulations which are as tough as, or tougher than, some of these Federal laws and regulations.

National social goals have thus become State P-R goals through such laws as Title VI of the Civil Rights Act of 1964, the Age Discrimination Act of 1975, and Section 504 of the Rehabilitation Act of 1973. The State fish and wildlife agencies have truly been conscientious about these. Paperwork burdens for recordkeeping and reporting are the chief complaint, particularly when similar but different records and reports must be kept for various State and Federal agencies and purposes.

There are a number of environmentally related compliance requirements which include coastal zone management, exotic organisms, endangered species, flood plains and wetlands, pesticides, and historical and cultural preservation. An important but troublesome one has been the National Environmental Policy Act (NEPA) of 1969. A lawsuit against the P-R program over NEPA compliance by an anti-hunting organization in the late 1970's dragged on for three years, causing a tremendous paper workload for both the Service and many of the States. After this was resolved, the Service provided considerable NEPA training to its own people and the States in order to lessen the likelihood of such legal action in the future.

There are more than 35 compliance requirements which relate to P-R in varying degrees. Together they constitute a sizable new workload to the States in recent years which evokes many complaints. It is not surprising, in the 1981 survey, that the States found these added administrative requirements to be "highly undesirable," since they divert money and manpower from purely wildlife purposes. Because the Service's regional Federal Aid specialist must continually help States sort out these requirements, provide them some training, monitor State compliance, and question some matters for compliance, it is easy to understand why State personnel laugh when a Federal specialist says, "I'm here to he'p you."

Concurrent with the incident in a State office building at the beginning of this chapter, other activities in P-R administration take place in Washington, D.C. These involve the Fish and Wildlife Service and its Division of Federal Aid, other elements of the executive branch of government, the Congress, and a variety of conservation organizations and special interest groups. Though we tend to

All P-R projects, like this wild turkey transplant of some years ago, must be Federally reviewed in planning stages to minimize wasted or overlapping efforts. But some States have reduced their day-to-day paperwork burden by adopting comprehensive wildlife management plans.

Chuck Post, South Dakota Wildlife, Parks and Forestry

Canoeing is only one of the many non-hunting uses of lands acquired with P-R aid. Non-hunters far outnumber hunters visiting most of these areas. Some acquisitions have been funded jointly with the Dingell-Johnson Federal Aid in Sport Fish restoration program, a companion to P-R since 1950.

belittle the bureaucratic routines of government in Washington, these are the forces of our democracy by which P-R was born, has matured, and has grown through these 50 years.

The P-R Act itself has been amended but little through the years since its passage September 2, 1937. This indicates it was soundly conceived, well administered, and effectively performed by the States and the Service. Maintenance- and management-type projects were authorized by Congress in 1946 and 1955, respectively. Five territories and the States of Alaska and Hawaii were made eligible participants at different times. Originally, States received funds by submitting projects only, but in 1970 Congress authorized submission of comprehensive plans as an alternative. The hunter safety program was also added in 1970 and was funded by excise taxes on pistols and revolvers. In 1972, an excise tax was placed on certain archery equipment for hunter safety training.

Through the 50 years of P-R, various organizations and Federal agencies have been active in the financial affairs of the program in a variety of ways. The Treasury Department, for example, collects the excise taxes on arms, ammunition, handguns, and archery equipment from the various manufacturers and importers—based upon *their* price—and places these in a wildlife restoration account. The P-R Act, as it was passed, only authorized future Congresses to appropriate money collected each year; however, on September 6, 1950, Congress enacted a permanent-indefinite appropriation for P-R which remains in force today. Essentially, this allows P-R excise tax receipts to be used without specific action by Congress each year. This helps the Service and States to plan ahead without "feast or famine" variations in funding, and without the delays which are characteristic of annual appropriations. It is a major key to the effective use of funds paid as excise taxes by sportsmen.

Predictable Funding

The permanent-indefinite appropriation is not without its detractors, since it tends to limit a Presidential administration's budget authority. However, through the years the Congress has remained firm on its action taken back in 1950.

Under the continuing budget authority there are two processes in fund allocation. One is to withhold funds for Service P-R administration, and the other is the apportionment of grant funds to the States.

For its administration of P-R, the Service may, under law, withhold up to 8 percent of the total funds. This use, per se, has remained at only around 3 to 4 percent through the years. However, for more than 30 years the States have petitioned the Service, mainly through the International Association of Fish and Wildlife Agencies, to fund also certain projects out of administrative funds on behalf of all the States and Territories. This approach is more economical than if the States performed these projects separately or collectively. Two examples are the Fish and Wildlife Reference Service, which collects and makes available published and unpublished research reports of the Service and States, and the National Survey of Fishing, Hunting and Wildlife-Associated Recreation, for which the Service uses D-J as well as P-R administrative monies. The P-R Act also states that, within the authorized 8 percent, funds may be withheld by the Service for administration and execution of the Migratory Bird Conservation Act. These funds have been used mainly in migratory bird research.

Apportionment of grant funds to States is done by the Service's Division of Federal Aid, and each is signed by the Secretary of the Interior. Apportionment has two processes—the first allocates the arms and ammunition tax money plus half of the handgun and archery equipment funds for wildlife restoration, and the second allocates the other half of handgun and archery funds for hunter education.

From the wildlife restoration portion, first Puerto Rico receives a half of 1 percent and other four commonwealths or territories each one-sixth of 1 percent. The remainder is divided among the 50 States, half of it distributed according to the area of each State and half of it according to numbers of paid hunting license holders in each State. No State may receive less than half of 1 percent or more than 5 percent of the total.

The hunter education funds are apportioned only to the 50 States, not the Territories, on the basis of State population. No State receives less than 1 percent or more than 3 percent of the total. States have the option to use these funds for wildlife restoration purposes.

States and Territories are all notified of their apportionments, but the funds remain in the Federal treasury. P-R is a reimbursement grant; therefore, grantees receive payments *after* approved work is performed throughout the year. States must furnish at least one-quarter of the cost and P-R pays no more than three-quarters. The Territories provide no matching share; thus, P-R reimburses their total allowable costs.

P-R funds apportioned to the States are available to the grantees for 2 years. Those unexpended or unobligated after 2 years revert to the Service to accomplish purposes of the Migratory Bird Conservation Act. These have largely been used in connection with migratory bird research.

One further item needs to be mentioned. The Service's Federal Aid office in Washington maintains and distributes a *Federal Aid Manual* to provide the Regional Offices and States the policies and procedures required in grant administration. Following the 1981 administrative survey of the States (mentioned earlier), the Service made extensive revision of the manual and published it in 1982. This manual indicates a future direction for major administrative change discussed briefly below.

Comprehensive Plans

In the early days of P-R, technically trained people in the various disciplines needed for wildlife management were in short supply; therefore, the Service established a rigorous routine of project review and monitoring. Initially, it was centered in the Washington Office and later transferred to the various Regional Offices where the routine is still carried out today. The only substantial change is in three regions where a total of five States have approved comprehensive plans—Colorado, Kansas, Maryland, Tennessee, and Wyoming. With these States there are no traditional project approvals and, as a result, there is much-reduced monitoring by the Feds.

Today, trained and experienced wildlife managers are available and are on the staffs of all State wildlife agencies. The 1982 *Federal Aid Manual* provides the States with several options whereby the Federal role in P-R administration may be reduced. How they go, however, is the option of each State. They may continue to submit projects as in the past or they may adopt any of a number of options based on plans.

Both P-R and D-J Acts require the submission of projects or comprehensive fish and wildlife plans. The 1970 amendment to the two acts which authorized comprehensive plans was a recognition of State progress in management of fish and wildlife resources and the administrative advances of their agencies. This was reinforced through passage of the as yet unfunded Fish and Wildlife Conservation Act of 1980 (the Nongame or Forsythe-Chafee Act), which encourages States to develop conservation plans for all fish and wildlife, and authorizes plans of lesser scope than comprehensive, such as for nongame wildlife. Those portions of conservation plans which pertain to wildlife conservation are also approvable under the P-R Act.

A comprehensive plan must include the entire mission for resource management of the fish and wildlife agency, and it must be supported by a documented management system which controls the processes and procedures of the agency's planning, programming, budgeting, implementation, and evaluation functions. The development, implementation, and maintenance of such a planning system are very large and costly steps for any agency. A State which chooses this avenue must be completely committed to it at all organizational levels throughout the agency.

Therefore, the 1982 *Federal Aid Manual* includes the flexibilities of the Forsythe-Chafee Act and is open-ended to the options of planning available, if a State chooses to use this approach in its management. The State may develop and maintain plans for such modules of its wildlife program as big game management, nongame wildlife, migratory birds, upland game birds, furbearers, or hunter education. It may choose either to document management systems for these plans or to continue controlling work by simplified projects. Each step a State chooses will increase its own responsibilities and reduce the Federal role in that State's affairs. Any time, a State may increase the scope of a module developed previously, or add modules, and if that State should ultimately decide to embrace comprehensive planning, modules already developed will fit right in.

P-R has a long history of excellent performance, free of scandals and serious problems. Costs of administrative overhead have remained low. To maintain this enviable record into the next five decades, performance and accountability must be maintained regardless of what management systems a State chooses, and regardless of who exercises various roles. Not only must there be proper accountability for property and funds as in the past, but there must be equal diligence by State and Federal people alike to show all concerned, from sportsmen who pay the taxes to the Congress who authorizes and appropriates them, that every dollar spent has produced wildlife and hunter education benefits worth many dollars. If the program is to continue another 50 years, the sportsmen and industries who pay the excise taxes and those millions of others who enjoy and appreciate wildlife will be the force that causes it to happen.

Acquiring, planning, and developing areas with P-R funding aid is a State function.

Success Story: Wild Turkey

by John B. Lewis

The wild turkey *(Meleagris gallopavo)* may have had a greater influence on our culture than any other wildlife species. At Thanksgiving time it symbolizes the riches of a great new land and even gave the holiday its nickname.

The wild turkey has affected our lives in other ways too. It has influenced our music ("Turkey in the Straw"), our speech and our geography. If you've traveled the back roads of this country, you've probably encountered names like Gobbler's Knob, Turkey Creek and Turkey Foot Mountain. There's little doubt that the wild turkey played a significant part in the lives of the early settlers of our country by providing food and a source of badly needed income. Turkeys were so abundant that at times they sold for 6 to 12 cents apiece at the game market, with large gobblers maybe selling for a quarter.

Estimates of the pre-settlement turkey population in what is now the United States ranged from 7 to 10 million, and this may have been conservative. Accounts of "so many wild turkeys that there's no need to raise the domestic variety" appeared in the history of Montgomery County, Missouri about 1830. But within 100 years, the wild turkey had become a rare bird in most of its former range.

In appearance the wild turkey is long, lean and slender, whereas the domestic varieties are now basically short, heavy and stocky. The wild turkey spends much of its life walking, running and flying. Although it is a large bird it can fly up to 55 miles per hour.

Adult wild turkey gobblers are almost twice as large as hens, averaging about 20 pounds, compared to 10 pounds for adult females. Weights vary among the 6 subspecies, with the Gould's turkey apparently the largest.

Gobblers and hens have noticeable color differences. Breast feathers of hens are lighter colored and tipped with brown; gobblers are darker due to the black edging on their body feathers. In both sexes, the body plumage shines with iridescent shades of bronze, green, brown, blue, red and purple in the sunlight. This iridescence is most noticeable in adult gobblers.

In addition to their spurs and beards, gobblers develop wattles (folds of skin below the beak) and caruncles (wartlike growths on the neck) and a dewbill or snood. These growths are also present in hens but aren't as pronounced. During the spring breeding season, the caruncles and wattles of the gobbler may be fiery red, white or blue depending on the bird's mood. Adult gobblers lack the feathers on the neck that give the hens a fuzzier look from a distance. In the spring, the top of a gobbler's head is sometimes as white as a cottonball, one of

Mr. Lewis, now a Wildlife Research Supervisor for the Missouri Department of Conservation, worked for 31 years on wild turkey research and restoration in Missouri, during which time the State's wild turkey population grew from 2,500 to more than 250,000. He has provided technical aid to other States on wild turkey management, and has written several popular and professional articles on the subject.

31

the clues that hunters look for in telling gobblers from hens during the spring hunting season.

Wildness is the key to understanding this bird. Wild turkeys are wary and will react instinctively to danger by flying, running and hiding. These behavior patterns have been important to the species' survival.

Wild turkeys seem to have eyes in the back of their heads because they are able to see in an almost complete circle. This, plus their ability to detect the slightest movement at long distances, equips them with exceptional vision. Some turkey hunters say that if wild turkeys could smell as well as they can see, they would be impossible for a hunter to kill. They also have a highly developed sense of hearing. They can pinpoint the location of another turkey or a hunter calling with remarkable accuracy. It would almost appear that wild turkeys have a built-in "sonar" which directs them.

Wild turkeys like company. When lost or separated from one another, they communicate with a variety of calls. This togetherness in turkeys is another trait that has survival benefits, for in numbers there is strength. Flocks of wild turkeys in the fall and winter usually include the adult hen(s) and broods. Adult gobblers may join the hen and brood flocks occasionally, but mostly remain apart in the their own bachelor flocks. During periods of severe weather or when food is scarce, several flocks may "gang" together. These "gangs" may continue for a brief time, but when the weather moderates they separate into the original flocks. By mid-winter the young-of-the-year gobblers begin to drift apart from the brood flocks and start running together. When this occurs three separate flocks may use the same general area, while maintaining their own identities.

As spring approaches, the flocks' integrity begins to break down and all of the groups join in courtship flocks. Courtship flocking rarely lasts for more than two or three weeks, after which small groups of hens begin to move off in search of nest sites, followed by one or more adult gobblers.

Most of the actual mating probably takes place following the breakup of the courtship flock. Small groups of hens accompanied by one or more gobblers can be seen for a couple of weeks after they have left the courtship flock. As each hen begins to lay and nest, the number of hens with gobblers declines daily. After the last hen has left, the old gobbler soon joins up with other lonesome gobblers and they remain together until next spring. Wild turkeys travel over a fairly large area throughout the year in their daily movements in search of food and cover. The area covered during the year is known as "annual home range" and may be several square miles in size.

Historically wild turkeys were native only to the North American continent. Their range included all or parts of 39 States, plus the southern tip of Ontario and south into Mexico and Central America. Six distinct geographic races or subspecies of turkeys are recognized, all slightly different in color and behavior. The eastern wild turkey *(M. g. silvestris)* was found throughout the hardwood and mixed pine-hardwood forests from Maine to Missouri and south to the Gulf of Mexico, the largest range of the six subspecies. The Florida turkey *(M. g. osceola)* was restricted to the Florida peninsula, the smallest area occupied by any of the subspecies.

The Rio Grande turkey *(M. g. intermedia)* inhabited the grasslands and mixed mesquite-grassland areas of Texas, northeastern Mexico, western Oklahoma and extreme southwest Kansas and possibly a small portion of New Mexico. The original range of the Merriam's turkeys *(M. g. merriami)* included the mountain woodlands in Arizona, New Mexico and southern Colorado and perhaps a small extension into Texas. The Mexican turkey *(M. g. gallopavo)* and Gould's turkey *(M. g. mexicana)* primary range is in Mexico.

32

Wild turkey gobbler in flight. The author says these birds seem to be constantly in motion.

Wild turkey habitat has changed tremendously since Europeans first settled here. Gone are the almost endless expanses of virgin timber in the Eastern United States. Forests that once supported a diversity of trees have been replaced by pure pine stands that are now harvested every 25 or 30 years. Gone too are the unbroken prairies. Where there used to be tall and short grass prairies, there are now corn, soybean and wheat fields. Despite these dramatic changes the wild turkey has persisted.

The fact that wild turkeys were able to survive these drastic habitat alterations at all is a demonstration of how adaptable they are. Even during the pre-settlement period wild turkeys occupied a wide range of habitats and environmental conditions. Basically they are habitat "generalists", occupying several plant communities.

During the winter, turkeys need high-energy foods, especially where the winters are long and the ground may be covered with snow for extended periods. Acorns, beechnut, pine seeds and other sources of hard mast are preferred winter foods, but if they are unavailable, turkeys in grain-growing areas will forage for waste grain. Turkeys are forced to move when their natural winter foods fail, and when this happens they often suffer increased losses to predators and poaching.

As spring approaches, wild turkeys move from their winter habitat to areas that provide nesting and brood-rearing habitat. These shifts from winter to spring habitat may be quite long, especially for the Rio Grande and Merriam's subspecies; movements of 10 to 30 miles are not uncommon for these western subspecies. The eastern and Florida subspecies also move between winter and spring, but not as far.

These winter-to-spring shifts occur mainly because hens need a diet high in Vitamin A and these foods are usually found near preferred nesting and brood habitat. Green forage makes up a high percentage of the turkey hen's diet prior to the onset of egg laying and nesting. Hens will move to more open areas where

33

Source: National Wild Turkey Federation, Inc., Edgefield, South Carolina.

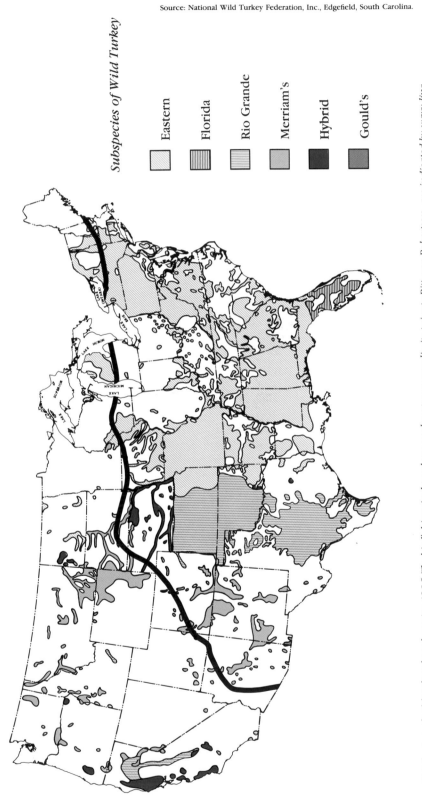

Subspecies of Wild Turkey

- Eastern
- Florida
- Rio Grande
- Merriam's
- Hybrid
- Gould's

Distribution of wild turkeys by subspecies, 1986. The bird's historical northern and western range limits, prior to Pittman-Robertson, are indicated by wavy line.

Source: National Wild Turkey Federation, Inc., Edgefield, South Carolina

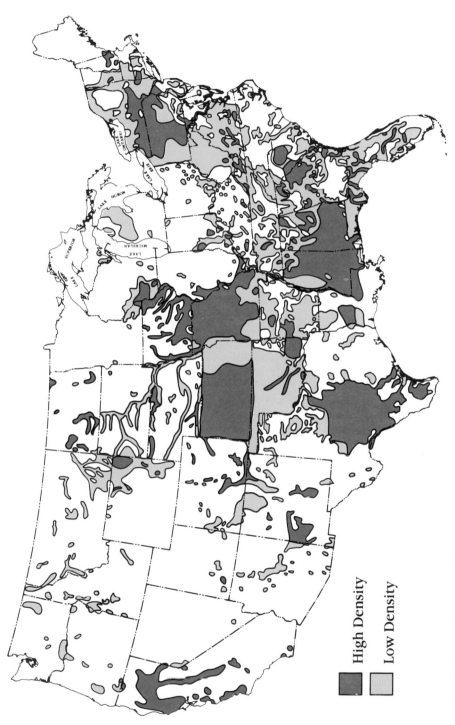

Density of wild turkey populations, 1986.

High Density

Low Density

35

vegetation green-up occurs earlier than in the timber. Nests have been found near old logging roads, old fields, hay fields and cut-over areas. Although nesting locations would appear to be selected at random, some common denominators are usually involved. Nests are usually fairly close to water, and often at the base of a tree. Normally the nest is screened by shrubby vegetation ranging from 2 to 4 feet high. Wild turkey hens lay an average of 11 eggs per clutch in a process which takes about two weeks to complete. They then spend another four weeks incubating. Only about 30 percent of the hens are successful in bringing off a brood. Shortly after the poults are hatched, the hen moves them to areas that offer foraging opportunities and security from birds of prey. While the poults are still too young to fly, the hen will keep them in areas that provide good ground cover, which is fairly dense but not to the point that it restricts movement. Brood range size increases as the poults grow. Late summer brood range often includes old fields, pastures, savannahs and timbered roads' right-of-way. Insects, such as grasshoppers, beetles, millipedes, walking sticks and others, and grass seeds, plus fruits and soft mast are the principal food items for turkeys at this time.

Thus, wild turkeys need a diversity of habitats, which vary seasonally. The opportunity for a high-density turkey population is greater if all the needed habitats exist close together than if they are widely separated.

The Mexican turkey is given credit for being the ancestor of our present domestic turkeys. Mexican turkeys were being raised in captivity by Indians when the "New World" was discovered by Europeans. Turkeys were taken to Europe by the early Spanish explorers and ultimately were established throughout the Continent. Domestic turkeys were brought to America by the English colonizing the east coast, but the time and location of these early imports is not well established. It was noted, however, that these early settlers preferred the wild turkey to eat, indicating that the domestic variety was a poor substitute. Wild birds were saved for festive occasions.

Wild turkeys' nutritional needs vary according to the season of the year.

U.S. Fish and Wildlife Service

36

As the frontier moved westward and more and more land was cleared, wild turkeys became scarce. The seemingly inexhaustible supply had been completely eliminated in some regions of the country by the mid-1800's. Where populations could still be found, they were greatly reduced. The last record of a wild turkey in Connecticut was in 1813; in Massachusetts the last was reported in 1851. Wild turkeys had disappeared from most of the Midwestern States by 1900.

The conversion of forested lands to pasture and croplands in the Eastern United States reached such intensity by the end of the 1800's that it virtually eliminated the wild turkey's habitat. Added to the loss of habitat was constant hunting pressure, especially market hunting. In St. Louis, an exporting firm filled an order for the London market for 700 dozen wild turkeys in 1881. We might wonder if the turkeys were edible when they got to London. Market hunting reached a peak after the Civil War and extended into the early part of the 20th Century. Concerned sportsmen appealed to their State governments to prohibit this commercial slaughter. Laws were passed, but were largely ineffective. It wasn't until the supply of wildlife had diminished to a point where it wasn't profitable that market hunting disappeared.

Hunting as we know it today, for sport or recreation, didn't exist during the early settlement period in this country. Wildlife was generally considered either a nuisance or a commodity by the early pioneers—something to eat, sell, or get rid of. It wasn't until hunting for sport became fashionable that concern developed over the continuing decline of wildlife. This concern by public-spirited sportsmen started during the middle of the 1800's and was responsible for the enactment of seasons and limits. By 1880, all of the States had passed some type of game law. The first bag limit was established on prairie-chickens in Iowa in 1878. Market hunting was first outlawed in Arkansas in 1875. Massachusetts and New Hampshire developed the first "Game Warden" programs about 1850. In Missouri an "Act for the Preservation of Game Animals and Birds" was passed in 1874; it established open and closed seasons on most wildlife species. The turkey season was closed from April 1 through September 15, but no mention was made regarding bag limits.

Early game laws were seemingly designed to ration the dwindling stocks of wildlife. Lawmakers believed that these restrictive measures would only make what was left last longer, before it completely disappeared. While most of the early game laws had little impact on the continuing disappearance of wildlife, they were in fact the beginnings of wildlife management in this country. It wasn't until the early 1900's that the idea of "conservation through wise use" was made popular by Theodore Roosevelt. He viewed wildlife, forests, rangelands, and water power as renewable organic resources that might last forever if harvested scientifically and not faster than they could restore themselves. Before the Teddy Roosevelt era, "conservation" had been an obscure word, one the public had hardly ever heard and rarely associated with wildlife, woods or water. The dominant philosophy in this country prior to Roosevelt had been one of "conquering the land." The 19th Century pioneer's attitude toward complete mastery of the land became an obsession; subduing the wilderness was viewed with a sense of national pride and was proclaimed as America's "Manifest Destiny." The disappearance of the wild turkey along with numerous other wildlife species was hardly noticed by the vast majority of the people during the 19th Century.

Roosevelt's ideas for the development of game preserves or refuges and using science as a tool were new concepts in the young conservation movement. Game preserves were established throughout the country during the early 20th

A gobbler's head may be red, white or blue, or a combination of all three, depending on the season and his mood.

Century, but were largely ineffective in halting the decline of wildlife populations. The scientific approach was also ineffective. The state-of-the-art at that time could only provide measurements and plumage color, not information on what animals ate or where they lived. The scientific experts at that time devoted most of their energies in classifying and cataloging, while ignoring almost totally the environments which produced the animals they were studying.

The first detailed life-history investigation on a major wildlife species was done on bobwhite quail by Herbert L. Stoddard during 1924-28 in South Georgia in a project funded by a group of public-spirited sportsmen in cooperation with the Bureau of Biological Survey of the U.S. Department of Agriculture. The fact that this very important study was initiated and partly financed with private monies was an indication of the problems associated with wildlife management and research. Very few if any of the States' natural resource agencies had personnel capable of conducting intensive wildlife research, and money to fund such projects was not available. Wildlife research and management as a science was still in its infancy during the 1920's and early 1930's. Very few colleges and universities were capable of training students who wanted to enter the wildlife profession.

Two events in the 1930's changed the course of wildlife management in this country—the creation of the Cooperative Wildlife Research Unit Program in 1935 and the passage of the Federal Aid in Wildlife Restoration (Pittman-Robertson) Act in 1937. The Unit program created the means for training a cadre of wildlife professionals. The P-R program provided the monies needed by the State agencies to hire wildlife professionals and put them in the field. Together they lifted wildlife conservation out of the dark ages and sent it down the road toward the most aggressive and constructive wildlife-restoration campaign ever known.

These two programs started to produce results almost immediately. A major research effort on the propagation of wild turkeys was initiated in September 1935 through the Virginia Cooperative Wildlife Research Unit. The scope of the project was broadened in 1938 to include the status, life history and management of turkeys in Virginia. In 1939, the investigation was continued under Federal Aid in Wildlife Restoration Project 2-R of the Virginia Commission of Game and Inland Fisheries. The results of these studies were combined and published as "The Wild Turkey in Virginia, Its Status, Life History and Management" (Mosby and Handley 1943), the first comprehensive study concerning the wild turkey. Although portions of the study dealt with rearing wild turkeys in captivity, it also presented for the first time habitat requirements and specific management recommendations needed to restore wild turkeys. Much of the information is as relevant today as it was more than 40 years ago.

Soon after the passage of the Federal Aid in Wildlife Restoration Act, several other States initiated wild turkey research projects, among them Alabama, Louisiana, Texas and Missouri. Following Virginia's lead, many of these early studies focused on population status and distribution. Previously little if any factual information was available concerning how many wild turkeys the States had or where the birds were located. Results of these early studies established the basis for setting hunting seasons, selecting areas for restocking, and identifying the need for additional research.

One of the major problems confronting managers early in this century was how to restore wild turkeys into unoccupied areas of suitable habitat. Early restoration attempts, for the most part, took the easy way out and used game-farm-reared turkeys. Very few of these game farm birds survived. How could a bird raised in captivity make it in areas where the native wild turkey had been eliminated? So long as game farm releases were made in areas where no native wild turkeys occurred, the only loss would be the game farm stock. However, if game farm birds were released near existing wild propulations, then the chances for hybridization and disease posed a real threat to the few remaining wild birds. This no doubt happened, and rather than enhancing restoration just set it back. Restoration efforts involving game farm turkeys were limited primarily to those States which had or formerly had eastern wild turkeys. The Florida, Rio Grande and Merriam's wild turkeys had not been totally eliminated from their historical range so there wasn't the same incentive to release game farm turkeys in those areas.

A P-R funded study demonstrating the differences in the heritable wildness between the native wild turkey and hybrid or game farm turkey put an end to the release of game farm birds in Missouri in 1942. The researcher, A.S. Leopold, showed that the adaptability that allowed hybrid turkeys to be successfully raised in captivity worked against their survival in the wild. Although the release of game farm turkeys didn't stop in some States, Leopold's work did slow it down and had the effect of directing wild turkey managers to look for other ways of restoring wild populations.

Most wildlife research programs either came to a halt or were drastically curtailed during World War II; turkey restoration efforts almost stopped for about five years.

Dr. Henry Mosby, reporting in 1949 on the present and future outlook for the eastern and Florida wild turkeys, indicated that the prospects were not good and that the only hope of saving these birds would be found in proper and intelligent management on public land. He stated that the eastern and Florida wild turkey range had been reduced to 12 percent of the ancestral range and that the birds had been completely eliminated in 19 States. In the 17 States with remaining population of wild turkeys, 5 States reported them to be at dangerously low levels with complete extirpation not improbable; 3 States thought they were increasing; in 2 States they were just holding their own, while in the rest they were either static or declining. Mosby went on to say that some work had been done on live-trapping native wild turkeys for restocking and that this approach did offer some hope of halting the decline. He went on to say, however, that live-trapping native wild turkeys was difficult and expensive and neither live-trapping or using captivity-reared birds would be the answer to stopping the decline in the eastern and Florida races of wild turkeys.

However, E.A. Walker's 1949 report on the status of the Rio Grande and Merriam's turkeys wasn't quite as pessimistic. Walker indicated that the Rio Grande turkey was slowly decreasing in Texas, but increasing in western Oklahoma. The Merriam's turkeys were thought to be increasing within their former range in Arizona and Colorado, although decreasing in New Mexico. The really bright spot was that introduced populations of Merriam's were increasing, especially in States outside the birds' historic range. Fifteen Merriam's turkeys trapped in New Mexico had been released in Wyoming in 1935. These birds had multiplied to an estimated 10,000 by 1958. South Dakota successfully introduced Merriam's from New Mexico and Colorado into the Black Hills in 1948-1951. The turkey population increased from the original 29 to an estimated 5,000 to 7,000 birds by 1960. The South Dakota wild turkey restoration project was financed in part by the Pittman-Robertson program.

Encouraged by the success achieved by South Dakota and Wyoming, Montana obtained Merriam's turkeys from Colorado in 1954 and from Wyoming in 1955. One additional release was made in the fall and winter of 1956-57 with birds secured from Wyoming. Populations increased so significantly in a short time that hunting was permitted after just four breeding seasons. Similar success in introducing Merriam's turkeys was accomplished by several other western States soon after the Montana establishment.

The spectacular results that had been attained in live-trapping native wild Merriam's and Rio Grande turkeys were yet to be duplicated for the eastern and Florida species. The trapping methods used to capture turkeys in the West weren't very successful when tried on the eastern turkeys.

Several trap designs employed in the West with success (roll-front, open-front, drop-front, slide-front, and drop-net) were used in early attempts to capture eastern turkeys in South Carolina. The researcher, W.P. Baldwin, reported limited success with some of these traps, but added, "in general it would appear that turkeys of the southwestern brush areas are more likely to enter open-front traps than those of the eastern forests."

The capture of the eastern and Florida turkeys using "walk-in" type traps was time-consuming and expensive and didn't appear to be the solution to providing enough birds for restoration programs. In 1948, a cannon-projected net trap was developed by H.H. Dill and W.H. Thornsbery on Swan Lake National Wildlife Refuge in Missouri. The inventors of the cannon-net trap intended it primarily for capturing waterfowl, but they believed that it offered a practical and economical means for trapping large numbers of any species of birds tending to flock together. This break-through in trapping technology made it possible to capture enough eastern and Florida turkeys for large scale restoration programs.

Cannon-nets were used to trap turkeys successfully in South Carolina on the Francis Marion National Forest Wildlife Preserve in the early 1950's. Missouri used cannon-nets to trap turkeys during the winter of 1953-54. Later modification in cannons, nets and charges improved the overall effectiveness for capturing turkeys. Narcotics applied to cracked corn also have been used effectively for capture.

Turkeys will shortly be captured in this drop-net trap.

Ron Spooner, Kansas Fish and Game

Perfecting capture techniques certainly played an important role in wild turkey restoration; many other elements were also required before the restoration programs were successful. Better habitat conditions, due to improvements in forest management both on the State and Federal levels, proved vital to the success of the restoration effort. Better law enforcement and a groundswell of public support for conservation measures in general also contributed substantially. These factors, plus the wild turkey's ability to accommodate to habitats previously thought unsuited, made it possible for the turkey to expand its range across ecological barriers.

In 1959, at the First National Wild Turkey Symposium, Dr. Mosby presented a report on the general status and management of wild turkeys in the U.S. This report, just 10 years after similar reports by Mosby himself and by E.A. Walker, presented a much different outlook. The financial support provided through the P-R program had enabled 30 States to participate in active turkey management and research. Seven States had biologists assigned full-time to turkey management and research, with 85 individuals preforming part-time work on turkey programs. Almost $400,000 was being allotted to turkey management and research in 1958, with most of this money coming through P-R.

Wild turkey populations were responding to the restocking and habitat improvement programs. During the 10 years between 1948 and 1958, populations had been re-established in several States within ancestral range and had been successfully established in a few States outside their original range. This dramatic turn-around reaffirmed that Theodore Roosevelt's idea of "conservation through wise use" could work, and it did.

Even though the wild turkey had been saved, there still remained many questions concerning the management of the species. Attention had been directed primarily during the late 1940's and through the 1950's toward trapping and relocation, with very little thought given to the bird's basic life history. Before managers could effectively manage wild turkey populations they needed to know the answers to such questions as how far turkeys move, what they eat, what constitutes good turkey habitat, the effects of predation and disease, and many more. It would seem that the answers to the above questions should have been known before any successful restoration could take place. Although there

A cannon-net trap is prepared, with cannon muzzles visible above ground.

was some knowledge, detailed data were lacking. Ironically, wild turkeys had to be re-established so they could be studied in detail. Studying a bird as elusive as the wild turkey is difficult—but when the populations are low, it's next to impossible. The re-established and expanding populations provided the opportunity for wild turkey researchers to answer many basic questions and thus to be more effective in turkey management.

The introduction of miniature radio transmitters into the wildlife research field during the 1960's made it possible to take a closer look at the private life of the wild turkey. The use of telemetry provided precise data on home range size, daily movements, and habitat use throughout the year. The results of these studies enabled managers to manage specifically for wild turkeys. Wild turkey research studies, supported primarily with P-R funds, were solidly in place in practically every State during the 1960's. The data from many of these research projects were presented at the Second National Wild Turkey Symposium in 1970, when Dr. Mosby summarized the past 30 years of wild turkey management and reported that the prospects for the future welfare of the wild turkey had brightened considerably in that time. In 1968, an estimated 1,250,000 wild turkeys were present and the legal harvest of the four subspecies had increased 2.8 times since 1952.

The Nation's wild turkey population did not show any significant increase from 1968 to 1974, according to estimates available to Mosby. However, the harvest by hunters increased 41 percent during the same period, indicating continued population growth and expansion. Progress in the wild turkey restoration effort is perhaps best measured by the number of States with legal hunting seasons. Sixteen States allowed turkey hunting in 1952, the number rose to 31 by 1968, and was up to 39 in 1970. Today the Nation's wild turkey population is conservatively estimated at between 2 and 3 million and hunting seasons are presently permitted in 46 States including Hawaii.

In closing the Fifth National Wild Turkey Symposium, W.D. Ziedyk and J.G. Dickson in 1985 summarized the great strides in status, distribution, and biolog-

Cannons are fired, projecting the net over the birds. The dark cloud consists of forest floor litter and debris. Turkeys quickly recover from the experience, evidently none the worse for it.

ical knowledge of the species since the first symposium 26 years earlier. They encouraged wild turkey investigators to design and conduct long-term studies that would evaluate the impacts of weather, vegetation response, and land-use changes on wild turkeys. They discouraged researchers from dealing in short-term studies involving small numbers of birds and then extrapolating and projecting their findings to large areas and long-range planning. They stressed the need for better habitat models, with the emphasis on testing and improving existing models. Harvest management was noted as an area where additional research was needed, to enable managers to utilize the turkey resource better. Their final comment was that although we have enjoyed success with wild turkeys, we shouldn't become complacent.

At this point there certainly doesn't appear to be any complacency concerning the need for additional information on how to sustain and increase our wild turkey populations. P-R funded wild turkey research efforts can be found in almost every State and should continue for a long time.

To briefly summarize what has happened to wild turkeys during the past 50 years: they were in trouble in 1937; today they're not. Wild turkeys have been restored to much of their former range due primarily to the success of the trapping and transfer of wild birds. Viable wild turkey populations have been established via the introduction of wild-trapped birds beyond their ancestral range. Wild turkey populations have responded favorably to improved management programs based on research studies. Continued loss of habitat still remains a serious threat, however, to the future welfare of the wild turkey. During the late 1930's there was a lack of both factual information about what was needed and of money to accomplish the task of restoring wild turkeys. Thanks to some very farsighted individuals, both these problems were overcome with the passage of the Federal Aid in Wildlife Restoration Act in 1937 and the establishment of the cooperative Wildlife Research Units in 1935. If it hadn't been for these two events occurring at about the same time, and when they were badly needed, the wild turkey might not have returned.

Success Story: White-tailed Deer

by Robert L. Downing

One must agree with R.E. and T.R. McCabe, who in a definitive 1984 book on the species wrote: "In the annals of wildlife management in North America, there are few success stories as great as that of the white-tailed deer. Some persons contend that the impressive whitetail record is a direct consequence of scientific management. Others point to the animal's innate resilience to altered environments, particularly those of human design. In addition, there are those who consider the recent history of white-tailed deer anything but a success and are quick to note crop and other damages and highway accidents that are direct consequences of abundant whitetail populations . . . No one, however, can deny that the whitetail's modern history has been remarkable." I have witnessed and taken part in a great deal of that recovery myself and will describe it to you as best I can. It is fitting that much of this chapter was mentally composed in a deer stand, while hunting a herd that was restocked and managed with the aid of Pittman-Robertson (P-R) funds.

McCabe and McCabe described three distinct stages in the decline of the whitetail. The 24 to 34 million deer estimated to have ranged over much of North America in 1500 A.D. had declined by 50 to 65 percent by 1800 because of massive killing by Indians as an item of trade to European settlers. Some deer herds rebounded from 1800 to about 1865 because the Indians had been mostly driven out of the East and the Europeans had not fully settled in remote rural areas. Uncontrolled hunting for market and for home consumption from about 1850 to 1900 further reduced the deer population to a low of perhaps 300,000 to 500,000, only 1 to 2 percent of the number present in 1500. Exploitation did not slow until the Lacey Act of 1900 forbade interstate traffic in wild game. Whitetails survived the late 1800's and early 1900's only in sparsely settled regions, inaccessible swamps and mountain ranges, or on large landholdings where they received the personal protection of the landowner.

Although laws protecting whitetails were enacted as early as 1646, the conservation movement did not receive widespread public support until the very early 1900's when public indignation became aroused because of the endangerment or local extinction of many species. Many game and nongame species then began to receive the enforced protection of both State and Federal law, and additional public lands were set aside—a National Wildlife Refuge System (1903) and a National Forest System (1905). The pendulum of deer abundance did not swing sharply to the "plus" side until the Great Depression of the 1930's, however, when much of the rural human population in the South, Midwest, and East began to abandon small farms and move to the cities. Not only

Mr. Downing worked on Pittman-Robertson-financed deer studies for one year in Texas and seven years in Georgia before devoting 13 years to intensive deer research in North Carolina and Virginia as a wildlife research biologist for the U.S. Fish and Wildlife Service. Now retired, he has written more than 25 scientific papers on deer.

did the deer's worst enemy, man, move away, but the abandoned farm fields grew up in weeds and brush, an important component of whitetail habitat. People who for generations had virtually no big game to hunt understandably supported the establishment of refuges and other special areas, of State wildlife departments, and of the new game laws. People were even willing to tax themselves to restore the game that had been missing from their lives for so long, and eagerly supported the P-R Act of 1937. From then on, every effort, every noticeable success financed by these monies brought with it increasing support by the public. The stage was set for an unimpeded rise in the population of white-tailed deer.

Mere protection of the deer was not enough in many areas, however, because there were no remnant herds to spread and repopulate vacant habitats. At first, there were few deer herds that had enough surplus animals to be used for restocking. Trapping techniques were primitive and uneconomical and progress at establishing "new" herds was slow. Furthermore, personnel, equipment, and gasoline often were not available during the World War II years to carry out large-scale restocking.

After the war, however, a lot of returning veterans took advantage of the "GI Bill" and went to college, many getting degrees in the new educational discipline called wildlife management. These new scientists quickly developed new ways to capture and transport deer, reestablished local herds, and set about learning how to manage them properly.

Two early research efforts are outstanding among those sponsored by P-R to hasten recovery of our deer herds. C.W. Severinghaus in 1949 noted the pattern of tooth replacement and wear, giving biologists a tool that is used even

Whitetail doe hastens to get away during a 1956 release in Indiana. Deer transplanted from herds surviving in remote areas helped managers make the restoration work spectacularly successful.

Indiana Department of Natural Resources

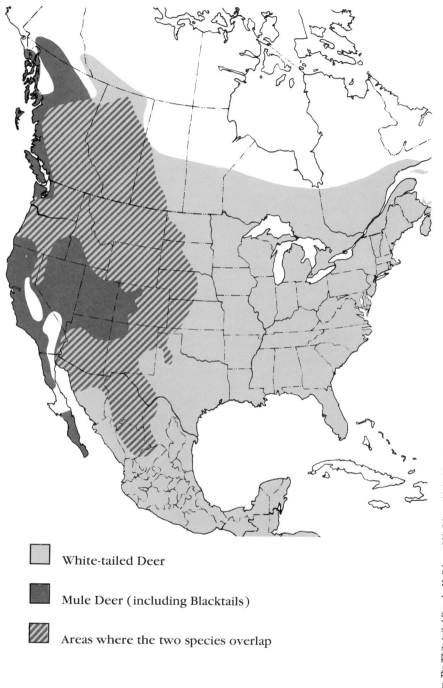

Source: *The White-tailed Deer*, by McCabe and McCabe, published for the Wildlife Management Institute, 1984.

White-tailed Deer

Mule Deer (including Blacktails)

Areas where the two species overlap

Distribution of White-tailed and Mule Deer

47

today to "age" deer, to study how and why their populations change, and to reconstruct and model herd size and composition as an aid to selecting future management goals and harvest levels.

J.A. Crockford and three associates in the late 1950's developed a dartgun system for capturing deer in the wild. Early investigators actually employed the blowgun technology of South American Indians and progressed through literally hundreds of combinations of increasingly sophisticated darts, dartguns, and drugs to develop today's relatively safe and foolproof capture systems. Dartgun technology, initially developed within the P-R program, is now used worldwide by wildlife biologist and is also widely applied in the livestock, zoo, animal control, and even the human criminology fields. Dartguns are used not only for capture purposes (restocking, tagging, physical examination, etc.) but also for humane killing of animals and remote injection of pharmaceuticals. Some agencies still rely heavily on dartguns to capture deer and other animals, while others use a variety of other devices such as traps and nets that have been developed in recent years.

Modern research and management have been so successful that there are now at least 14 million whitetails in North America, some in areas at the extreme northern and western edges of their range that had never supported whitetails before. More likely than not, our major problems today involve too many deer, rather than too few, because deer have proved to be so adaptable to the human-altered environment. There has been a lot of change in the last 50 years, much of it due to the P-R program.

The Deer and Its Habitat

The white-tailed deer is so adaptable that I have often said (rather facetiously) that it could find something nutritious to eat anywhere in the East except a paved parking lot. I have had to qualify that statement because I have seen parking lots that periodically contained discarded cigarette butts, popcorn, potato chips, candy, and hotdogs, all potential deer foods. Of course, I recognize that some habitats are better than others. Some are consistently poor because of inherently poor soils; others are periodically poor when winter or a drought make most available foods tough and woody. The quantity of food also can be low when it has been overused by livestock or even by deer themselves, or when it is being shaded out by a dense, uninterrupted stand of large trees. As preferred foods decline, deer are forced to eat things that are less palatable and nutritious.

Based on P-R studies of deer food habits, it has been found that whitetails will eat everything from mushrooms and lichens to fruits, nuts, and even fish and insects on rare occasions. Anything that is green in winter, whether it be white cedar in the North, Japanese honeysuckle in the South, or grasses and forbs in the West, is an important component of deer habitat. When fruits and acorns are available, they dominate the deer's diet. Mushrooms are seasonally important as well. Deer have the remarkable ability to select the choicest leaves off each plant, to pick these leaves at their most nutritious stage, and to find mushrooms and acorns under the leaves using their keen sense of smell.

The best deer habitat has a lot of diversity, so that deer can select a variety of foods or shift their feeding patterns to better habitats nearby in response to changing seasons and the accompanying changes in both palatability and availability. Unless restricted by deep snow, deer are not averse to moving several miles to obtain better foods, if necessary.

In many well-nourished herds, healthy females often breed for the first time at about 6 to 7 months of age. These young mothers usually bear only one fawn.

Yearling does usually have two—one if they did not breed the previous year. A healthy adult doe will generally give birth to twin fawns each year. When fawns cease to breed and few adults rear twins, the habitat may be deteriorating for some reason. Fawn survival is quite variable, depending on the health of the mother and the prevalence of predators, insects, and diseases.

It is impossible to generalize about weights of white-tailed deer because of basic differences in size of the 15 U. S. subspecies. Each subspecies differs in average weight and other characteristics, but the problem is complicated by the fact that many areas were restocked with deer of several subspecies. Therefore, what is "normal and healthy" must be determined for each herd individually. In many healthy herds during fall, fawns will weigh 50 to 80 pounds, yearling bucks will weigh 90 to 140 pounds, and adult bucks 130 to 220 pounds. However, exceptional deer on excellent range occasionally exceed these weights by 50 percent or more, and the largest whitetail on record, killed in Minnesota in 1926, weighed more than 500 pounds.

Antler size varies from herd to herd for a number of reasons. Foremost among these are variations in habitat quality. Antler size is also influenced by genetics. For decades, small spike-antlered bucks were protected in many herds before it became known that antler size was partly hereditary; genetically inferior bucks may grow only spikes during their first year or two even when the habitat is good. Genetically superior bucks on the same range will produce eight points as yearlings and may have 10 points and a 16-inch spread by 2-1/2 years of age. Most States no longer protect spike bucks. Some have even devised systems to protect young bucks that exhibit good antler characteristics while heavily cropping those that do not. Yearling bucks that were born late in the season also

A healthy adult whitetail doe commonly bears twin fawns each year, but this normally high fertility may vary according to availability of nutritious forage.

James C. Leupold, U.S. Fish and Wildlife Service

49

Not a bit intimidated by humans peering through cameras, a whitetail buck aggressively defends his territory and his doe.

do not produce as many points as those born early, another reason for each herd having different antler characteristics.

Changing land uses have had considerable impact on deer. Before the coming of European settlers, the dense forest overstory was broken to the benefit of deer only by strong winds or uncontrolled fires, started either by Indians or by lightning. Early settlers cleared small patches of forest to obtain lumber and to plant crops. Whitetails near these settlements were hunted heavily year-round for food, so these improvements in habitat did not result in an increased deer population. By the late 1800's, forest clearing and agriculture had spread throughout the East; and although deer habitat was improved immensely by these practices, uncontrolled market and subsistence hunting by the expanding human population further reduced the herds. Agriculture continued moving westward because food and fiber production there was often more economical than in the East. As many small eastern farms were abandoned, some were planted to trees and many more eventually reverted naturally to woodland, thus reversing the trend that had begun a century before. The early stages of forest regrowth produce ideal deer habitat, especially if there are adjacent stream bottoms, old house sites, and woodlots that contain mature hardwoods to provide fruits and acorns as food for deer.

Modern, intensively managed pine forests, especially in the South, are now cut over frequently and in small blocks so that young growth beneficial to whitetails is constantly available somewhere within the cruising range of individual deer (from one-half to one square mile). Northern evergreen forests grow much more slowly than southern ones and, therefore, are cut less frequently. Unfortunately, many northern forests are nearing maturity or have been over-browsed and no longer provide the quality of deer habitat that they did a few decades ago. Hardwood forests, because they mature more slowly, are often not replanted to hardwood trees after cutting but are converted to faster-growing pines or to agriculture. Soybeans, in particular, grow well on newly cleared hardwood sites and are attractive food for deer, creating a serious conflict between farming and wildlife interests. Most modern farmers and foresters now have a fairly high tolerance for deer, however, demonstrating how human attitudes and behavior have changed. There are exceptions, of course, and crop damage in some areas is so severe that farmers are sometimes allowed to shoot deer during the summer to protect their crops. Riparian (streamside) deer habitat in the West suffers from livestock grazing and clearing for agriculture. Offsetting this trend is the increased tolerance and protection of deer. Urban sprawl and highway construction are consuming deer habitat throughout the Nation, but scientific management and the adaptability of the deer are keeping pace, and the overall trend is for slowly increasing whitetail populations in most regions.

Causes of Death

Many of the natural predators of the whitetail have been eliminated or greatly reduced. The cougar and wolf originally were the chief predators of deer throughout their range, but the cougar is now present in whitetail range only in isolated parts of southern Florida and portions of the Rockies and Southwest. The wolf has been eliminated in much of the whitetail's range and is now present in significant numbers only in Alaska, northern Minnesota, and parts of Canada. While most bobcats do not prey on deer, some have learned to do so and are very efficient at it, partially filling the niche vacated by the cougar. Coyotes are extremely effective predators on young fawns, enough to hold some south-

51

Philip K. White, U.S. Fish and Wildlife Service

Whitetails have adapted well to people and their structures. Livestock fences normally pose no obstacle to their movement.

western deer populations in check. Black bears also kill fawns when they have the opportunity but probably do not do so often enough to significantly affect population size. Free-ranging dogs are presently the most widespread predators of deer, but they seldom catch healthy adult deer and are mainly a harassment. Dogs kill fawns and disease-weakened adults with enough frequency to cause some concern, but cannot limit deer population size except during deep snows and other unusual circumstances. However, anything, including the snowmobile, that puts stress on deer during severe winter weather can sap their limited energy stores and lead to early death. Thousands of deer die annually on our highways and railroad tracks, possibly more than die from all predators combined.

Starvation is another important and dramatic cause of death for deer, especially in the northern part of their range. Whitetails concentrate during the winter in low-lying areas called "yards" because the shelter and food supplies there are generally the best available. If the winter is severe and long, however, these limited food supplies become exhausted, the deep snow prevents the deer from moving on to greener pastures, so to speak, and a portion of the herd may die of starvation. Farther south and west, malnutrition comes on less suddenly because the deer are not confined by deep snow to small areas. Furthermore, deer respond to slowly deteriorating habitat by having fewer fawns and poorer fawn survival, and approach the point of actual starvation much more slowly. The few adults that do die of starvation are so scattered that they are usually overlooked and the problem does not receive the publicity that it does in the North.

Parasites and diseases are rarely an important cause of death. The worst killer disease of deer is epizootic hemorrhagic disease (EHD), which some consider to be a form of the disease called bluetongue. The virus causing EHD is carried by a bloodsucking gnat, and epidemics usually occur in late summer or during an unusually warm autumn. The most important bacterial disease of deer is anthrax, a now-rare disease of special importance because it can be transmitted to man and to livestock.

Several devastating foreign livestock diseases would be extremely difficult to control if they reached the U. S. because deer are among the potential carriers. It is easier to treat or destroy livestock to block the spread of a disease than it is to catch or kill an entire deer herd, thus making eradication of such a disease extremely difficult. There have already been two dramatic examples of disease

It's not only their tails that show up white if there's snow on the browse.

53

control programs that proved quite costly because deer were involved as a carrier. In 1924, a foot-and-mouth disease outbreak in California forced the killing of 22,000 mule deer and in 1939-41 an estimated 10,000 whitetails were killed in southern Florida in an attempt to eradicate the cattle fever tick. Deer were also an important host of the screw-worm fly, a parasite responsible for much deer and livestock mortality through the late 1950's. However, the screw-worm fly was eradicated by releasing sterile male flies, not by eliminating its host.

By far the most important cause of death for deer is legal hunting. For example, hunting was responsible for six times as many deer deaths as highway accidents (148,530 versus 24,699) in Pennsylvania in 1981. Hunting mortality is believed to be largely compensatory partly because it takes place before the harsh winter period, when most natural deer deaths occur. Because hunting keeps deer density below maximum, the deer surviving a hunt have more food (better habitat) and come through the winter in better condition than those in unhunted herds. It has been demonstrated that deer populations can be purposely eliminated by hunting, long and hard; but I know of no case where a herd has been eliminated where modern hunting regulations were being enforced. When the Indians and early settlers drastically reduced or wiped out deer populations prior to 1900, they did so by hunting year-round, with dogs, and by "jack-lighting" at night, when deer are especially vulnerable.

Veterinarians at Southeastern Cooperative Wildlife Disease Study in Georgia take blood sample from tranquilized whitetail doe to test for brucellosis, as part of routine monitoring of deer herd's health.

Susan K. Snyder, College of Veterinary Medicine, University of Georgia

Whitetail sampling the grass and browse in "edge" habitat characteristically used by this species.

Erwin and Peggy Bauer/Outdoor Life Magazine

Scientific Management

Research, the basis of scientific management, has been carried out on deer by virtually every State since monies to support such activities were made available by the P-R Act of 1937. Universities and Federal agencies also have conducted deer research; but the bulk of it has been done by State wildlife departments, who have responsibility for virtually all non-migratory wildlife within the State.

Much of the earliest research concerned food habits. These studies, especially the ones based on stomach analysis, have led to the conclusion that deer will eat almost anything at some time during the year, either when it is most nutritious or when other foods are in short supply. A highly diverse habitat, which combines grasses, weeds, shrubs, and trees, should be provided as part of good deer management. As a result of this research, the U.S. Forest Service and many private timber companies now cut timber mainly in small tracts and leave groups of oaks and other hardwoods to provide this diversity. State wildlife departments also plant small patches of winter grass and clover to provide something green during the critical winter period. Prescibed fire is also used to reduce the height and density of certain browse species and to stimulate succulent and nutritious new growth.

State wildlife departments rarely have enough money, personnel, and equipment to perform more than "token" habitat improvement on their own. Massive habitat alteration is so costly that it must be done with the cooperation of the landowner as a modification of a timber sale, farming operation, etc. Where habitat improvement is not possible or cannot keep pace, deer herd managers manipulate the density of a herd in order to maintain its health.

Management of deer habitat at the fringes of whitetail range in the North and West is particularly difficult. When snow depths exceed 18 inches, deer usually remain in small areas where food is concentrated or there is shelter from the wind and cold, or preferably both. Here they often depend on a very few species of browse, so deer managers must work closely with foresters to protect and encourage those key species and, at the same time, maintain adjacent evergreen cover. Even under the best habitat management, deer herds near the limits of their range may decline significantly after a year or two of extreme, prolonged winter weather; but these herds may rebound quickly after several mild winters.

Pest control is rarely practiced in deer management. Natural predators are a serious problem only in isolated instances such as when an abnormally high coyote population is present and its members become skilled at finding new-born fawns. Dogs usually have to be controlled only near deer "yards," especially when the surrounding snow is deep and the crust is thick enough to support a dog but not a deer. No predator, insect, or disease has much effect on whitetail herds except at high deer densities. Therefore, the most practical management is to keep deer populations well below maximum density where they are individually healthy enough to resist most pests.

Individual herds are managed under different sets of objectives, depending on the desires of landowners and other local citizens. Some are managed for maximum sustained yield of deer for the benefit of the hunter; some, for minimum damage to forests, farm crops, orchards, ornamentals, or motor vehicles; some, for maximum public opportunity to observe deer; and still others, to provide the optimum mix of two or more such uses. The most difficult part of population management is knowing how many deer of which age and sex to

Even after the "velvet" has been rubbed off a buck's antlers, he may polish the regrown rack on trees.

remove each year to meet the objectives for that particular herd. Even though considerable research has been done, white-tailed deer are extremely difficult to "census." It is also becoming recognized, especially in the South, that only a deer can interpret its complex habitat realistically; biologists usually cannot detect the early stages of habitat deterioration without performing time-consuming browse surveys. For that reason, most management is prescribed and evaluated by monitoring the deer's reproduction, mortality, sex and age ratios, antler size, and average weights. Each of these sensitive yardsticks changes with density and habitat quality—the trick is in determining, usually by trial and error, what rate of reproduction, weight, etc. is best for that particular herd.

Hunting is by far the most economical way to achieve and maintain a particular deer density because of the free labor contributed by hunters. Hunters tend to be self-regulating in that they hunt harder when they are seeing lots of deer or signs of deer, and will remove more deer in areas where they are plentiful and fewer where they are scarce. You might also say that there is a built-in safety valve—the deer get wary and the hunters get weary long before an excessive harvest can take place.

The maximum sustainable yield of deer is attained by keeping herd density at about one-half to two-thirds of the maximum that the habitat would support if no hunting took place. Managers should keep populations at an even lower density if the herd threatens crops, and at a higher density if there is considerable public interest in observing deer. Deer are easier to kill at high density; thus the season must be short (or limited to bucks) if a high density is desired. Conversely, a low-density deer herd on good range will reproduce rapidly; thus hunting seasons designed to alleviate crop damage, produce the maximum yield, etc., require heavy hunting pressure directed at both sexes. Deer management thus becomes hunter management—we regulate hunter effort to achieve the desired density and health of the deer. Whether or not the objectives are being met is determined by looking at the deer that are killed to determine if they are achieving the desired reproduction, weights, and other indicators of well-being.

Thanks to the interest in managing deer so they will live compatibly with people, and the P-R monies that have been available, more research has been done and more is known about white-tailed deer and their habitat than any other wild animal. There is still much fine-tuning that needs to be done; but what we already know and the innate adaptability of the deer promise to keep them in their present position as our Number One big game animal.

Whitetails enjoy new browse growth in burned-over area.

Biologist uses radio tracking antenna to locate an animal bearing a radio transmitter. Radiotelemetry, developed largely with P-R funding, has been a breakthrough in determining wildlife movement patterns.

Substituting Facts for Myths

by Tony J. Peterle

Wildlife research was in its infancy when the Pittman-Robertson Act became law in 1937. Many of the Nation's valued birds and mammals were in serious trouble, their numbers sadly diminished and their habitats shrinking; also, the people who managed the States' wildlife agencies were chronically short of funds. The major advantage of the P-R law was to provide a continuous source of stable funding for wildlife research and management; it couldn't have come at a better time. The Dust Bowl was still a very real event, the extensive evergreen forests in the Lake States had been cut and burned over, productive wetlands in the Midwest were being drained and plowed, and wide expanses of rangelands in the West were overgrazed and eroded. Wildlife populations were being overexploited in some areas. This exploitation, together with habitat loss, had resulted in drastic reduction or even disappearance of wildlife species in some States. Quick-fix game farm rear-and-release programs didn't work, but little was known about the reasons why. With Pittman-Robertson money available for research, many States began to develop more accurate systems to survey their wildlife populations periodically. That led later to the studies of how best to restore habitats.

Another boost came from a quiet little program just then getting underway. Beginning in 1935, State wildlife agencies, the Federal government, and often the private sector as well, provided funding to State land-grant colleges and universities to undertake wildlife research through the new program of Cooperative Wildlife Research Units. The Co-op Units later were to grow and spread into 30 States. But even in the late 1930's, the Units were helping State wildlife agencies with needed studies, and developing small but influential cadres of potential research leaders. Graduates of the Units, familiar with State wildlife issues, were among the first hired by the State agencies. Other universities without Cooperative Wildlife Units also established excellent wildlife programs. The entire process of training and research was enhanced because graduate students could find employment, largely as a result of the developing Pittman-Robertson programs in the States.

By the late 1940's and early 1950's, the developing science of wildlife management was producing high-quality research to help managers make decisions. It wasn't long before an increasing number of researchers moved into management and administrative posts, developing a new breed of supervisors familiar with research concepts.

Restocking efforts continued during the early years of the P-R program, still with spotty results at first, but with a significant difference. The trial-and-error system was beginning to be scientifically documented, published, and dissemi-

Dr. Peterle, Professor of Zoology at Ohio State University, has had more than 30 years of research and teaching experience, working at both State and Federal levels. He has served The Wildlife Society as a Regional Representative, Vice-President and President, and has been Editor-in-Chief of the Journal of Wildlife Management for two terms.

nated in ever-widening circles. It soon became evident that habitats were an essential key to restocking success; that the genetic make-up of the birds and mammals transplanted was important in evaluating how these species would adapt to new environments; and that a sensible first step everywhere would be to regularly seek detailed information on existing wildlife populations, their sizes, locations, characteristics, and habitat needs.

The periodic species survey became the basis for further research. Population assessment continues to be a universal necessity—so much that some researchers question whether surveys ought to be counted against their budgets, because survey findings are also of direct importance in making management decisions. Surveys have become more sophisticated, getting deeply into the makeup of a wildlife population as related to male-female ratios, number of young born each year, rates of survival, population growth or decline, and so on. These data are now accepted as necessary, not only in fixing hunting season dates and bag limits, but in identifying issues still to be investigated.

A good wildlife manager now looks to his researchers for help in addressing many problems. Keeping hunters satisfied and wildlife populations self-sustaining is only part of his job. He must also develop plans to minimize damage done by wildlife to crops and domestic livestock—a problem that emerged in the earliest days of settlement and still remains; plans to make wildlife accessible to non-hunters, for educational values and esthetic enjoyment; and ways to cope with the impacts on wildlife of all sorts of substances discharged into our air, land, and water by American technology. The desperate struggle of endangered species has been added to this steadily lengthening list.

Research is called upon to define the basic nature of these problems; to provide techniques for information-gathering; to provide managers with options to solve problems; and to seek to predict the outcome of various decisions in relation to the long-term impacts on species, populations, and environments.

Facts produced by wildlife research have ranged from practical, management-oriented information to improve game populations or harvests, all the way to basic biological facts that seem, at first, to have no direct relationship to management decisions, but may later turn out to be critical. As the volume of available information began to build, some became buried in P-R reports in dusty archives, some was published in State or Federal bulletins, or in scientific journals, monographs, and books. Handling this vast amount of information on wildlife research and management became—in itself—a major challenge.

Much information has become more readily available to researchers and managers as a result of the recent development of the P-R-supported Fish and Wildlife Reference Service in Rockville, Maryland. Computerized search systems provide background material on a great variety of species, research accomplishments, and management techniques for planners, researchers, and managers throughout the Nation. All State P-R programs have access to this Reference Service, which leads to more efficient planning and less duplication of effort for researchers. Managers can and do review cost-efficient methods applied in other States before beginning research or development projects at their State level.

Research developed the methods for obtaining quick responses to questions from the public and hunters related to "How many deer did we kill?" or "How many geese were shot last weekend?" These answers were needed, not only to respond to questions from the public, but—over the long term—to predict future population trends, and to set hunting and trapping quotas to protect the welfare of the wildlife species being managed.

As the early P-R research projects began to produce solid, useful information about wildlife numbers and distribution, the type of research gradually shifted to better respond to the need for basic information about the biology of species and a better understanding of special habitat and nutritional needs. The public, particularly the avid hunters, sometimes could not understand why wildlife biologists needed to study the composition of microbes in the stomach of deer and elk, but these basic facts all came to be important to the understanding of digestive efficiencies, winter survival, and conversion of food to more fawns or calves. For years, biologists correctly recommended against feeding big-game herds during the late winter because these animals could not adapt to high-grade alfafa hay or grain. Research demonstrated that the unique fauna of deer, elk or antelope intestinal tracts was adapted to specific natural vegetation, and that artificial feeds were not digestible. Now, as a result of additional research, a suitable pelleted food has been developed that reduces winter mortality. Whether using this pelleted food is economically, politically, or ecologically the best thing to do in a given locality is still a matter for intelligent management decisions.

As big game populations recovered in a number of Western States, ranchers and landowners became concerned about competition between livestock and game, and about direct losses of crops to wildlife damage. Excellent State P-R research programs developed information on how to better manage deer, elk, bighorn sheep, and antelope in relation to livestock grazing. Detailed studies of food habits showed that on some ranges there was little overlap in diet as a result of seasonal use, while in other areas continuous livestock grazing and restriction of wildlife movements resulted in reduced habitat quality for all species. For some game species in some types of habitat, removal of certain plant species

Computers are now an essential part of wildlife research—used to retrieve information from many sources and to calculate wildlife population and habitat trends.

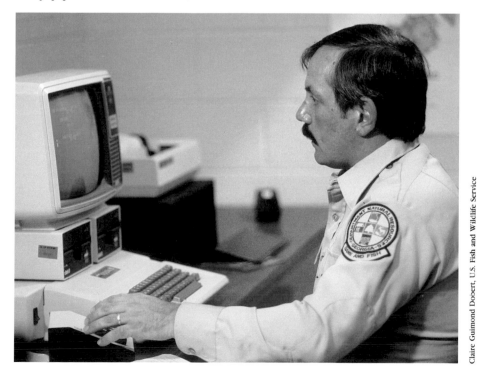

Claire Guimond Dooert, U.S. Fish and Wildlife Service

improved range quality; in other areas, controlled burning provided palatable plants of higher quality. There were some concerns as well over potential disease problems; several wildlife species were widely suspected of carrying and transmitting diseases to livestock. Although big game ungulates (hoofed animals) and livestock do harbor some diseases in common, research disclosed that the direct spread of disease as a result of concurrent use of habitat has not emerged as a serious problem. Cooperative studies among various States, particularly in the Southeast, have been important in evaluating losses caused by disease for both wildlife and livestock.

The computer age has made an enormous impact on wildlife research and management. Population indices and estimates, together with harvest surveys, have shown that some species can tolerate longer hunting seasons and greater harvests than people previously believed, without adverse effects. Population models show that about 30 percent of a healthy deer population—including does—can be harvested each year without reducing the next year's population. The hunting seasons for such short-lived species as ruffed grouse, cottontail, and fox and gray squirrels have been extended in many States. In some States the grouse season is four months long, and populations remain healthy within the limits set by natural fluctuations and habitat changes. For other species, we know that limiting mortality may be the only way to save the populations that remain. That is certainly true for the grizzly or brown bear in our Western States, where population models have shown that the bears' chance of surviving in a wide area may depend on sparing the lives of only two or three females a year. We know much about the brown bear and its cousin, the black bear, because of long-term research, aided by development of immobilizing techniques and improved radio-telemetry methods. These tools, too, were perfected largely by researchers with P-R funding.

Maine research biologists take measurements of a tranquilized bear.

Research has made a major difference in management of migratory bird species, a shared Federal-State responsibility. Researchers have shown that surveys of wetlands and of breeding birds can help predict autumn populations with considerable accuracy. We know that habitat loss and annual fluctuations in water levels are important factors in determining how many ducks fly south along the flyways and are available for harvest and for reproduction in the following breeding season. We know more about where ducks nest, how many nests are hatched, and how many are lost to predators, all as a result of radio-telemetry studies of breeding hens. Hen mallards, we now know, can tolerate high nesting densities, but those same densities make them more vulnerable to predators when they are on land. Research results have shown how to manage for waterfowl, how to improve their nesting areas, what kinds of habitat are needed during migration, how to prevent disease outbreaks, and how to reduce mortality once disease is found in the population. All of these research findings lead to recommendations for management. However, decisions are also obviously affected by social, economic, and political considerations. Wildlife managers must take into account other Federal and State programs related to agriculture, power production, reservoir impoundment, stream channelization, and flood control. But, without wildlife research, we would not have the correct information input to influence these management decisions.

Some of the most notable successes in P-R research have been related to the introduction of animals into areas where those species had never existed, or where they had vanished. P-R research was involved in how to determine critical elements in habitat, how to catch the animals, rear them in captivity, feed and transport them, and release them with the best opportunity to survive and reproduce.

Checking a mallard for avian influenza in a
Mid-Atlantic State cooperative study.

Gary Doster, Southeastern Cooperative Wildlife Disease Study, University of Georgia.

As discussed elsewhere in this book, the successful relocation and subsequent buildup of deer and wild turkey populations is one of the major modern success stories in American wildlife management. These achievements were made possible largely by research, which discovered locations of suitable habitat for repopulation, and provided better means for capture and handling of the animals being transported. Much of this research, as well as the actual capturing and transplanting, was accomplished with Pittman-Robertson funding. Early methods for immobilizing animals, such as administering ether on swabs, masks, and sprays, were ineffective and dangerous to use. Now, dart guns with safe and effective drugs are used to immobilize animals in traps and—sometimes—by shooting from aircraft. Effective mixtures of modern drugs and the use of antidotes has reduced trap-caused mortality, and animals can be transported and released in better condition. Radios that are attached by collars or harnesses, or are surgically implanted, are used to determine animal movements, locations and in some sophisticated studies even to determine heart rate and other physiological information. Some radios can be used to trigger a powered syringe to inject and immobilize free-ranging animals a second time for study.

Research has led the way to a better understanding of the dynamics of wild populations and, thus, of population management. The major key is the ability to gather appropriate information about the proportionate sex and age composition of, for example, a deer herd or a subpopulation of birds. Research has developed new methods for use on live animals as well as for postmortem examinations. Plumage and body structure characteristics in birds have been important for the determination of sex and age. Wing, bill, foot, and feather lengths and diameters can indicate sex and age in a variety of bird species. The weight of the eye lens increases with age and—for some mammal species—this method can be used to determine how old the animal is, up to 2 or 3 years. Tooth length, diameter, and pulp/enamel ratios can be used to determine the ages of various mammals. The enamel layers in mammal teeth are laid down much the same as rings in a tree, so some researchers have extracted a tooth from live animals (bears, for instance) for the purpose of determining age. Sex in some species of birds can be determined by chemically analyzing blood, urine or fecal droppings. Minor surgery (called laparotomy) is sometimes necessary to determine the sex of eagles, among other birds. The determination of the age and sex of individuals and groups in the population in necessary for inclusion in computer models of population growth or decline. If we understand the age and sex structure of the population of long-lived species, we can also understand specific reproductive rates for various ages of females and better predict the total rate of increase of the population. If we know the age structure, we can better understand the rate of mortality, and how this rate effects population status.

Research on animal feeding habits has advanced from simply determining what they eat to questions of why, where, and how much energy they use to get the food they need. We now better understand competition for food between deer, elk, antelope, and domestic livestock. We know how food preferences change with weather conditions, and in response to forest cutting, burning, or grazing by livestock.

Food preferences also change in relation to the season and reproductive state of the animals. Prior to nesting, hens of most waterfowl species select more animal foods than do males during the same period. More research effort is in progress to study waterfowl populations and their wintering grounds, with an eye toward management decisions that may help them return to their breeding areas in the best physical condition. Some wintering areas are better than others, and send back mallards to the breeding grounds in better condition following

This biologist is measuring out dosage of a drug to immobilize a mountain lion. The dose will be delivered in a special syringe fired from *the gun at his feet. Once captured, the animal can be safely handled, examined, and released.*

severe winter weather, but the various factors need more analysis. The great importance of good nutrition on the wintering grounds is just beginning to be understood.

Basic studies of animal behavior have been important to wildlife management. We know that dominance of certain individuals plays a role in reproductive success for many species of birds and mammals. Dominant sage grouse, prairie-chickens and pheasants do most of the breeding. In deer and elk, dominant stags have larger harems and do most of the breeding, but we also know under what circumstances some younger males find it possible to breed, as well. Hunter harvest of large trophy animals may not influence the actual rate of breeding, but we do not yet understand how this might relate to natural selection and to the future genetic composition of the population. Social systems in many animals are quite complex, and provide a fertile area for study as such systems might relate to management decisions.

Information on behavioral traits has been developed by research biologists to allow managers to count, survey, or census animals. Birds sing on territories and can be counted during the spring. Booming grounds or "leks" can be censused for various grouse species. Cooing mourning doves, crowing pheasants, and calling bobwhites and woodcock can be counted along survey routes. Wind, rain, and cold temperatures influence call-count surveys. Aerial counts of waterfowl and many large mammal species have proven to be an efficient means of surveying such populations, but research was necessary to determine the most opportune time to count, what proportion of the animals was being observed, and differences between results obtained from different aircraft types and different observers.

Wildlife habitats, some of which were purchased with P-R funding exclusively for research, have received an increasing share of attention with substantial results. Recent work has shown how to produce high-quality native foods for wildlife in wetlands, through carefully controlled water-level manipulation. These practices can often complement or even replace expensive time-consuming traditional cultivation of croplands for waterfowl and other wetland wildlife. Much of this pioneering research was done on State-owned lands purchased with P-R funds; the results have broad application in many parts of the United States as well as abroad.

Research to improve and expand methods of wildlife habitat inventory and evaluation has progressed, often aided by Pittman-Robertson funding. As a result, we are in a better position to predict the effects of large water-development projects on wildlife habitat, to provide standards for mitigation of habitat loss, and to better manage habitats for many species of wildlife on lands in varied ownerships.

As land-based resource use became more intense, and higher technology brought about the increased use of synthetic chemicals to enhance industrial and agricultural production, some of these toxic substances began to harm wildlife populations. Some such chemicals killed wildlife directly, while others produced long-term chronic effects, primarily on reproduction. Research developed an understanding of the entrance pathways and effects of accumulation of toxic wastes on wildlife populations, and provided data for the development of regulations and laws to protect both man and the environment from the effects of toxic chemicals. Some predatory birds, such as bald eagles and pelicans, were affected severely and served as a warning of environmental contamination—and perhaps also allowed us to avoid more serious impacts on other species, including humans.

On the other hand, chemicals have been used to control and remove pest animals that have caused public health problems or damage to crops and livestock. Some of these chemicals are immediately lethal, some are less toxic, and others simply cause wildlife to avoid the crop or area protected. Chemicals also have been used to alter vegetation for the benefit of wildlife species being managed. Methods of applying chemicals or dosing wild animals for the control of parasites and diseases are under investigation.

Chemical analyses of feathers from birds can indicate their general nesting areas. The development of more sophisticated chemical analytical procedures will permit further applications to wildlife research.

Wildlife research has greatly improved in design and conduct, and in the production of sound biological and statistical results that can be used for management purposes. Greater improvement is possible. Added emphasis on the peer review of research projects might improve their design, content, analytical procedures and probability of success. This might impinge on some decision-making by local and State research biologists, but the P-R law provides funds for review and control of research at the Federal level. Research direction and supervision could be strengthened at both the Federal and State levels. Many biologists who began their careers 20 or 30 years ago in the P-R research program need to be re-educated in more modern research approaches and techniques.

Pittman Robertson-supported research has had a great impact on the welfare of wildlife resources in the United States and abroad. Production of wildlife through research-based management options has improved populations, saved species, enhanced the harvest of wildlife by hunters, and improved the availability of wildlife for observation and enjoyment.

Increasing human population density, greater and more rapid use of our natural resources, the continuing reduction in wildlife habitat, and the pollutants associated with highly developed technology—all will require even greater research and management efforts if wildlife are to continue to be part of the American landscape. Wildlife populations will have to be managed more intensively on less land. Urbanization and agriculture are rapidly encroaching on habitats required by many wildlife species. If these species are to survive in suitable numbers for the benefit of man, research must be carried out to develop management schemes that are compatible, alternate habitats must be developed, and more intensive management must be applied to the limited habitat remaining. P-R supported research has a fine record of accomplishment over the past half century. It will have to be even better if wildlife is to retain its place in our culture during the next half century.

Seasonal dove count. Periodic population surveys are essential research tools.

Cooperative management agreements between State wildlife agencies and private land owners cover an average of 50 million acres nationwide at any given time.

Restoring a Land Base

by John R. Langenbach

When Congress wrote the Pittman-Robertson (P-R) Act, it used language that made clear its recognition that wildlife needs a land base "as feeding, resting, or breeding places." The law empowered the States to use P-R funds to obtain the needed properties—whether "by purchase, condemnation, lease, or gift."

Progress in setting aside lands for wildlife was slow in the early years. The State wildlife agencies needed to obtain assent legislation from their legislatures before they could participate, and only small amounts of money were available initially. During the first five years of the program a total of $8,310,600 in Federal dollars was available to the States, with some State apportionments only about $10,000 per year. Yet land acquisition was the first project in 13 of the States, and among the first five projects in 29 States. These 29 States acquired over 400,000 acres at a Federal cost of $2.5 million during that early spurt. During the first 15 years of the program, the States acquired in fee title over 1.5 million acres at an average cost of $12.57 per acre. On today's market, even if the same land types were available, the cost would be well over $200 million. (For each $75 of Federal money, States put up at least $25 while some contributed considerably more. The exact amounts the States paid out for land acquisition are largely unavailable, especially for the early years. Hence, only the Federal outlays are cited in this chapter.)

Naturally, the acquisition effort was aimed primarily at providing suitable habitat for "wildlife." However, the legislation did not define the term "wildlife" as to species. To most people at that time, it meant simply game birds and mammals. Yet the lands that were acquired and the habitat that was developed benefited all species, including man.

In many States the acquisition philosophy was to acquire any available habitat to prevent further loss or destruction. The Nation's wetlands were especially threatened, largely because of drainage programs vigorously supported by agencies in the Department of Agriculture. P-R projects in Iowa and Minnesota, for example, stressed the acquisition of the remaining marshes and waterfowl breeding habitat. Where there was multiple land ownership on a marsh, they often followed a strategy whereby the purchase of a single wedge or "piece of pie" would preclude any further drainage efforts. Although the total acreage acquired may have been small in comparison to some other State acquisition programs, the benefits far exceeded the amount of land by saving some of the remnants of vast waterfowl production areas in all the prairie "pothole" States.

In the early years of the program, most State fish and game departments did not have professional land appraisers on their staffs. Therefore, the Fish and

---

Mr. Langenbach spent nearly 40 years in the wildlife profession, mostly in Federal Aid, retiring as Chief of USFWS' Federal Aid Division. He earlier worked for the State wildlife agencies of Connecticut and Pennsylvania in research and management; was Assistant Director of USFWS' Patuxent Wildlife Research Center; and was a USFWS Assistant Regional Director-Operations.

Wildlife Service's Division of Lands (now Realty), with the use of P-R administrative funds, provided appraisals of areas approved for acquisition under the P-R program. The States, then using such appraisals, negotiated with the landowners. If agreement was reached but the agreed-upon price exceeded the appraisal, a justification by the State was needed.

With the post-World War II increase in available funds, the States stepped up their acquisition programs. As their programs expanded, they employed land appraisers, many of whom were trained and tutored with the assistance of the Service's Division of Realty.

Similarly, few States had professional engineers on their staffs adequately familiar with low-head water impoundment and control structures. Some States contracted with private engineering firms, but they too lacked expertise in this facet of water control, usually resulting in over-design. However, the Fish and Wildlife Service Engineering Division was recognized as the authority in this type of construction. The postwar boom permitted the States to employ engineers who, with the help, training, and guidance of Service personnel, became competent in this field, gradually reducing the States' dependence on the Federal Aid-financed Service engineers.

Acquiring Wetlands

The State acquisition and development of waterfowl habitat in the postwar period was enhanced by the passage of the Federal Aid in Sport Fisheries Restoration Act, or Dingell-Johnson (D-J) Act, in 1950. In certain cases, these new funds could be combined with P-R to acquire and develop aquatic habitats. The two programs shared the cost in proportion to the expected benefits for fish and for wildlife. Not only hunters and fishermen, but all people, be they birders, shutterbugs, hikers, picnickers, or just enjoyers of the outdoors, benefited from these programs.

To date, almost 2 million acres of waterfowl habitat have been acquired by the States under P-R. These areas range in size from small prairie potholes in the northern Great Plains, to sizable migration stopover areas in Oregon, Missouri and Arkansas, to vast tidal marshes and wintering areas in Louisiana, Texas and California. Naturally, the protection of these areas from needless drainage, farming, grazing and other intensive uses also helped all the local species from quail and rabbits to deer. Furbearers, songbirds, fish, amphibians, reptiles, and even the lowliest insect and worm enjoyed the glorious habitat provided.

Control of these waterfowl lands cost about $60 million; another $185 million was spent for development, operation, and maintenance of State waterfowl areas. (During roughly the same period, the Fish and Wildlife Service also purchased about 2 million acres for waterfowl on National Wildlife Refuges, and about 500,000 acres for Waterfowl Production Areas.)

Development of waterfowl areas covered a gamut of activities depending on the condition of the site and the expected use. In the prairie pothole region of the northern plains—Minnesota to Montana and south to Nebraska—the principal management tool was fencing to exclude domestic livestock. The old adage that the most efficient and economical game management tool is the three-strand barbed-wire fence still holds true. In some instances, the plugging of a drainage outlet and the encouragement of nesting cover converted the pothole into a productive area. Such actions also greatly benefited resident game species—pheasants, Hungarian partridge, prairie grouse and quail, as well as deer and antelope.

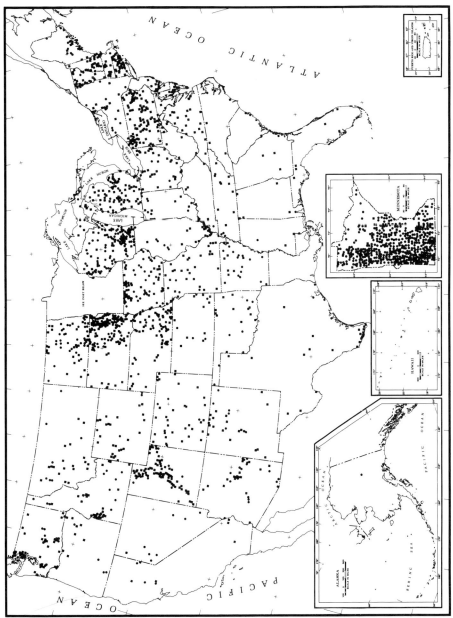

This map shows where States have used P-R funds to acquire lands "in fee title" or to control lands through easement agreements on behalf of wildlife. Note heavy concentration of small wetland areas in "prairie pothole" region of the Upper Midwest.

71

Dams for Ducks

In many of the major waterfowl-oriented units, more elaborate undertakings were essential to provide the habitat required. Low-head dams, dikes and levees with necessary water control structures were developed. These could vary from minor contour levees to stairstep the shallow impoundments (commonly used in the States in the Mississippi Delta) to elaborate water diversions and impoundments. The Duck Creek-Mingo National Wildlife Refuge joint venture diverted water from the Castor River into the Mingo Swamp of southeast Missouri to be used by both the Federal and State wildlife agencies in the prescribed water management program.

On the 75,000-acre Rosseau project in Minnesota the water was diverted from Pine Creek in Manitoba, Canada. This required considerable negotiation which included the State of Minnesota, the Province of Manitoba, the U.S. Fish and Wildlife Service, the Canadian Wildlife Service, the U.S.-Canadian International Boundary Commission, and other agencies, all consummated by the Wildlife Management Institute, which acted as the banker to legalize the transfer of funds from the State of Minnesota to the Canadian contractor who did the work. It was a real accomplishment in international cooperation, yet at reasonable cost for the benefits derived.

Along with water control, adequate feeding units were necessary, especially in management of Canada geese. Food was necessary to attract and hold migrating geese and also to reduce their depredations on private agricultural land. Many landowners did not take kindly to the big-footed gray birds gobbling up their corn and soybeans and grazing on their fall-planted grain crops. This was an important issue on the southern Illinois complex initiated by the State at Horseshoe Lake, later fortified by Union County and then extending to the Crab Orchard National Wildlife Refuge and still later to the State of Kentucky's Ballard County unit. It has been estimated that this complex has been host to about 75 percent of the Canada geese migrating along the Mississippi River. Thus, agricultural cropping by the States was and is an important facet in providing a well-rounded waterfowl management area.

Maintenance Costs

Naturally, with such large capital outlays, maintenance and operation became important and costly ventures. Frequently, the cost of providing substantial acreages of agricultural crops exceeded all other annual management costs. The original P-R Act did not provide for maintenance or management. However, an amendment signed July 24, 1946 permitted maintenance of capital improvements acquired or constructed with P-R funds; an August 12, 1945 amendment authorized States to use P-R funds for management of wildlife and of human activities on acquired areas.

Many State waterfowl areas were acquired adjacent to, or in conjunction with, units of the National Wildlife Refuge System. These included numerous types of waterfowl habitat, from the prairie pothole production areas of the Great Plains to the areas where migratory ducks and geese stopped for food and rest, to the wintering grounds of forested river bottoms, and resting reservoirs with adjacent feeding grounds and coastal marshes. Every State has participated in one or more facets of the waterfowl program and together they have spent more than $45 million in grants from Pittman-Robertson on waterfowl research and inventory activities.

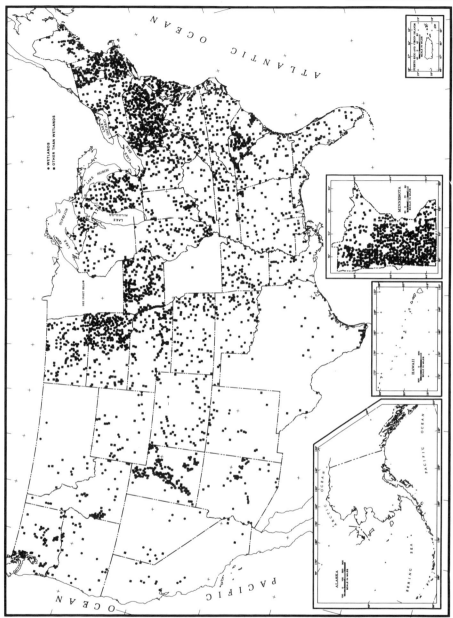

This map shows areas where P-R funds are being used by State wildlife agencies for active land management and operations. Included are areas owned outright by the States, plus others managed under cooperative agreements with Federal and private land owners. Some States prefer to use their own funds for such management so they can use their P-R allotments for other kinds of wildlife projects.

In the State waterfowl programs, cooperative agreements were negotiated with Federal agencies controlling land and water. These agencies included the Army Corps of Engineers, Bureau of Reclamation, Bureau of Land Management, Forest Service, Bureau of Indian Affairs (on specific tribal lands), Tennessee Valley Authority, Fish and Wildlife Service, military installations, etc. Lands held by agencies in State government were also the subject of mutually beneficial agreements as were waterfowl habitats controlled by private foundations, timber companies, oil companies, and other industries.

Nonhunters Benefit, Too

In the post-World War II period, with the large increases in P-R funds, opportunities arose to set aside wildlife management areas providing not only excellent habitat for most native species of birds, mammals, and even plants, but also some first-rate opportunity for public use. The nonhunting public which continues to visit these areas includes students on school field trips, birdwatchers, nature photographers, hikers, picnickers, swimmers, berry-pickers, snowmobilers, etc.

Use of State-owned wildlife management areas by the nonhunting public tends to outnumber use by hunters where the lands are within reasonable driving distance of major metropolitan areas. The State of Michigan, for example, found that its southern wildlife management areas were used by non-hunting recreationists up to 20 times as much as by hunters. Actually, this is not surprising, as in most States major game species are hunted only 30 to 60 days

Perhaps 75 percent of all Canada geese migrating along the Mississippi River use a complex of wetlands acquired with P-R aid in Union County, Illinois and nearby in both Illinois and Kentucky — all augmenting a Federal wildlife refuge in the same vicinity.

Paul Willms, Illinois Department of Conservation

74

each year, which leaves over 300 days for a host of nonhunting users. Many of these users were hunters who learned of the areas from their hunting forays, then came back with family, friends and relations to share the outdoor experience. Such increased public use put an additional burden on the States for sanitary facilities, potable water, parking areas, structures to aid the physically handicapped, etc. All these facilities used by the general public were provided by self-imposed taxes on the sportsmen without the need for any State or Federal general tax revenue.

Upland Acquisitions

In addition to waterfowl, Pittman-Robertson funds were used by the States to acquire an almost equal amount of land for other game species. These acquisitions varied in size from over 76,000 acres on the Catoosa Wildlife Management Area in Tennessee to the 34-acre Bahr Creek Area in Wisconsin. The larger management areas were primarily for such big game as elk, deer, bear, bighorn sheep, wild turkey, etc., with many benefits to grouse, squirrels, quail, rabbits, etc. The Bahr Creek Area acquired by Wisconsin was made a refuge to protect migrating birds of prey "riding" the updraft created by the dunes on the Lake Michigan shore. Operation of the area was accepted by the Milwaukee Museum and locally interested bird-study groups. This probably was the first acquisition (1949) using P-R funds specifically for nongame species.

Along with outright purchase of land, an extensive program of cooperative agreements, leases or other land-use devices provided additional millions of acres for the hunter and the general public. One of the largest is the State of Florida's management of surface use of about 1.5 million acres in the Everglades under a comprehensive cooperative agreement involving several agencies including the U.S. Army Corps of Engineers.

The Western States in particular acquired large tracts of big game habitat, primarily for elk and deer, but numerous species were benefited, principally through elimination of grazing by domestic livestock. The initial development on these ownerships was usually fencing, not only to keep domestic livestock out, but also to provide an area highly attractive to big game, especially elk, thereby reducing wildlife depredations to orchards, haystacks and other domestic crops on neighboring private land. In addition, other activities were initiated to benefit the habitat, the game, the hunter, and the public. Such things as food plots, watering tanks, and forest openings greatly enhanced the population of grouse, quail, chukar partridge, and a host of other species of animals and plant life.

In many instances, these tracts of private land acquired by the States abutted lands controlled by other State and Federal agencies, particularly the U.S. Forest Service, the U.S. Bureau of Land Management, and State forests. Cooperative agreements ensured the consideration of wildlife. Frequently, the acquisition of private tracts included the ranchers' grazing permits on the adjacent Federal land, which the State then retired to eliminate overgrazing.

Cooperative Agreements

Not all cooperative agreements involved gaining control of land use on Federal land. Some were negotiated directly with the landholding agencies to open large areas to increased habitat improvement, and to open the land to greater use by the hunter and the general public. Many such lands were inaccessible to the public due to closed private land which blocked entry, or because there were no roads or trails leading inward. Sometimes the terrain was just too rough, and an entry route would be too costly or would cause environmental damage. Therefore, the States acquired title or perpetual easements to access routes that were compatible with the environment and acceptable to the landowner. Many of these were dual-purpose agreements, providing access to fishing waters also, and involving participation with the Dingell-Johnson program. Over 800 public access sites were acquired at a cost of over $1 million in Federal outlays. The development of these sites cost more than $3.25 million and involved 40 States. They opened up hundreds of thousands of formerly inaccessible Federal and State acres.

Even though the primary reason for the increased access was to benefit the hunter, the total use by non-hunting outdoor enthusiasts exceeded visits for hunting. Fishermen, hikers, and others made extensive use of them.

Total figures for all such agreements cannot be accurately compiled because the agreements were generally of limited duration. In fact, the number of such agreements with private landowners and the acreage involved varies from year to year, but averages over 50 million acres nationwide. Every State has participated in this type of activity in one form or another.

Although this emphasis covered more land in the West, it was equally important in the East and South. Here the agreements were with the U.S. Department of Defense, the U.S. Forest Service, other State landholdings and such private landowners as forest products, oil, and mining companies.

Working With Farmers

Many States were held back by land prices, especially on land for quail, pheasants, cottontail rabbits, and other small game. These species, known commonly as farm game, inhabit and breed primarily on private agricultural land. In order to provide access to and an opportunity to hunt on farm lands, the States devised a host of incentive programs, activities, and relationships with the landowner—farmer or rancher. The myriad practices that evolved from these programs cannot be listed in this brief summary of cooperative farm-game habitat development. The minimum compensation was probably in the form of seed for annual food plots or perennial plants, shrubs and trees.

Probably the oldest and most extensive program of this type is the Pennsylvania Cooperative Farm-Game Program. It provides hunter access to the farm, but also designates refuges and safety zones (protected areas surrounding occupied buildings) where hunting is prohibited. For this the landowner could be paid to plant food plots, nesting areas or permanent cover, raise State-provided pheasant chicks to be released on site (a favored activity for the 4-H program), leave unharvested part of a regular crop (corn for winter food or hay for nesting), etc. Meanwhile, the State established and posted refuges and safety zones; erected signs showing the rules, regulations and boundaries; provided additional law enforcement officers during the hunting season; offered assistance in soil conservation practices like contour farming, crop rotation, farm-pond construction; and similar activities which benefited the land, the farmer and farm game.

In the late 1940's, a cost analysis was made on four Cooperative Farm-Game Projects. The study revealed that the cost to the Pennsylvania Game Commission, which gets its funds from the hunter, for the privilege of hunter access to farm game hunting, was about 50 cents per acre per year. As of July 1, 1985, the State had 184 Cooperative Farm-Game Projects in 58 counties, covering almost 2.5 million acres owned by well over 20,000 farmers. This program coupled with other types of leasing programs with private forest landowners, such as the Cooperative Forest Game Program, is making available 5,500,000 acres to the hunters who pay for the program and also to the general recreation-seeking public.

Every State has some from of program of land control on wildlife management areas operating under the P-R program. Collectively, these lands encompass almost 50 million acres. This land is under State control due to "acquisition by purchase, condemnation, lease or gift." All four forms of acquiring land for hunters and the general public have been used under the P-R program. However, condemnation—the right of eminent domain—has been used very rarely because the States have been reluctant to employ this process except in cases where judicial procedure was necessary to clear the title to the land. This is generally termed "friendly" condemnation, as both parties agree to the process.

Passage of the Uniform Relocation Assistance and Real Property Acquisition Act of 1970 (P.L. 91-646), aimed at correcting abuses and inconsistencies in certain Federal programs, tended to complicate the acquisition process and caused some State administrators initially to employ various other forms of leases and cooperative agreements to which the new law did not apply. However, States have gained experience under the standards of this law and landowners now enter into sales agreements with increased assurance of fair treatment.

60 Percent of P-R Funds

In the first 50 years, the obtaining of land control and the ensuing development, operation, management and maintenance of these areas has utilized well over $800 million, or about 60 percent, of the P-R funds available. The States have matched that sum with at least $270 million of their own, virtually all of it from hunters' license fees.

To speculate on the future is, perhaps, an exercise in futility. Nevertheless, land acquisition by purchase in fee title using P-R funds will probably continue to decline for two principal reasons: (1) a predicted leveling or future decrease of revenue from the taxes earmarked by the Act; and (2) the increasing cost of land coupled with further statutory requirements.

Similarly, the acreage under cooperative agreements between the States and other public agencies will probably not increase appreciably, as the most desirable areas are already covered. However, there certainly will be adjustments, addenda and other changes to accommodate the ever-changing conditions in State-Federal relationships. The States' development, operation, maintenance, and even management of specified high-use areas for hunters and the general public is expected to increase.

By the same token, there could well be a strong increase in various forms of cooperative agreements, leases and other land-use instruments between the States and private landowners. Many large tracts owned by oil, mineral, timber and industrial companies may be brought under varying types of cooperative agreements for public hunting. In many instances, this is a well-used local public relations tool which is beneficial to the industry and the public.

The need for small-game hunting opportunity will undoubtedly increase in direct proportion to the loss of public access to privately owned hunting areas. Thus, more, and more kinds, of cooperative agreements between the States and private landowners, primarily farmers and ranchers, can be anticipated. This may increase the total acreage available to the hunting public, and the general public, on a nationwide basis.

Helicopter seeds and fertilizes newly cut-over forest area in Oregon. The new grass will stabilize soil and provide food for elk.

Managing Habitat

by Keith W. Harmon

Without habitat there is no wildlife. Although widely accepted today, this truism was not so self-evident half a century ago.

Habitats differ as do the species occupying them. And habitats change with time, sometimes due to natural causes, sometimes because of human activities. European settlers made sweeping changes in North America's habitats. They felled the forests and plowed the prairies. Their descendants continue to do so.

As human-induced habitat changes threatened many wildlife species, a national concern began to surface. This turn-of-the century concern centered on protection of the animal—bounty payments for predators, curtailment of hunting and restocking of game birds and mammals. But little attention was given to whether the needed habitat was present. As a result, successes were limited, and, for the most part, wildlife continued to decline.

While the Pittman-Robertson Act recognized that to survive wildlife needed places to feed, rest and breed, its passage in 1937 did not automatically usher in enlightened management. Few wildlife agencies, State or Federal, were staffed or funded to deal with habitat even when the need was apparent. Years of trial and error passed before the young wildlife profession settled on a course of actively managing habitats to make them more productive and supportive.

Luck played a major part in the early P-R years. The searing drought of the 1930's eventually yielded to increased moisture, and then uncropped fields on farms and ranches that had been abandoned during the Great Depression began to grow profuse stands of untamed vegetation favored by many wildlife species. On Western ranges, big game restocking became more successful than previously, thanks largely to the newly abundant food and cover.

As deer, elk and pronghorn antelope herds expanded, and new Pittman-Robertson research findings came on line, the States directed more effort to habitat as a means of managing animal populations.

Many Western deer and elk herds spend spring, summer and fall at high-mountain altitudes in the publicly-owned national forests. As winter settles in, deep snows make this range uninhabitable, forcing deer and elk to move to lower elevations where snow depths are less. Here the land often is privately owned. On both ranges, land-use conflicts arise, requiring different solutions.

A host of decisions that affect wildlife are made on the "multiple-use" Federal lands. The States use P-R funds to coordinate with the Federal land management agencies to ensure that wildlife habitat needs will be considered—and accommodated to some degree—in their plans for managing timber, grazing, recreation, etc. The old cliche that "good timber and range management are good wildlife management" is no longer accepted as gospel. coordination is required in early planning to modify timber production and harvest plans to incorporate practices that affect forest openings; size, timing and distribution

---

Dr. Harmon, Field Representative for the Wildlife Management Institute, has devoted more than 20 years to habitat-related programs, including protection of wetlands, farm wildlife restoration, and protection of in-stream water flows for wildlife. He also has worked on economics of wildlife and land use and governmental programs affecting habitats.

of cuts; diversity of resulting vegetation; and road construction and closure, so that results will generally benefit wildlife.

Similar coordination also is needed for grazing allotment management plans on Federal lands to reserve adequate forage for wildlife, exclude livestock from critical habitats, regulate livestock numbers, and determine seasons and lengths of time livestock may graze given areas. Needed modifications of grazing and timber management plans to benefit wildlife cannot be left to chance, particularly as demands for economic outputs increase.

In addition to coordination, Pittman-Robertson dollars are used directly for habitat work on public lands. To increase deer and turkey numbers on the Kisatchie National Forest, Louisiana constructed fencing to restrict livestock grazing. In South Carolina, P-R monies were used to develop wild turkey habitat on the Francis Marion National Forest, while Virginia established clearings, waterholes and other management practices for deer and turkey on the George Washington and Jefferson National Forests and several State forests.

A number of Federal laws require that wildlife habitat be considered on public lands, which gives State wildlife agencies at least legal entree to the planning coordination process. Where big game herds winter on private lands, no such authority exists. Private recreation, housing developments and ranching operations therefore continue to reduce habitat on historical big game winter range. Often, purchasing the land to head off development is the only alternative. Montana, for example, used P-R funds to acquire land in the Blackfoot-Clearwater, Sun River and Judith River Game Ranges. Currently Utah continues to expand its holdings in the Twelve Mile, Lost Creek and Lake Fork-Mill Fork big game winter ranges.

Once in State ownership, winter range for big game is often manipulated to maintain plant vigor and productivity. These manipulations include planting of browse species, reducing height and density of taller woody vegetation and rejuvenating over-age browse plants. Rejuvenation of browse, for example, is generally accomplished by removing or reducing unpalatable woody growth with herbicides, controlled burning or mechanical means such as hand pruning or crushing with huge chains or discs pulled by dozers. When the old growth is removed, the plant is stimulated to sprout new palatable growth from the root system. Prescribed burning is gaining wider acceptance. Where appropriate and correctly applied, fire provides excellent results at low costs.

P-R funds are used on public lands in the arid Southwest for constructing watering facilities to benefit scaled, mountain, valley and Gambel's quail. Because the distance these birds can travel is limited, the distances between water sources may limit their distribution and numbers. By installing watering sites at proper locations, populations of these and other species can be considerably expanded. A popular watering device called the "gallinaceous guzzler" was developed in the Southwest and became common in much of the arid habitat of the Western States. It consists of a watertight storage basin or tank with a rain-collecting apron and a cover to reduce evaporation.

The States increasingly have used P-R funds for other forms of coordination on Corps of Engineers, Bureau of Reclamation and Soil Conservation Service public works projects. These agency projects generally include dams, channelization of streams and drainage of wetlands, which may eliminate or degrade important wildlife habitat. A number of Federal laws now provide for preventing or offsetting habitat losses, but the degree of consideration that must be given wildlife is not defined. Therefore, the amount of habitat saved or replaced depends on aggressive coordination by the State wildlife agency during the planning process.

Paul Willms, Illinois Department of Conservation

Food plot planted specifically for wildlife. The sorghum is planted close to two kinds of cover—woody and grassy/weedy—and therefore is available to birds and mammals large and small, game and nongame.

Although lost habitat seldom is fully replaced, various methods are used to offset losses. The level of mitigation, as it is called, depends on the success of the coordination effort. Most frequently, excess project lands are leased free of charge to the State wildlife agency for management. It may then establish tree and shrub plantings, grass-legume nesting cover and food plots. Where the lay of the land is suitable, small water impoundments may be constructed for waterfowl management. For the most part, these mitigation areas are open to public hunting.

Nowhere has habitat loss been more dramatic and widespread than on private agricultural land. Prior to the 1940's, drought and the Depression littered the Midwest and northern plains with abandoned cropland. As rainfall increased, habitat improved, creating a situation to the liking of the introduced ring-necked pheasant. During the next 10 years, hunters in the Dakotas, Minnesota, Iowa and Nebraska harvested an estimated 80-plus million pheasants. But soon, advancing technology and growing demand for food and fiber changed all that. Idle cropland went under the plow, and the small family farm, raising a variety of crops, increasingly was replaced by large operations dependent on large capital and energy investments to grow a single crop. Odd parcels of uncultivated land and weedy fencerows no longer had a place in the scheme of things, nor do they today.

*Constructing a dike and water impoundment
system, Crex Meadows Wildlife Area, Wisconsin.*

With Pittman-Robertson dollars, State agencies attempted to bolster declin-ing farm-wildlife habitat through cooperative programs with farmers. In return for setting aside small areas, the States provided fencing material to exclude livestock, and planted trees, shrubs and grasses and legumes. In a different approach, Ohio and Pennsylvania used P-R funds to purchase uncut hay crops for nesting cover and standing grain for food plots. Existing woody cover was leased for winter habitat. In South Dakota, where blizzards can eliminate a wintering population of pheasants in a few hours, the wildlife agency established wide shelterbelts or improved existing ones.

Despite this effort, only a minute portion of the cropland acreage was touched, and pheasant numbers continued to dwindle. By the mid-1960's, few pheasant States still operated cooperative programs with private landowners. The wildlife agencies' emphasis shifted to acquiring and managing their own land. Habitat developments on State-owned lands consisted of tree and shrub plantings, establishing nesting cover and planting annual food plots. As an econ-omy measure, most States depend on sharecropping with local farmers to establish and maintain such habitat. Although acquisition of land has benefited pheasants in some localities, regional populations remain depressed compared to a generation ago.

Use of P-R funds for providing bobwhite quail habitat in the East and Southeast paralleled those of the pheasant States. Cooperative efforts on private land began in the 1940's, and mainly consisted of furnishing lespedeza seed or seedlings for establishing cropland field borders. Unlike the programs in the pheasant range, private-land habitat programs for quail persisted into the 1970's, after which these States also directed their P-R funds to acquiring their own land.

For several reasons, mainly higher prices for cropland (potential quail habitat) compared to forested land and an increasing interest in deer and turkey, few of the lands acquired by the States held potential for quail management. Where such potential did exist on lands acquired, strips of cropland were allowed to revert to annual weeds favored by quail for a period of years until woody vegetation began to invade. The site then was disced to eliminate or set back shrub stages, and again allowed to produce annual weeds. Adjacent to these sites, food plots of corn, sorghum or other grains were planted by local farmers under sharecropping agreements, whereby the State's share was left standing for winter food and cover. In large measure, however, the P-R private-land program for quail was never successfully replaced by other habitat programs.

The major share of P-R funds spent for quail, rabbits, pheasants and other farm-associated wildlife still is directed to State-owned lands, with only minor amounts used to address habitat problems on private land. Several States have begun to establish and manage nesting cover in roadside ditches in intensively farmed areas. Others have secured supplemental, dedicated funds (habitat stamps, for example) that are used to pay landowners annual rental payments for establishing and/or maintaining existing habitat. The amount of acreage affected is limited by available funds.

The first project approved under the P-R program was Utah's Ogden Bay Waterfowl Unit. Other States quickly followed that example. Oregon acquired the Sauvie Island Waterfowl Area, Kansas the Cheyenne Bottoms, Missouri its Fountain Grove Waterfowl Area and Wisconsin the famous Horicon Marsh.

These early waterfowl habitat projects usually involved restoration or creation of aquatic habitat to realize their potential. Utah's Ogden Bay project consisted of constructing exterior and interior dikes to control water diverted from the Weber River. Flood flows from the Grand River provided Missouri's Fountain Grove areas with water following construction of a system of dikes.

The water table is so close to the surface of the land in some wet meadow areas that new surface water can be created for breeding ducks or geese simply by level ditching, as was done here. In background is a natural pothole.

Ken Moum, South Dakota Wildlife, Parks and Forestry

Controlled burning of old undergrowth clears the way for newer and more tender plant life, benefiting many wild species.

Mississippi Department of Wildlife Conservation

Research has demonstrated that waterfowl produce at peak levels on the northern prairies where there is a combination of grasslands and small scattered wetland areas. To waterfowl's misfortune, their prime breeding grounds lie in the heart of the Nation's grain-producing region where wetlands often are viewed as potential cropland. Wetland losses have been drastic.

Few real choices presently exist for protecting waterfowl habitat where drainage can mean attractive economic returns. The "Prairie Pothole" States have thus far concentrated on acquisition. Three States—Minnesota and the Dakotas—account for about 25 percent of all the P-R funds expended nationwide to acquire waterfowl habitat.

Habitat development on small waterfowl production wetlands is less spectacular than that on larger wintering and migration areas. In the arid northern plains, naturally fluctuating water levels alternately expose and reflood wetland basin soil, producing a variety of aquatic plants and insects needed by breeding waterfowl and their young. In limited cases, low-head dams have been constructed to increase water depths in very shallow wetlands (seldom deeper than three feet).

When possible, each area purchased for breeding waterfowl includes some adjoining upland. These uplands, normally in crops before being acquired, are seeded to native and introduced grass-legume mixtures to provide nesting cover for ground-nesting species such as mallards and pintails. Long-term management to maintain plant vigor involves periodic discing or burning. Burning is especially useful where native grasses and legumes are used.

Loss of wetlands in the Mississippi Delta States, Texas and California likewise has been severe, which is bad news for wintering waterfowl. Once wetlands have been acquired in these areas, habitat development is usually intensive and expensive. In the Delta, for example, providing flooded timber (greentree reservoirs) for wintering waterfowl may require extensive diking, water control facilities and pumping of water. When the water is drained (or recedes naturally) during the growing season to prevent killing important trees and shrubs, selective timber harvesting may be used to favor trees which produce mast (acorns, for example) for species such as the wood duck. Such high quality wetlands determine wintering waterfowl's health and ability to reproduce at desired levels when they return to the prairie breeding grounds.

In California, not only have many wetlands been eliminated, but historical water supplies also are diverted to sustain a large irrigated agricultural economy. Intricate water-rights agreements are necessary, as well as extensive water control facilities, to permit intensive State management of the few remaining wetlands for wildlife. The costs of managing wintering habitat compared to breeding habitat is unavoidably expensive. For example, California has used 15 percent of all P-R funds expended nationwide for waterfowl management as opposed to Minnesota, which has expended only 4 percent. Yet both have equally aggressive waterfowl programs.

Although P-R funded habitat programs have concentrated on selected game species, a multitude of nongame species also have benefited. Many people and organizations currently espouse the concepts of diversity, holistic and/or ecosystem management as the ultimate goal. Unfortunately, they take them beyond "real-world" limits. Every acre of land cannot produce everything, and each land-use decision, even one to leave land unmanaged under the Wilderness Act, favors some species (game and nongame) over others. While certain nongame species may not thrive at desired levels in a game-oriented habitat program, nongame species as a broad group have benefited much more with it than without. Least bitterns and marsh wrens fare better in a prairie wetland saved and managed for mallards than one drained and raising wheat or corn. Bald eagles and catbirds fare better in a streamside habitat protected and managed for deer than one grazed and trampled by livestock.

Monies provided by the Pittman-Robertson Act, along with hunting license revenues which under the Act may not be diverted to non-wildlife purposes, have financed a habitat program unequaled anywhere in the world. While it may fall short of halting or reversing overall habitat losses in the face of an ever-expanding human population, wildlife and habitats would be far worse off without it. The foundation for future action has been tested for 50 years and found to be firm. With the flexibility to accommodate change as needed, P-R will remain the crown jewel of wildlife habitat management for another 50 years.

Adjustment of water levels helps the same area to accommodate different species.

The seven major ecological regions of the lower 48 United States, as set forth in this map, follow the basic outlines defined by distinguished American geologist and geographer Nevin M. Fenneman in 1928, and used by scientists ever since. For the sake of brevity, Alaska is treated in this book as a single region although it contains several ecological regions of its own. The "Fenneman" maps used to introduce chapters in this section of the book are intended only to depict regions with certain common characteristics, and not to indicate ranges or distributions of any wildlife species.

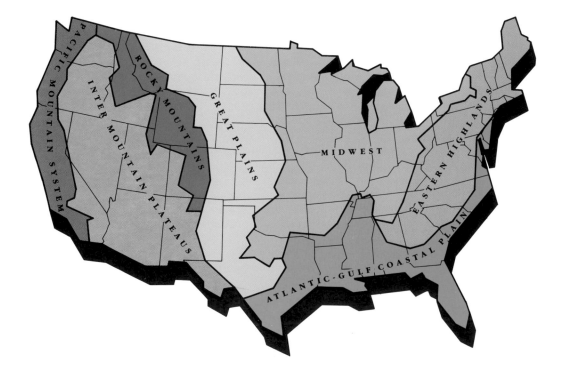

Species and Regions

The explorers and early settlers who came to North America, and the generations who succeeded them, were united by a sense of mission to civilize this wild continent and make it productive for them and their kind. It was surely one of the most ambitious goals in human history, and it resulted in enormous changes to the land's basic character. Wildlife, always a product of the land, was affected drastically—first by indiscriminate killing, and later by the disappearance of habitats under the plow, the axe, and other tools of civilization. So severe and widespread were the impacts that as the 20th Century dawned, even conservationists accepted as inevitable that wildlife would disappear entirely, although they felt it important to postpone the sad day as long as possible.

How conditions reached that point in great regions of the United States will be sketched in the next eight chapters. Each chapter will focus on a wild species typical of the region, how it declined, and its partial restoration, thanks to scientific wildlife management.

Scientific management was little more than a concept 50 years ago. Its growth and development since then have reversed the trend of thinking about wildlife resources, which now are recognized as renewable. It was the scientific approach which put systematic research into the picture and thus led to effective restoration of animal populations, management of wildlife harvests and habitats, and other biological support systems.

The Pittman-Robertson Federal Aid in Wildlife Restoration Act has contributed more than any other law to this process of learning, healing, and restoring in every State. It has received significant help from many other laws in the past half century aimed at improving management of soils, forests, rangelands, air and water. Pittman-Robertson is not a cure-all; wildlife is influenced even more by economic pressures, changes in land use, altered farming and ranching and forestry practices, and major shifts in public attitudes. How all these factors have affected wild populations will also be discussed in the following chapters.

Still another chapter, later on, will examine how Pittman-Robertson and other influences are interacting on wildlife in the special environments that exist in the Hawaiian Islands and the United States' mid-ocean commonwealths and territories.

Each author is an experienced authority on the species and region under discussion, and each one has been encouraged to state his or her own scientific views and conclusions. The opinions thus expressed are their own and do not necessarily reflect governmental policies at either Federal or State levels.

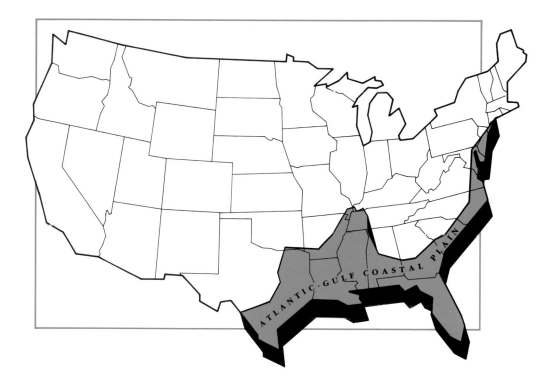

Wood Duck Domain: The Coastal Plain

by Joseph P. Linduska

All along our Coastal Plain and the attendant great sodden basin of the lower Mississippi, it's "water, water, everywhere"— and scarcely a drop absents the wood duck. More than any other type of wildlife, this popular and plentiful bird identifies with this unique area. But a great host of others also find the makings of a good life here. So much so, that it can fairly claim to sustain more kinds of wildlife, in greater numbers, than any region of comparable size in the United States.

This vast water-world that makes up our Atlantic-Gulf Coastal Plain begins at Cape Cod and Nantucket, skips down to embrace Long Island and, in an ever-widening serpentine arc, wends south and west, taking in the New Jersey

Dr. Linduska has served the U.S. Fish and Wildlife Service as Chief of Game Management, Associate Director, and Senior Scientist. He also has been Vice President for Science of the National Audubon Society, and Director of Conservation for Remington Arms Company. Now retired, he remains active as an outdoors writer. He is author of two books and numerous technical and popular articles.

pine barrens and all but the northern tip of Delaware. Meandering southward, it easily includes the great Chesapeake and Delaware Bays, then continues on to surround two of the Nation's mighty swamps—Great Dismal and Okefenokee— along with the seaward halves of both the Carolinas and Georgia and all of Florida. In Alabama, it jig-saws northward as far as Cape Girardeau in southeast Missouri, then winds south and west to end on the Rio Grande in Texas. Wood ducks follow it throughout its breadth and length.

Including its diversionary bulge northward along the Mississippi River, the Atlantic-Gulf Coastal Plain is over 2,500 miles long and embraces more than 300 million acres of highly diversified land and water. From its slice-like beginning in New York to southern Georgia, its inland edge is determined by the fall line, an escarpment that marks the inner margin of an ancient sea. It is here that inland waters in their path to the ocean spill over the hard rock of the continental plateau onto the softer sands and clays below. Cataracts and falls of varying size mark the place as well as the end of ocean-to-inland ship travel. New York, Philadelphia, Baltimore, Richmond and other great cities of our eastern sea-board are perched atop the fall line.

One additional feature adds to the variety of habitats which characterize this region—the longest stretch of barrier islands in the world. The chain begins off Long Island and hugs the coast for 2,500 miles to the southern tip of Florida, then extends for an additional 1,300 miles along the Gulf Coast to Mexico. Among the most fragile of the earth's formations, they serve, nonetheless, as our foremost bastion in protecting the mainland from assault by the sea, particularly a sea whipped to full fury by a tropical storm, northeaster or hurricane. Within such barrier islands, sheltered by wind-blown dunes, there lies a small world unto itself, vegetated by a variety of trees and shrubs and supporting an assortment of birds, mammals and other wildlife. Along the shoreward side, fresh and salt waters blend to form estuaries, mixing a magic broth that is more supportive of living things than any other environment. Salt marshes, bays, lagoons, and, in the tropics, mangrove swamps, all lend further enhancement for numerous marsh birds and other inhabitants of brackish waters.

Over its long north-south dimension, the region experiences a broad range of climatic conditions, although temperatures are less extreme than they become farther inland. The Atlantic Ocean, for some distance landward, exerts a moderating influence, particularly from Florida north to extreme southeastern Virginia. There, the warm waters of the Gulf Stream follow closely along shore until clashing head-on with a cool, southward-flowing current off North Carolina's Pamlico Sound. At this point the Gulf Stream turns north, then eastward. Geographers call the climate of this southerly coastal zone Humid Subtropical. A number of typically southern plants and animals reach their northern limits where the Gulf Stream heads out to sea. Only South Florida and the lower Rio Grande Valley of Texas are classified as Tropical.

The coastal fringe, from upper North Carolina to southern New England, is remarkable for its heavily indented coastline which measures, straight line, a scant 600 miles north to south. But the meander line delineating this labyrinth of bays, streams and tidal guts adds to a distance of 14,000 miles. Nearly a third of this coastal fringe is covered by water ranging from fresh to salt, a boon to great colonies of gulls and terns. Also, it is the major wintering area for the Atlantic brant and greater snow goose. But while some species appear bountiful in certain specialized habitats, the wood duck calls most of it home. And, in addition to its wide distribution, it makes up one of our primary sporting species as well. To this extent it could serve as an indicator of how well we tend this bountiful land.

The Banner Bird

Depending on where you live, you may know it as the tree duck, swamp duck, summer duck or squealer. But, whatever the local name, all agree that the wood duck is the dandy of the duck clan. Even its Latin species name, *sponsa,* translates into "betrothed" in reference to the bridal-gown splendor of its plumage.

Weighing in at about a pound and a half, the wood duck is larger than the several species of teal but noticeably smaller than the mallard or black duck. While not as drab as other female ducks, the hen is still a bird of somber colors. In contrast, the drake's plumage is brilliant almost beyond description. The iridescent feathers in its prominent crest, alone, reflect all colors of the spectrum, and the whole bird is an artistic melange of black, white, red, yellow, green, purple, bronze—and more. Like a kaleidoscope, the rainbowlike plumage reflects an endless combination of colors.

Such eye-catching beauty is an all-out must for bench dogs and show horses in quest of a blue ribbon, but for people and wood ducks it often leads to trouble. In the case of the "woodie", being highly prized as a table bird is liability enough but, additionally, its colorful plumage is much sought after by fishermen. The feathers go into the making of a variety of artificial flies. And still other nature buffs see in this handsome bird a brightly-hued taxidermy mount for rec room or den.

Woes of yet another nature have plagued the wood duck; both its nesting and wintering grounds have been under long-time assault. Throughout its range, vast tracts of woodland habitat have been cleared to make room for agriculture; river bottoms have been logged off and pond- and field-edges cleared of timber. More recently, flood control reservoirs in many major drainages have drowned out substantial areas of forest trees, and also eliminated the prolonged and

A wood duck pair. Female is drab, but the drake is a dazzler.

Dave Menke, U.S. Fish and Wildlife Service

91

regular flooding necessary for the wood duck's fruitful use of lowland hard-woods downstream.

The wood duck is a dabbler by nature, preferring its acorns under a blanket of water. Yet, as ducks go, it's a graceful walker and, if need be, it will hike a mile into upland woods in search of these prized nuts. But, alas, seeds of oaks and other hardwoods are staples as well for a host of other wildlife ranging from mice and tree squirrels, to deer, bear and wild turkeys—and other waterfowl. By spring, the autumn-winter bounty of such foods is exhausted and the wood duck finds sustenance in insects and other animal life, and a great variety of green plants.

Courtship and mating occur on the wintering grounds, and nesting in a hollow tree or a simulated man-made site begins any time between mid-January and early April, depending on the latitude. The average clutch of 10 to 15 eggs hatches about 30 days after the last egg is laid. The actual nest site may be as much as five feet below the exit hole, a puzzling circumstance which led early naturalists to believe the hen carried the flightless young from nest to pond in-beak or on-back. Not so. Modern-day biologists took a closer look and found that the little ones do it all on their own. Sharp, curved claws enable the young to gain a toe-hold on rough wood and a succession of lurching jumps gets them to the rim of the hole. Then, with quiet "kucks" of reassurance from the mother, the near-weightless nestling jumps from a height of as much as 50 feet to a soft landing alongside the waiting hen.

In all of life's stages, the wood duck faces a precarious existence. Eggs in the nest are fair game for raccoons, opossums and several kinds of snakes and birds. From hatching until flight is gained, the predator list is augmented by snapping turtles, mink, a number of large fish—and more snakes. If half the ducklings in any nesting season reach flight stage, the woodie calls it a good year. The lucky survivors then face hunting season.

*Baby wood duck preparing to leave nest box,
never to return.*

Soil Conservation Service, USDA

By distribution and temperament the wood duck is as American as the Stars and Stripes. It occurs *only* in North America and, in a large measure, over most of the middle part, except for a few States in the highly arid and mountainous West. From the southern Canadian provinces, throughout the States to the south, it's been known to take up abode wherever its minimum requirements for a grove of hardwoods and a patch of water exist. And it's as outgoing and adaptable as any back-slapping Texan. If ever you see a duck near Town Hall calling down a brood from a nest in a hollow elm, then leading them to the municipal reservoir, it's sure to be a woodie. Quite likely, traits such as these help explain the heroic restoration efforts humans have made in their behalf. To paraphrase an old saying, "One doesn't mind helping those willing to help themselves."

In spite of its reputation as a "can-do" bird, able to get along where others of the duck clan might fail, the wood duck has definite preferences. While its nesting range extends over a wide area, the major concentration, by far, is in the eastern third of the United States, where its numbers are about equally divided between Dixie and States to the north. Both afford the kind of habitat the birds seek out for nesting and rearing young—bottomland hardwoods bordering rivers and streams with a generous admixture of swamps, ponds and small lakes. But the nickname "summer duck" has a sound basis; while northern States may serve it well in mild weather, the birds abandon that harsh land well ahead of the first sign of winter. Their short migratory flight to the South begins in September and October.

Eyes of Discovery

Well ahead of landfall, early voyagers to the eastern seaboard were greeted by a fragrance that wafted for miles on the open sea. In those primitive days, virgin forests covered most of this province; pines of several species dominated, but bottomlands supported hardwoods and an undergrowth of shrubs in endless variety. Marshes rimmed the coastline, and their flowering added to the mingle of aromas. There were shrub bog habitats along the mid-Atlantic coast, mangrove forests in south Florida, and southward from the Ohio, Shenandoah and Kentucky rivers, the valleys were filled with a jungle-like growth of cane. In the luxuriant South, these "brakes", several miles wide, often stretched for a hundred miles. But the canebrakes sat astride the most fertile of soils and were more easily cleared than the woodlands; the land-hungry settlers quickly converted most of them to farm fields.

The early settlers viewed with awe and, at times, fear, this primitive wilderness, and they were equally impressed by the abundance and variety of wildlife it supported. Some of these species have since disappeared, while others are at precarious levels. There was the passenger pigeon, a symbol of extravagance, often condemned by the Pilgrims for the forays it made on their gardens; nonetheless, it found its way into many a settler's belly that might otherwise have gone empty. The heath hen, also now extinct, was extremely abundant from New England to Virginia in the scattered pine plains, grasslands and blueberry barrens. In the prairie areas of Louisiana and Texas, the Attwater's prairie-chicken was common. A close relative of the heath hen, this bird survives, but only in an endangered status.

The Carolina parakeet (now extinct) was abundant then, as were turkeys, grouse and waterfowl. Occasionally bison and elk ranged this far east, while deer and black bears were common. The cougar and gray wolf were present in disquieting numbers and became targets for early extermination. In 1630, the first of many bounties to follow was placed on the gray wolf by the Massachusetts

Bay Company. It is unclear as to whether the meager penny-per-scalp payment reflected great numbers of wolves or a scant Colonial budget.

The Settlers

While first European settlement of the country may well have gone forth without this great overflowing of wildlife, it is likely that the human hardships would have been greater and the pace of development slower. As it was, by 1850 most of the eastern half of the country had been occupied. Pioneering spirit was at a fever pitch and exploration had become largely exploitation. America, then, was conquering a wilderness and building a nation, and lumber was a prime requisite—for homes, fuel, fences and endless other needs. By 1850, Maine was logged off, then New York, then Pennsylvania. By 1870, they were logging the Lake States, and from there it moved to the South. Not all forests were put to good use; enormous quantities of prime trees were felled and burned to make room for farms.

The consequences for wildlife of this widespread deforestation cannot be documented in good detail. However, mature, even-aged stands of trees characterized much of the forest primeval, and the closed canopy so shaded the woodland floor that few shrubs or other food-producing plants useful to wildlife could gain a foothold. As a result, the logging (and the fires which frequently followed) led to shrubby regrowth which helped many species. Also, the partial clearing for agriculture of large continuous stands of forest resulted in a patchwork of open fields and woodlands in a way to satisfy an axiom of modern-day biologists which states: "Wildlife is a product of the edges." Given this greater diversity of vegetative types (edge), the cottontail, bobwhite, red fox, skunk, white-tailed deer and others were able to thrive for a time, while some true wilderness lovers, such as the turkey and larger predators, suffered a decline.

Nowhere was this beneficial effect of "edge" more evident than in the Black Belt, a prairie area of black soil running from central Alabama into northeast Mississippi. From settlement in the early 1800's until the Civil War, this was plantation country and cultivated by slaves. After that, until about 1940, tenant farmers worked the ground. In both periods, fields were small and of irregular outline. This "patch farming" produced the golden era of quail hunting in the South. As one small indication of numbers, market hunters in the winter of 1905-06 shipped over a half-million bobwhites to market in the North and East.

Benefits for wildlife do not always follow the drastic alteration of virgin woodlands. Consider the floodplain forest, a unique mixture of trees, shrubs and other plant life—and water. It once covered all the drainage ways of the eastern seaboard, the Gulf Coast and far inland along the Mississippi River and tributary waters. These bottomlands feature a broad range of water depths, and periodic flooding which varies in time and intensity. Moreover, they contain the richest of all soils, silt from the uplands deposited by flood waters. The result is varied strata of wildlife habitats which reflect the varied conditions of water.

In what is left of our floodplain forests, a great many wood ducks still find all of life's necessities and remain the year around. With the coming of winter, they are swarmed over by a surge of their kind which had ventured north to nest. The woodies, numerous in themselves, are not alone. The rich supplies of acorns, seeds and other foods are relished equally by mallards, black ducks and other waterfowl. But a big chunk of this wildlife paradise proved, as well, a lumberman's dream and was logged off early. Even so, most of what remained may have continued to serve a useful purpose for wildlife had not a legislative calamity brought doom to a vast part of this zone.

The Destroyers

In 1849, 1850 and 1860, the United States Congress passed several Swamp Land Acts which, by 1954, had resulted in the transfer of 65 million Federal acres of swamp and over-flow lands to 15 States, most of them in the Mississippi Valley. The States let nearly all these acres go, at fire-sale prices or even free of charge, to promoters eager to drain them and make them "useful." Naturally, floods followed, and within a few decades Congress was passing laws to build flood-control dams and levees to protect developers' investments. Now, as we shall see, agriculture threatens to take over still more of our forested wetlands.

The frontier settlers of the mid-1800's, like the early colonists, were forced to live off the land. Native fruits, nuts and berries continued to be common in the diet, but what sustained them most of all was the wildlife. Game was the one easily obtainable staple that made life bearable along the new edges of settlement.

Had this been the only direct drain on wild populations (substantial though it was), all species probably would have continued indefinitely in good supply. But that was not to be, either. City dwellers had developed a taste for game, and with that new demand there arose a new occupation to fill it—market hunting. It was a lucrative trade, even with ducks selling at 50 cents a pair, and these professional hunters made the most of it. There was no end to the call for game, and the extension of the railroads, later equipped with refrigerated cars, made it possible to deliver fresh meat to all parts of the country, in all seasons. Grocers routinely stocked iced barrels of ducks, geese and quail, and hotels everywhere featured wild game menus. Millinery fashions of that day called for feather adornment, and untold numbers of birds were killed only to be stripped of a few plumes or breast feathers. The effects of this wanton slaughter were soon to be seen. Between 1840 and 1910, five species of birds had been completely eliminated, and a number more—the hapless wood duck among them—had been trapped, netted and shot almost to the vanishing point.

Market hunters decimated waterfowl around the turn of the century. Not until their slaughter ended did the wood duck and other wild waterfowl have a chance to come back.

The Savers

The last half of the 19th Century (and one decade beyond might well be added), was the bleakest of all times for the living natural resources of America. Wildlife, in general, was driven to a scarcity never seen before or since, and forests and fields were abused in like fashion. One good came of all this. An aroused public was stirred into action and became organized in ways to be effective politically.

First came a flurry of new laws designed to regulate the kill of resident species (those living year around within State borders, like quail, rabbits and deer). But migratory birds enjoyed no such protection. There was no incentive to grant succor to a group of birds just passing through only to be shot by others down the line. Even into the beginning of this century, the vast majority of States appeared wholly indifferent to the welfare of this interstate (and international) resource.

The piece-meal regulations of the States (for the most part unenforced), did little to curb market hunting. This, together with the failure of States to regulate on behalf of migratory birds, prompted Federal intervention. In 1900, the Lacy Act applied Federal muscle to help end commercialization of wildlife; in 1913, the Weeks-McLean bill placed a limited custody of migratory birds in the Federal Government; a 1916 treaty gave protection to birds moving between the United States and Canada; and, in 1918, enabling legislation placed the Federal Government firmly in authority for management of this group of birds. The treaty called for immediate protection for the banner bird of the Coastal Plain, and a total ban on the taking of wood ducks promptly followed in both the United States and Canada.

There is little doubt that the outlawing of market hunting was the salvation of the wood duck—and, for that matter, a number of other species. However, a conspicuous recovery was slow to materialize, a failure which some blamed on the harsh economic times of the Depression years, which hit farm country in the early 1920's and continued through the 1930's. Over that extended period, hard-pressed rural dwellers, like their pioneering ancestors of an earlier era, were forced to take from nature's larder what a scarcity of dollars failed to provide. But with economic revival there followed a recovery of wood ducks as well. After 25 years of total protection, the ban was lifted and, in 1941, a single wood duck was allowed in the daily limit for 15 States in the Atlantic and Mississippi Flyways. In the following year, all hunters in these two flyways were allowed a bag limit of one bird.

The era of protective legislation was also followed by near-frantic efforts to restore wild populations. Game farms appeared in many States but with uniformly discouraging results, as artificially propagated animals failed to augment the populations of wild stock. Predator control, as practiced under the fraudulent bounty system, proved largely to be "money down a rat hole." The protection of sanctuary areas did not produce excess numbers of resident game which would overflow onto adjoining lands. They remained in place and at static levels.

A Profession is Born

Only after a variety of such expedients had been tried and found wanting did the truth begin to dawn. There were no short cuts to building the supply of game. As a product of the land, wild populations responded mainly to improved conditions in their habitat. It became apparent that game management is inherently land management. With this realization there came a rapid conversion of wildlife management to a science-guided profession from that of trial-and-error groping. An event of 1933 pinpointed and highlighted this truth; it was the appearance of the book, "Game Management," by Aldo Leopold, patron saint of the new profession.

Many other achievements marked the 1930's as a period of enlightenment to match in magnitude the dark years of a half century earlier. Three pieces of Federal legislation deserve special mention: 1934 saw passage of a Migratory Bird Hunting Stamp Act (Duck Stamp Act) and a Fish and Wildlife Coordination Act; and, in 1937, a Federal Aid in Wildlife Restoration Act (Pittman-Robertson Act) laid claim to a 10 percent excise tax already in force on sporting arms and ammunition.

Wildlife in all its diversity benefited from one or another of these far-reaching laws, and the wood duck was a prime beneficiary of all three. Under the P-R program, lands acquired by the States helped safeguard critical habitat; and research produced knowledge of the bird's habits and needs in ways to make management effective. A measure of the widespread attention given to wood ducks under this program is the 108 publications and project reports from 31 States which have appeared in the Pittman-Robertson annals over the past 40 years. One activity which saw widespread application was the installation of nest boxes, which the birds readily used, to offset the loss of natural tree cavities resulting from indiscriminate logging. State game departments and many sportsmen's organizations entered into the nest box program enthusiastically, and Federal biologists bolstered that effort in the two eastern flyways by installing nest boxes on national refuges which appeared to offer production potential. The success of these cumulative actions became apparent in 1984 when, for the first time, the bird ranked number one among ducks taken by hunters in the Atlantic Flyway and second in the bag for the Mississippi Flyway.

This same Pittman-Robertson era marked, as well, programs of intensive management for other wild residents of the Coastal Plain, including the wild turkey and the white-tailed deer, both discussed extensively elsewhere in this book. The mourning dove, the most numerous and widespread of American game birds, reaches its greatest numbers in the Coastal Plain States where up to half of the annual hunting kill of 50 million birds occurs. More than 175 substantive reports detail work done on mourning doves under P-R. Numerous other game and nongame species, predators and fur bearers have likewise profited from the P-R program. One fur species, the beaver, merits special mention, since our theme bird, the wood duck, has been a prime beneficiary of its growing numbers.

Losses and Gains

The beaver was both plentiful and widely distributed over Colonial America, but excessive trapping in the 19th Century caused a great decline in populations of this valuable fur species. Since then, the popularity of fur for clothing and decorative wear has declined sharply, which together with harvest restrictions and enforcement, enabled a great recovery of beaver and other fur animals. In particular, beaver are now re-established in many areas from which they had been trapped out, as well as in new habitats. The rapid spread of the animals, in many cases augmented by live-trapping and transplanting, has brought them into frequent conflict with man, as evidenced by numerous P-R reports dealing with "problem" beavers over the past quarter century. But, if their dammed and overflowing waters bring grief to landowners and highway maintenance crews, they bring only pleasure and joy to wood ducks. The sharp

Nest boxes have done much to restore wood
duck numbers in otherwise suitable areas
where hollow trees are scarce. Note metal
guard designed to keep raccoons away.

increase in beaver dams in recent years has added a substantial amount of high grade habitat for wood ducks and other waterfowl.

The interval from World War II to present has also been noteworthy for the rescue of some species perilously close to extinction. The Key deer of Florida has grown in numbers from a few dozen to several hundred—probably close to what its limited range will support. The whooping crane and bald eagle, one the symbol of endangerment, the other the symbol of the Nation, have shown noteworthy improvement in their numbers. While the former, at 100-plus individuals, is still at a critical level, it is a comforting number alongside the baker's dozen (or a few more) that marked its low. The brown pelican of the Gulf Coast and the peregrine falcon, along with the bald eagle, are experiencing revivals since the banning of DDT. And the alligator has responded to widespread management enough to be relieved of its endangered status through most of its range.

Although the past 40 to 50 years have been notable for the enlightenment and achievement they brought to wildlife management, there has been slippage as well. Much of it has been due to political, social and technological changes, largely beyond the control of professionals in wildlife management. Recent years have witnessed a growing trend away from the family farm and into agribusiness. In the resulting consolidation of ownership, diversified farming is being supplanted by a single cash crop. Field borders are being removed and roadways incorporated into adjoining croplands. Wet areas are being drained and filled, and further land clearing is taking place. The resulting combination of many-into-one, and variety-into-uniformity, works against the wildlife requirement for edge. The widely-hunted cottontail rabbit, bobwhite quail, many species of songbirds, and even the prolific, adaptable white-tailed deer are finding the new pattern of land use much less livable.

Adapting to Change

One exception is the Canada goose. It has learned to accept crop residues in lieu of declining amounts of natural food in and around coastal waters, and the new enlarged fields relieve the birds of fear they normally feel in entering smaller fields closely bordered by woods or other heavy cover. Also, their capacity for sustained flight can carry them long distances, if need be, to the safety and shelter of open water. Today, the Delmarva Peninsula, east of the Chesapeake Bay, harbors more of these geese than at any time in recent history.

It's not always been so. A half century back, give or take a decade, a dozen Canadas in a Maryland cornfield brought excited comments. Today, 5,000 of them gleaning kernels in the same field go unnoticed. What made the difference, mainly, was the mechanical corn picker, (followed by the combine), a time-saving but wasteful innovation, compared with hand picking which left few unclaimed ears of corn.

Prior to widespread adoption of the picker in the 1940's, honkers wintered mainly in North Carolina and south into Georgia and Florida. Today, a mere handful reach the Tar Heel State and fewer yet Georgia and Florida. What it amounts to is that geese, like others of their kind, are opportunists. They'll migrate no farther than necessary to make a decent living. Biologists have a phrase for it—"Short-stopping." It's happened with other species in other areas, notably geese in the Mississippi Flyway.

Additional to a new-found source of food, Delmarva's attraction for these birds has been enhanced further through the addition of State and Federal refuges, and farm ponds too numerous to count. That may be enough to perpetu-

Porter B. Reed, Jr., U.S. Fish and Wildlife Service

Some hardwood-growing bottomland areas are being acquired with P-R funding, but not as rapidly as others are being cut over and drained.

ate the Shore as Goose Capital; or it may not. Similar developments to the north are being reflected in increased wintering populations in Pennsylvania, New Jersey, New York and New England. It could lead to further short-stopping.

Other new trends in agriculture brought us the use of pesticides from pre-seeding to post-harvest. We have yet to assess all the implications this may bear for wildlife, but our experience with DDT may indicate the insidious nature of some. The burning of soft coal and the use of fissionable materials for power generation have resulted in acid rain and warming waters. These and other by-products of today's economy may also have consequences for wildlife as yet unseen. However, few events of modern times can match for severity the blight cast upon wildlife through wetland drainage. An original 215 million acres of wetlands at the Nation's beginning have since dwindled to less than half that in the lower 48 States. In recent years (from the mid-1950's to the mid-1970's), 9 million acres were lost nationwide, nearly 90 percent of it in the Southeast; of this total, over 5.5 million acres involved forested wetlands, mainly bottomland hardwoods, one of the most productive wildlife habitats in the United States. Their rich, heavy soils proved to be ideal for soybeans, and drainage for this purpose, much of it made possible through government funding, has gone on apace and without regard for the many other values inherent in such areas.

In combination with estuaries and tidal marshes, these bottomlands support, in large measure, the bulk of the migrating and wintering waterfowl from three of the four major Flyways—Atlantic, Mississippi and Central. And the attraction of these watery oases extends beyond water-oriented species. More than nine-tenths of *all* bird species in eastern North America find their way to these bottoms at some time. Fur bearers, by kind and total numbers, abound; fall and winter, bears seek out these low-lying wetlands for the assured food supply and the denning sites afforded by numerous hollow logs; and our number one big game species, the white-tailed deer, is both larger and several times more plentiful here than in most comparable areas of upland forests. Forested bottomlands are also home to the reclusive wild turkey, and they may well serve as the final haven for some of our endangered species.

Two-thirds of our major commercial fishes depend on our coastal wetlands for nurseries or spawning grounds, and many shellfish are produced there as well. The fresh waters sustain a thriving sport fishery. In numerous unseen and immeasurable ways, they perform useful functions in flood and erosion control, wave damage protection, the maintenance of water quality and the recharge of ground water supplies. These waters of the Coastal Plain have values as natural systems which far exceed their worth as cropland.

In Retrospect

Viewing events over a historical span of time, we can see that the rapid conversion of Colonial America into the wealthiest nation on earth hasn't occurred without the piling up of substantial debits. Twelve generations of tenants have taken freely from the land and paid back sparingly. For the first hundred or more years, the human occupants depleted but they didn't despoil. In the last century, technological developments have combined with population pressures to bring long-lasting, maybe even irreversible, scars to America the Beautiful. The area longest to suffer these human transgressions is the full sweep of the Atlantic seaboard. Conditions here now have led one writer to refer to it as, ". . . the most heavily populated, heavily industrialzed, heavily polluted, drained and despoiled zone in the Nation." A good case can be made for this statement.

Along all of our eastern seaboard, then in large measure around the Gulf, a megalopolis overlooks the not-so-shining-sea. Major cities and towns sit astride all the river systems which carry the offal of a civilized society to the estuaries and the ocean. Some, such as "the immense protein factory," (words used by critic H. L. Mencken, in describing Chesapeake Bay) are so polluted by silt, municipal and industrial waste, and agricultural runoff as to be only marginally productive. Industrial plants, resort hotels, second homes, first homes, and high-rise hotels and condominiums, blanket both seashore and barrier islands.

For half a century, ocean waters crept up beach lines and threatened to dispossess the occupants, who fought back—mostly with public money, and lots of it. Efforts were made to contain the sea with concrete walls and other engineering stopgaps; dune stablization programs evoked enthusiasm and optimism. But in most instances, the winds and the waves won out, and the engineers, and the public as well, have come to appreciate a rising sea level, fed by thawing glaciers, for the indomitable force that it is.

Looking Ahead

The surprising outcome is not that wildlife has fared so badly through all the changes, but that it has done as well as it has. Except for a few highly specialized species, most wildlife continues in reasonably good supply. At least part of the explanation may be found in the unexpected ability of many wild creatures to adapt. For some, it has meant conspicuous changes in food habits; for others, that they accept man as part of an altered landscape. Most small game find the gleanings of farmlands fully as acceptable as their traditional fare. Some of the duck clan, Canada geese and white-tailed deer have come to ignore native foods in some areas in favor of domestic grains—especially corn. And, in the small town of my residence, gray squirrels, cottontail rabbits and mourning doves—along with a number of songbirds—have adapted well to the city scene and are present in greater numbers than in nearby rural habitats.

Of course, the numbers necessary merely to ensure survival of a species fall far short of the flourishing populations required to allow sport hunting. Providing for the latter is largely the job of professional managers in State and Federal agencies. So far, they have done reasonably well. Research into the habits and requirements of nearly all game species has provided the background for effective management. Land acquisition by the States (much of it under P-R) has preserved substantial amounts of habitat while providing access for at least a modest number of sportsmen and the general public. A far-flung system of Federal refuges has preserved critical nesting, migration and wintering grounds for migratory birds, and helped to offset, somewhat, the widespread drainage and filling of wetlands. Yet, these programs in their entirely, if standing alone, may have little more than survival value for many species—if that. The key to game abundance still rests largely with the private landowner, who controls, by far, most of the lands.

In a large measure, people and wildlife do compete for food and space. But the presence everywhere of water marks this particular strip of land as something unique in the Nation, and directing the destiny of water is even more tenuous. The ocean, the Gulf, the major bays and other bodies too big to drain are serving as the Nation's cesspools, yet people still throng here by the millions. Some seaboard States have zoned waterside and wetland areas in the interest of bringing order to future development. However, much of this vital habitat continues to be subject to the whims of developers. Government-aided programs of pollution control have been put in place, yet water quality continues as a major problem. The drainage of low-lying wetlands over much of this coastal region continues at an alarming pace.

The Challenge

The future of some resident species along this half of the country's rim is neither bleaker nor brighter than it is for the rest of the Nation. But for many migratory birds, it's a different story. For them, this is a critical stopping point, a place of annual refuge where they wait out the winter months. From late fall to spring thaws, the bulk of the Nation's waterfowl assemble along the south Atlantic and Gulf Coasts. The Wilson's snipe and woodcock come here, as do 26

Coastal marshes are still being lost at an alarming rate, despite increasing awareness of their many practical values.

Joe Knecht, U.S. Fish and Wildlife Service

species of colonial birds, many of which remain for most of the year. Virtually all wood ducks winter here, and fully half of them nest here, too. For several other species of southern ducks, the Coastal Plain is a yearlong residence.

Occasional seasons of drought and, more importantly, the loss to drainage of breeding grounds in the North have led to a decline in the numbers of waterfowl. In 1985, the lowest breeding population in over a quarter of a century was recorded for ducks in general. Furthermore, for the much-sought-after mallard, the percentage of the fall population taken by hunters has increased in the face of declining mallard populations, a condition which some biologists attribute to overly liberal regulations which permitted an invasion into the breeding stock.

Whatever the causes for the slump in duck numbers, restrictive regulations adopted in the mid-1980's were designed to reduce the hunting kill substantially. It all augurs ill for the wood duck. Prior experience has shown that, under these conditions, the buffer bird—the one to pick up the slack—is the woodie, a fact which may help account for its ascent to positions one and two among all ducks bagged in the Atlantic and Mississippi flyways in 1984. And all of this happens at a time when the main rallying grounds of the birds, the Mississippi River bottomlands, are being drained at the rate of 300,000 acres per year. That's 10 percent each year of the remaining 3 million acres, out of an original 25 million.

Nearly a century has passed since the wood duck last faced a desperate battle to survive. Its "bailout" began in 1916 with a complete ban on taking. At that time, its human competition numbered much less than half what it is today; and its habitat base, diminished as it then was, must certainly have offered more than it does today. Yet 25 years went by before recovery was such as to warrant a daily bag of one bird, and another 20 years before it reached two. Over part of this period, its recovery was aided, as well, by such technology as was then known, plus several funding sources (P-R among them) which enabled building on their habitat needs.

Today's crisis may not offer the same happy ending. We can't very well shelter and foster something that hasn't been produced and provided for in all of its year-around needs. Should we fail to make secure the remnants of our riverine and related habitats, the wood duck as a sporting species may well be doomed. More so, this handsome bird is but one sample of a vast array of wild species whose fate also is tied to the rich resources of our Coastal Plains. They, likewise, would be heavy losers.

Muskrats are among many fur-bearing species dependent on the watery habitats of the coastal plain.

The Black Bear:
Home in the Highlands

by Jack W. Raybourne

Although it is one of the most commonly recognized of North American mammals, the American black bear also is one of the most maligned and misunderstood of all animals on the continent. The mere presence of a black bear near a residential area is often enough to cause instant panic in the whole neighborhood. Fearful parents may quickly gather children behind locked doors and windows and nervously await the arrival of authorities who, all too often, needlessly destroy a very frightened animal whose only crime simply was being in the wrong place at the wrong time.

Strangely, the general public seems to be quite familiar with bears. Nearly everyone from the Blue Ridge to the Bronx has heard of "Smokey the Bear" or has followed the exploits of "Gentle Ben." Every school child is familiar with "Goldilocks and the Three Bears," and it is a rare youngster who has not gone to

Mr. Raybourne has devoted most of his 18-year career in the wildlife field to research and management of black bear and wild turkey populations. He is currently Chief, Division of Game, Virginia Commission of Game and Inland Fisheries.

sleep clutching the security of a well-worn "Teddy Bear." A host of cities, towns, mountains, valleys, lakes and streams are named for bears; and early residents nicknamed at least two States, Kentucky and Arkansas, "Bear State" for the large number of bears they found there. Slang expressions such as "strong as a bear," "hungry as a bear," "bear hug," "grumpy as a bear" and others have resulted from human perceptions of bears. Countless park visitors have learned first-hand about bears at park roadsides and campgrounds, and many can attest to the "bone-crushing ferocity" of bears from the sensationalized accounts of popular outdoor magazines.

Most of us seem naturally to fear or mistrust those things which we don't know or understand fully, and old misconceptions and half-truths die slowly. It is understandable, then, that many of us have grown up with a great deal of knowledge about bears, most of it wrong.

Historically, black bears are thought to have ranged over much of the North American continent except for the Great Plains. They are the most numerous and widely distributed of the three members of the family *Ursidae* on the continent. Primarily a creature of remote forested regions, the black bear has proven to be somewhat more tolerant of human intrusion than its larger cousin, the grizzly. As a consequence, black bears still occupy much of their former range; and, although less numerous today, they are still one of the most widely distributed big game animals in North America.

Bears are large, powerful, carnivorous (meat-eating) mammals which are related to raccoons, foxes, dogs, coyotes and wolves. Although bears are well-equipped for meat eating, they are primarily *omnivorous* in their feeding habits. Like teenage boys, bears will eat virtually anything in whatever quantity is available, plant or animal; but their diet is largely nuts, berries and other plant materials. Bears have large non-retractable claws which are useful for climbing, food gathering or defense. They can stand erect on their hind legs, and, like raccoons, they walk on the soles of their feet rather than on their toes as do most other carnivores. Male bears are known as "boars"; females, "sows"; and the young, usually in litters of one to four, are called cubs. Perhaps it is these designations, as well as their feeding habits and gruff vocalizations, that have led to a popular but mistaken belief that bears are somehow related to pigs.

Black bears are smaller and more numerous than their two other North American cousins, the grizzly and the polar bear. Although adult males may exceed 700 pounds, most average 200 to 400 pounds, a size often wildly exaggerated in human estimates. When visitors in the Great Smoky Mountains National Park were interviewed a few years ago, most correctly estimated a bear's weight at about 400 pounds. However, some visitors thought 800 pounds was about average and other estimates ran as high as 2,000 pounds! Adult females are smaller, usually ranging from 100 to 200 pounds.

Although not all black bears are completely black, the name "black bear" was an obvious choice of early settlers for this New World animal. Nearly all black bears of the eastern United States and Canada are black with brown eyes and a brown muzzle.

Unlike their grizzly relatives, black bears are adept climbers which can nimbly scale most trees for food or protection. Despite their short legs and chunky appearance, black bears are capable of speeds of up to 30 miles per hour for short distances. However, they seldom run unless they have to, preferring to wander slowly over large areas in search of food or mates. The black bear, usually a committed creature of the forest, may feed occasionally in nearby open or bushy areas. He can be found equally at home in mixed hardwoods or evergreen cover.

106

Black bears, unlike grizzlies, are adept at climbing trees.

John Hall, Vermont Fish and Wildlife

Although black bears continue to be scattered over much of their former range, there are broad gaps brought about by the axe, fire and other forms of land clearing in the advance of human civilization. Today, black bears exist in no more than 30 of the 49 States in which they formerly roamed, and their range continues to shrink. The fact that black bears have managed to survive at all in many areas of the Eastern U.S. is little short of amazing. In spite of the fact that bear numbers have remained relatively abundant and widely distributed, it is important to recognize that they are restricted largely to the most remote and inaccessible portions of their former range. This is nowhere more evident than for the Eastern Highlands region which stretches from Maine to Georgia, and it is this area that will serve as the principal focus of our discussion.

Unlike the white man, most Indian groups generally treated the black bear with great respect and admiration although they killed one occasionally for food, warmth or religious purposes. However, when one was killed, it was usually afforded much different treatment from a deer, turkey or other game owing to its special status in Indian cultures. Its flesh was often eaten ritualistically as a symbol of courage, strength or wisdom. The fur was used for robes and bedding while the claws were worn as amulets and the paws and other parts were objects of "powerful medicine." The bear's fat was prized for cooking, tanning hides, softening and waterproofing clothing and moccasins, and as a skin and hair oil. Some tribes accorded human attributes to bears, often referring to them as the "Great Bear Spirit," "Little Brother," or Grandfather." Still other tribes refused to kill bears at all, believing they were reincarnations of departed family members. Indian tribes of the Ohio and upper Mississippi River Valleys constructed magnificent effigy mounds in the form of bears as well as deer, wolves, bison, eagles and others as objects of respect and worship.

107

Historically, black bears inhabited most of the forested areas from Maine to Louisiana and were often mentioned in the accounts of early explorers. From nearby Virginia settlements, Captain John Smith explored the upper Potomac River dividing present-day Maryland and Virginia and noted that on

> *the 16 of June [1608] we fell with the river Patowomak [Potomac] ... Having gone so high as we could with the bote [Little Falls of the Potomac] we met diuers Saluages in Conowes, well loaded with the flesh of Beares, Deere, and other beasts, whereof we had part.*

Since the fresh meat of these "Beares" and "Deere" would have spoiled rather quickly in the summer heat, they were, necessarily, present in the vicinity of the Nation's Capital nearly 400 years ago.

Near Boston in 1634, Captain Abraham Wood wrote that: "Beares they be common, being a great blacke kind of Beare ..." Wood also mentions the mauling of a waterfowler who made the unfortunate mistake of pelleting a startled bear with goose shot on nearby Pond Beach. Wood's 1671 expedition in Virginia recorded that a bear was killed almost daily in the Blue Ridge Mountains, often three a day.

Early settlers valued bears for their meat and skins. The flavorful meat usually was cured as a substitute for pork. It was also sold in markets and traded for staple goods along with venison, turkeys, waterfowl and furs. The bear's pure white fat yielded a light, sweet oil and was prized for frying (especially of doughnuts and fish) and for medicinal use. Like the Indians, early settlers used the oily fat as a scalp and hair oil and as a lotion for chapped hands and faces. When mixed with various herbs, it became a popular salve against a host of ailments, including baldness.

Bears likely benefited from the early slash-and-burn land clearing techniques of early settlers. Limited logging activities and the clearing of small tracts of land by burning stimulated the growth of fruit-bearing plants such as pokeberry, blackberry, dogwood and others which are relished by bears. Any such benefits were short-lived, however. As human settlements began to increase, bear numbers began to decline. New settlers hacked away the forest as they cleared the land for plowing, planting and grazing. The brush and timber so vital to the black bear's welfare began to disappear to provide for homesteads, fortifications, cooperage, tanbark and heating.

As forested areas dwindled, bears were forced increasingly into more rugged, inaccessible areas for survival. So complete was this shift that many people believe such areas were always the animal's preferred range. Naturally, foraging was more difficult in these less productive areas, especially in lean food years; and bears soon learned that Colonial farmsteads provided an abundance of food simply for the taking. Since the pioneer homesteader and his family depended upon their meager crops, livestock and stored foodstuffs for survival, few losses could be tolerated.

Bears soon became the bane of early settlers as they raided late summer cornfields and gardens. Although they were usually less destructive to livestock than bobcats or wolves, bears were often guilty of filching an occasional colt, pig or lamb, especially in late summer or when nuts and acorns were in short supply. Bears also played havoc with root cellars, meathouses and cabin homes. As might be expected, such actions did little to endear them to settlers. Bears and men became antagonists almost from the beginnings of the country's settlement, and bears would be regarded as little more than vermin for many years to come.

Faced with a persistent threat to their livelihood, colonists and homesteaders resorted to every conceivable method to rid the countryside of bears. The animals were trapped, shot over bait, shot in winter dens and pursued with dogs "at every occasion." Some colonists even hired Indians to hunt down marauding bears. Perhaps the most common method of encouraging the killing of bears was the bounty system, under which local governments or Colonial legislatures paid specified sums of money for the caracasses of predatory birds and mammals.

The Town of Fairfield, Connecticut, in 1666, was one of the earliest to adopt a bear bounty and paid 50 shillings for an adult bear and 20 shillings for a cub. Twenty years later the Town of Springfield, Massachusetts ". . . allowed & paid four shillings, for every grown beare & for every young Beare or Cub halfe so much out of the Town Rates . . ."

Bears were occasional nuisances in Delaware and New Jersey, and one county on Maryland's Eastern Shore was authorized to pay a reward of 100 pounds of tobacco for every bear killed. In Rhode Island, bears were such a persistent threat that the bounty was increased to 3 pounds sterling in 1736, and 50 years later some Rhode Islanders still regarded the bear as ". . . one of the most noxious animals in our forest." Following the American Revolution, several States including Vermont, New Hampshire, Virginia, West Virginia and others offered bounties of up to $15 (a very large sum). The exact number of bears bountied in the Eastern Highlands since Colonial times will never be known, but the figure must have easily exceeded 100,000 animals. Vermont alone bountied 2,595 bears from 1831 to 1941, and several other States equaled or exceeded this feat after having paid bounties for over 200 years. Maine, for example, bountied over 10,000 bears between 1946 and 1957!

Although bear numbers in New England were beginning to decline by the late 1700's, bear trapping continued as a profitable enterprise in many areas of the East until the early 1900's. During the 1920's, two West Virginia counties paid $40 bounties on bears, while the State of Virginia paid a $20 bounty. A resourceful hunter or trapper could bounty a dead bear and then sell its pelt for an added bonus.

West Virginia bear biologist Joe Rieffenberger described the general contempt for bears still prevalent in the 1930's when a bizarre technique for killing bears was described by Calvin W. Price, editor of the *Pocahontas Times,* and a vocal foe of the black bear:

> *Bears used to be caught and killed by driving murderous iron spikes through an oak beer keg at an angle so that the bear would force his head through the slanted spikes to get the bait (usually honey). The spikes would catch and hold him fast. He would perish miserably or be waiting helplessly for the trapper to finish him.*

In 1932, Mr. Price continued expressing his vehemence for bears in the following editorial:

> *The bear is no fitten companion either of man or beast. He is a barbarian and cannot be civilized. His preservation in West Virginia is not a question of saving an interesting biological specimen or desirable game animal—it is a question of people in Pocahontas County, or bears or other more valuable, interesting and productive creatures, from deer to snowbirds. The man who has to live in the same community with bears hates him with a cruel and lasting hatred and with good and sufficient cause.*

Before the white man appeared on the scene, bears had few natural enemies. Aside from the Indians, the only serious threats to black bears were wolves, mountain lions, porcupines and grizzly bears in areas where their ranges overlapped. Porcupines, of course, presented no direct threat to bears, but more than one unfortunate bear faced an agonizing death after having "bitten off more than

The black bear has survived centuries of persecution.

he could chew." Bears of the eastern forests even managed to hold their own in the face of the homesteader's rifle, the market hunter and the bounty hunter, but they were ill-matched against the plow and the axe, which nearly spelled their doom.

When the colonists arrived in the 17th Century, they were greeted with a veritable wall of virgin timber. Early colonists also found a tremendous *variety* of trees as they explored the Atlantic coast inland to the mountains—massive oaks and hickories, chestnuts and beeches, and magnificent stands of spruce, pine, hemlock, and cypress, ideal food and cover conditions for black bears, which were present in nearly all wooded areas. Just how many bears is difficult to say, but all evidence indicates they were very numerous. The combination of vast timberlands, the bear's general lack of enemies, and its varied diet could have produced a remarkably large bear population. Ernest Thompson Seton's 1909 edition of *Lives of Game Animals* suggested a primeval population of as many as a half-million black bears on the continent, but this estimate probably was conservative.

States such as Connecticut, Maryland, New Hampshire, New York, Vermont and Virginia, which had been almost entirely forest in Colonial America, had become nearly three-quarters farmland by the late 1800's. Large tracts of forested land in Kentucky, Pennsylvania, West Virginia and other States were being cut up into smaller tracts by roads, expansion of farms, mining operations and continuing timber harvests. The fertile and readily accessible flatlands and river valleys were the first areas cleared for agriculture. The wholesale clearing of other forested lands, including mountainous areas, continued rapidly to meet the demand for building lumber, mine ties, charcoal for iron and copper smelting, tanbark, railroad construction and fuel for steam-powered engines.

As the forests dwindled, so did the wildlife. The elk and the buffalo had all but disappeared from most areas of the East by 1850. They were joined quickly by the wolf, the mountain lion, the lynx and the fisher, which also stood in the "path of progress." The timber wolf, which had been systematically shot, trapped and poisoned for over 200 years, was the first major predator to be eliminated. The adaptive black bear, which is not much of a predator, was not as easy to eliminate. But uncontrolled hunting coupled with uncontrolled timber harvesting and burning, land clearing for crops and grazing, and other encroachments associated with an expanding civilization combined to reduce bear numbers.

In a scant 200 years, most of the virgin forests of the East had been cleared. Most attempts to continue farming the over-cropped soils usually failed within 20 years and wholesale abandonment of farm lands became the rule. Pioneer farm families had little choice but to move on in search of new land to be cleared for agriculture as the cycle repeated. Commercial logging had also reached the mountainous areas, and major sections of mountain ridges were soon cleared of trees up to 4,000 feet. The concept of reforestation was unknown in those days and the desolated mountainsides were also burned annually for blueberry production to supplement the incomes of local farmers and villagers. Whole communities turned out at "berry pickins," and the tasty fruits were shipped to eastern markets literally by the wagonload.

Forced to retreat into more and more remote areas, bears were running out of places to go. Vermont, for example, which had been 95 percent forested in the 1600's and which had served as a principal hunting and trapping ground and highway to Canada for over 100 years, had 218,000 people by 1810. Similar changes had occurred in nearly all of the New England and Atlantic States except Maine, and bears were becoming less and less common. Bears and wolves, which had been "plentiful and troublesome" in Connecticut, were largely gone by the mid-1700's. Land clearing and persecution had eliminated bruins in Rhode Island by 1800, and by the early 1830's only a few could still be found in the northwest mountains of Massachusetts.

The situation was delayed somewhat for the States southward and inland, but bear numbers in all areas of the East had ebbed to their lowest levels by the late 1800's. By the early 1900's, bears could be found in Kentucky, Maryland, North Carolina, Georgia, Pennsylvania, Virginia and West Virginia, but only in remote, mountainous areas. By that time, too, bears in Tennessee, formerly so numerous as to spawn legendary heroes, were restricted to a small mountainous section. Sadly, though low in numbers, bears were still considered to be outlaws by many people, especially by mountain folk who saw them as potential sheep killers and general nuisances. They continued to be maliciously harassed and wantonly destroyed—no longer just for food or even the excitement of the chase. They were simply slaughtered, whenever and wherever possible.

Fortunately, before it was too late, the pendulum began to swing in the opposite direction. With the abandonment of tens of thousands of worn-out farms of the past came a slow but natural reversion to woodland. Persecution, too, declined as bear numbers dropped and many people left farms for better-paying jobs in the cities. Ironically, the same conditions that were the bane of bears, deer, turkeys and squirrels were a boon to small game species such as bobwhite quail and cottontail rabbits, whose numbers flourished on the abandoned lands. As the former farmland continued its systematic recovery to woodland, more and more habitat came back for the black bear and remnant populations began slowly to recover.

The period from 1900 to 1940 marked a turning point for man as well as bears and wildlife generally in other ways, too. The Nation began awakening to the fact that our seemingly inexhaustible wealth of natural resources was not limitless after all, and that we had better set about the task of correcting our mistakes.

Nationally, groups of organized sportsmen and naturalists began to appear out of concern for the plight of wildlife and the need to acquire and protect our forests and other treasures from the abuses of the past. In response, States began to establish fish and wildlife departments to enact and enforce laws dealing with wildlife conservation. With the help of sympathetic administrations, concerned preservation and conservation groups pressed Congress into establishing our systems of national parks, national forests and national wildlife refuges. In time, some of the mature forests of Colonial days would return under the complete

Most black bears, like this Wyoming native, tend to avoid people—unless people make the mistake of feeding them.

E.P. Haddon, U.S. Fish and Wildlife Service

112

protection of the national parks, and the regulated logging of the national forests would provide habitat diversity for a wide range of birds and animals.

The timely establishment of the national parks and national forests in Kentucky, Georgia, North Carolina, Tennessee, Virginia and West Virginia was almost singly responsible for saving the black bear in much of the Eastern United States. Sportsmen had also become concerned and their support of the Pittman-Robertson Act by Congress in 1937 helped provide additional assurances. These "P-R" funds enabled State conservation agencies to supplement their own programs and begin an ambitious land acquisition and wildlife restoration campaign. Several States were soon able to amass sizable land holdings, largely from the thousands of acres that had been abandoned or taken for non-payment of taxes. Many of these lands lay in the mountainous regions of the Eastern Highlands, right in the very backyard of remnant bear populations, and served to supplement the national parks and national forests which were already benefiting bear numbers

Perhaps equally important, attitudes concerning bears and other game animals were also changing. Following the lead of New York and Pennsylvania, in 1904 and 1905, respectively, other States, with the support of game protection clubs and associations, began extending protection to bears.

While bear protection laws and habitat restoration had provided short-term gains, there were mild setbacks when the Nation returned to intensive agriculture and logging during World Wars I and II. However, a subtle, but more serious, setback was also in the making at this time. Just as the forests were again reaching maturity, a devastating blight struck the American chestnut tree. Once found from central Maine to Arkansas, the fast-growing chestnut provided a dependable food supply for many forms of wildlife at a time when the young, returning oak forests had yet to reach acorn-bearing age. Thus, when the black bear was just beginning to recover from over-hunting, over-trapping and habitat destruction, one of its major food sources disappeared from the Eastern Highlands. In time, the chestnut would be replaced by other but less dependably productive tree species, primarily the oaks and hickories, and bears would adjust to the change.

Following World War II, as its numbers continued to grow, the bear's popularity also grew; and its former position as despised vermin continued slowly to change. By this time, bears in most Eastern States had been elevated to the status of "game animal," and harvest restrictions had been implemented. Bounties, which had marked a 300-year trail of destruction for tens of thousands of bears and countless other mammals and birds, had all but disappeared. Maine, New Hampshire and Vermont were among the last to discontinue bounty payments in the late 1950's. However, the "war against the bear" persisted in some other areas. Pocahontas County, West Virginia, which had encouraged the destruction of bears as vehemently as any Colonial government, *added* panthers, coyotes and wolves to its $40 bear bounty system in 1946. The bounty system was brought to an end in 1969, however, when the West Virginia Legislature designated the black bear as a game animal. Highland County, Virginia, which is Pocahontas County's immediate neighbor to the east, may hold the dubious honor of having had the last remaining bear bounty statute in the East. When the local statute was discovered in 1972, the county had not paid its $50 bear bounty in over 30 years; and it officially came to an end in 1977 when the Virginia General Assembly eliminated all forms of bounties. No State now pays a bounty on any bear species, and it is very doubtful that any local bounties persist.

The stage appeared to be set for the bruin's return, but little practical information existed about how to manage bear populations. Although nearly

113

every State had a fledgling wildlife department in the early 1900's, virtually all efforts were devoted to the enactment and enforcement of game laws and the re-establishment of white-tailed deer, wild turkeys and small game birds. In addition to being relatively easy to handle and study, such species were popular with the sporting public and local efforts to restore them were highly visible. Bears, on the other hand, were still considered to be "second class citizens" by many folk. Besides, even if you caught one, what could you do with it? States had begun to use P-R wildlife restoration funds extensively to finance large-scale studies of wildlife, but bears were usually not among them.

As with human populations, data on trends in births and deaths by age and sex are indispensable for monitoring the growth and health of wildlife populations. Armed with new techniques derived from careful studies, wildlife managers were soon able to accurately "age" and "sex" most wildlife.

Bears, however, were difficult subjects for study. They live typically solitary lives in remote, inaccessible areas; and their acute senses and their natural wariness of man make them challenging animals to observe under natural conditions. Without a safe means of immobilizing such large, powerful animals, direct hands-on experience with bears is next to impossible. Consequently, for many years game departments had litle choice but to simply monitor estimates of bear populations and harvests and to respond to depredation (damage) complaints.

Ample evidence that little was known about bears until recently is seen in the 1973 publication honoring the 35th anniversary of the Pittman-Robertson Federal Aid in Wildlife Restoration Act. Bears received scant mention in the 36-page booklet which summarized the major accomplishments of the program. A portion of one sentence referenced the use of the "cap-chur" gun for immobilizing grizzlies in Montana and polar bears in Alaska. Although one such photograph appeared, there was no mention of black bears at all.

Thanks to some recent medical and electronic advances and the efforts of a small, but dedicated, band of wildlife researchers, more has been learned about bears during the last 20 years than in all of recorded history. Some of the fascinating new knowledge about bears is already aiding bear management by changing the attitudes of sportsmen, wildlife administrators and the public.

Much of the credit for our present knowledge of black bears must go to the collective efforts of a few dozen wildlife biologists who were challenged by the lack of information about bears and the hazards in collecting it. These weren't foolhardy men, but some of their earlier attempts to study bears must have seemed so. Techniques for safely trapping and handling such powerful animals had to be developed from scratch, and although there were occasional anxious moments for themselves, bear researchers were usually more concerned for the animal's welfare

While it would be impossible to identify all those who have been involved in bear research, it would be unthinkable not to recognize some of them. To pioneer the field, Albert Erickson experimented with trapping techniques involving culvert traps and foot snares in northern Michigan and anesthetized black bears with ether. Although much was gained for the effort, it was rough-and-tumble work, accompanied by some unavoidable bear injuries and losses. Charles Jonkel studied black bear behavior extensively in Montana, and his experience quickly taught him that they were not the aggressive, perpetually angry creatures once believed. Rather, he found them to be extremely intelligent, timid, and adaptive animals whose new image encouraged others to study bears. Working in Yellowstone National Park, Frank and John Craighead applied modern and innovative techniques to study interactions between grizzlies and man. National attention for their work involving the trapping, drugging and

114

Biologist enters den to tranquilize sow bear.

Cubs are checked and tagged before being returned to den.

Claire Guimond Dobert, U.S. Fish and Wildlife Service

Claire Guimond Dobert, U.S. Fish and Wildlife Service

radio-tracking of grizzlies dramatically focused the public's attention on scientific wildlife research. Media attention also played on Lynn Rogers, who further changed public attitudes as he entered Minnesota bear dens repeatedly in an intensive study of bear home range and denning behavior. Mike Pelton directed a host of studies involving bear reproduction, habitat use and human interactions with black bears in Great Smoky Mountains National Park; and Gary Alt's enthusiastic lectures and scientifically-based popular articles drew local and national attention to his numerous studies of bear biology in Pennsylvania. The list goes on with an impressive cadre of highly capable, though perhaps lesser known, wildlife biologists who have contributed, and continue to contribute, individual pieces to the puzzle that makes up the black bear.

Virtually none of our present knowledge about wildlife, and especially bears, would have been possible without the matching P-R funds. Lacking adequate funds, most States could not have bought and managed lands for wildlife or conducted needed wildlife research and restoration programs. Although no quality research comes cheaply, most bear research is necessarily expensive in terms of specialized equipment, drugs, travel, time, and manpower required. Also, because of the rugged conditions normally associated with large-scale bear trapping operations, results often come painfully slow for wildlife workers who frequently must spend long hours collecting meager amounts of information. Without such funding, few States would be able to devote the monies necessary for such intensive, long-term studies, and critical knowledge would continue to escape us.

As we noted earlier, certain age and sex information is the key to gauging the health of wildlife populations. Although most big game species can be "aged" readily, bears had defied any such attempts except for cubs or yearlings. Since bears may live 20 or more years in the wild, it was impossible to find the number of males and females in each year class. Researchers in New York discovered that bears' teeth contain microscopic rings that are formed annually, appearing much like rings in a tree. By removing a tiny tooth from a trapped or harvested bear and slicing it into thin sections for viewing under a microscope, biologists can now obtain an accurate age for any bear.

Miniature radio transmitters attached by neck collars to bears can be used to gather other information which could not be easily obtained. Electronic receivers, capable of detecting the transmitter's signal, are used to determine a bear's exact location at any time of the year. By continuously monitoring a large number of "bugged" bears in several States, biologists have obtained a vast assortment of new knowledge. For example, it is now known that the average home range of adult females is 5 to 15 square miles while adult males regularly use 75 to 100 square miles. Radio-tracking has also provided valuable insights into seasonal habitat preferences, activity patterns and seasonal movements related to breeding habits and dispersal of young. The tiny transmitters have also been used to evaluate the effects of various forestry practices on bears, the responses of bears to hunting, and the impacts of roads on bear movements. Tracking adult sows to winter dens, researchers often have the opportunity to tag entire litters of cubs at once while learning more about cub survival, methods of introducing orphaned cubs, and den site preferences.

A multitude of other research projects have been accomplished on food habits, livestock and crop depredation, effects of legal and illegal hunting, reproductive biology, behavior, and many other elements of bear life. Research dealing with hibernation and body responses to various immobilizing drugs offers potential for more knowledge about human health in such areas as anesthesiology, urinary and digestive disorders, and obesity.

116

*Radio collar will provide much information
on this bear's future movements and activities.*

Black bears have long played an important role in this Nation's history. For many years, along with other wild creatures, they provided many basic necessities of life to our pioneer ancestors. Then, almost without notice, the majestic forests, and much of their wildlife, were nearly gone. Although black bears had few natural enemies, they were ill-matched against gunpowder, fire, axe, greed, ignorance, and indifference. Happily, unlike some less fortunate creatures, bears were better able to adapt to remote regions until the forests returned and man had recognized the necessity of managing his natural resources wisely.

Today, the continent's black bear population is again estimated at 400,000 to 500,000 animals. Although the majority occur in Alaska and Canada, nearly half can be found in the lower 48 States, largely in the western mountains. The future of the black bear seems assured, even in the populated Eastern Highlands where an estimated 40,000 can still be found.

Bears are making a strong comeback aided by the return of the forest, regulated hunting, improvements in public attitudes, and scientific research. Although the outlook appears bright, much will depend upon what lessons we have learned from the past. As was true in pioneer times, bears will continue to face shrinking habitat as land and forests once more are increasingly cleared to make room for the homes, roads and agricultural needs of modern "settlers."

The challenges for black bear management, and our ability to meet them, will become increasingly difficult as human populations expand and bear habitat shrinks. On the brighter side, we have barely scratched the surface in our knowledge of this magnificent animal; and what we learn from future research may provide increased opportunities for man and bears to co-exist. Both species are remarkably adaptive, but our land changes and attitudes of today are likely to be more permanent than those of our ancestors. We have a choice. Let's hope we do better the second time around.

Prairie-Chickens: Survival in the Midwest

by Ronald L. Westemeier and William R. Edwards

The story of the prairie-chicken's *(Tympanuchus cupido)* rise and fall, and its limited comeback in recent years, contains some fascinating lessons about the past, present, and future of wildlife in the agricultural Midwest.

Today this remarkable bird is far less numerous and widespread than it was in its prime time a century or more ago. It has been wiped out of some States, perhaps forever, and is barely hanging on in some others; but it still thrives in some limited areas where favorable grasslands persist. There still is hope for its future, thanks partly to Pittman-Robertson (P-R) support of work done in a number of States. Much of what we know about the prairie-chicken has been learned through P-R research, which therefore deserves some of the credit for

Mr. Westemeier has done research, management, and preservation work with the greater prairie-chicken for a quarter of a century, mostly in Illinois, and has done studies of pheasants, bobwhite quail, and other grassland wildlife. Dr. Edwards spent 10 years in Ohio as supervisor of upland game research, followed by 24 years in Illinois with technical/oversight responsibilities for cooperative upland game research projects, and has long been involved in Illinois' efforts to restore prairie-chickens. Both men are wildlife ecologists for the Illinois Natural History Survey.

119

whatever we hope to do to save this species. Prairie-chickens also received a big assist, often unnoticed, from citizen-conservationists who put their money where their hearts were, enabling vitally important sanctuaries to be bought and managed as grassland habitat.

The subspecies known as greater prairie-chicken *(T. c. pinnatus)*, which we will discuss in detail, is still found in four States in numbers large enough to be hunted—Kansas, Nebraska, South Dakota, and Oklahoma, in that order of abundance as of 1986. There are smaller numbers in six States—Missouri, Minnesota, Wisconsin, North Dakota, Colorado, and Illinois. Greater prairie-chickens no longer occur in eight other States and four Canadian provinces where once they thrived: Arkansas, Indiana, Iowa, Kentucky, Michigan, Ohio, Texas and Wyoming, and Alberta, Saskatchewan, Manitoba and Ontario.

How did they disappear, and why? This was once a species of almost legendary abundance. Is its decline permanent? The answers center mainly on two factors, agricultural land use and (perhaps this will surprise the reader) the intrusions of the ring-necked pheasant, a popular species native to China and introduced to America in the late 1800's.

Greater prairie-chickens had their heyday in the years shortly *after* white people settled into the great valley between the Appalachian and Rocky Mountain chains. The "chickens" expanded their range northwestward by at least a thousand miles while the bison were being slaughtered wholesale, and while limited areas began to be farmed, logged, burned, drained, and sown to cool-weather grasses like bluegrass in Wisconsin and redtop in Illinois and Missouri.

Prairie-chickens continued to prosper in 24 States and provinces for a few decades until efficient farm machinery, overgrazing by livestock, tighter control of forest and prairie fires, and regrowth of some forests grossly reduced the quality and availability of prairie-chicken habitat. The decline worsened when pheasants were successfully introduced to the region, even where habitats remained favorable (and still are favorable) for prairie-chickens.

Habits and Habitats

The prairie-chicken belongs to the order Galliformes, which includes "chickenlike" birds such as quail, grouse, pheasants, and turkeys. It is in fact a grouse that has feathered nostrils and legs feathered to the toes. The grouse subfamily *(Tetraoninae)* includes ptarmigans, and ruffed, spruce, blue, and prairie grouse; the latter group includes prairie-chickens, sharp-tailed grouse, and sage grouse. Four subspecies of prairie-chickens have been recognized including the eastern heath hen (northern east coast), extinct since 1932; the endangered Attwater's prairie-chicken (Gulf coast of Texas and formerly Louisiana); the lesser prairie-chicken (eastern New Mexico, Texas and Oklahoma Panhandles, southeastern Colorado, and southwestern Kansas); and the greater prairie-chicken, which once inhabited all of what was the eastern and central tallgrass prairies—now better known as the Corn Belt, or to pessimists as the "great corn-soybean desert," for its lack of biological diversity.

The basic coloration of the greater prairie-chicken is one of various shades of brown in horizontal barred patterns that blend well into grassland habitats. Adult males weigh slightly over two pounds, and hens approximately one-half pound less. The most interesting features of the male prairie-chicken are the brilliant orange inflatable airsacs (tympani) on its neck, which serve to resonate the "booming" sound produced by the male's vocal apparatus. On a calm spring morning this may be heard for up to three miles. When booming, males erect

120

special pinnae feathers at the top of the air sacs, perform a foot-stomping dance, flutter-jump, click their tail feathers, spar with rival males, whoop, cackle, make nuptial bows to hens, and eventually mate with them. The displays and courtship performance of male prairie-chickens are truly among the most intriguing of natural wonders, and must be seen to be appreciated. Watching prairie-chickens on their booming grounds has been popular with hunters and non-hunters alike since the earliest times.

The ancient display rituals usually begin on calm, clear days in fall and continue off and on through winter. Typically, the peak of courtship activity occurs about the first week of April in Illinois, Missouri, and Kansas, and a week or so later in Wisconsin and Minnesota. Cocks arrive on booming grounds about 45 minutes before sunrise and continue to boom and display for two or more hours. The performance is resumed for an hour or more before dusk.

Visibility and ease of movement are clearly important in their selection of booming grounds. Most are on open ridges, knolls, or open level terrain. On today's landscape, plowed fields, soybean stubble, short new grass, wheat seedings, overgrazed pastures, and fresh burns all offer suitable booming grounds—if grassy cover adequate for roosting, escape, and especially nesting is available within a short flight distance (about one-half mile). Booming grounds tend to be traditional for prairie-chickens and some have been occupied each spring for as long as the oldest local residents can recall.

Booming grounds are typically occupied by about 10 males, although one ground in Illinois was regularly used by 65 cocks throughout the 1972 booming season. Each male establishes and defends a territory on the booming ground. Males occupying the central territories are dominant and perform most of the matings on an entire booming ground. Although booming and displaying announce the place for mating and provide for the natural selection of superior

Male prairie-chicken on a booming ground in Nebraska, with air-sacs distended in a typical display posture.

Nebraska Game and Parks Commission

individuals, the performance seems overly elaborate. Even newly hatched chicks have been observed to dance and to attempt the display antics typical of adults. Despite some fall and winter visitation by males, hens seldom visit booming grounds until late March. The greatest number of visits by hens occurs in early April and then sharply declines until even sporadic visits end about late May.

Nests are begun shortly after prairie-chicken hens have mated in early April. They are built on the ground, and most are within a mile of a booming ground, often within one-quarter mile. The booming ground nearest a nest site, however, is not necessarily the ground on which a given hen mated. Although grasslands are preferred, nesting may occur in fields of tame clover, weeds, grain stubble, or even growing small grains. The height and density of vegetation are more important than the plant species in the selection of habitat by nesting prairie-chickens. Because nesting begins in early April, the residual ground cover left over from the previous year is critically important in nest placement. Ideally, most of the residual grassy cover should be lower than about 16 inches and relatively dense.

Full clutches average 12 eggs, although they may range from 25 in early nests down to only 5 eggs in late nests. Typically, about 40 days pass from the time the first egg is laid until hatching. During this vulnerable period, an average of 50 percent of the nests and perhaps 10 percent of the nesting hens are taken by predators such as skunks, raccoons, mink, opossums, foxes, or coyotes. Hens may re-nest once or even twice if their clutches are destroyed during the laying period, but re-nesting by prairie-chickens is much less common than that by bobwhites and pheasants. Few chicken nests are active after mid-June.

Shortly after chicks have hatched, a hen will move her brood from the nest site to cover that offers freedom of movement and an abundance of insects to meet their dietary needs. In recent times, attractive brood cover included moderately grazed pastures, grasslands burned the previous year, fallow fields, small grain and clover fields, field borders, ditchbanks, and other disturbed areas. Like nesting, brooding is a vulnerable period in the life of prairie-chickens. Within the first two months after hatching, hens often lose half or more of their chicks to predators, farm machinery, and weather. The diet of young prairie-chickens is initially very high in insects, especially grasshoppers, but gradually becomes like that of adults—leafy greens, grains, weed seeds and such fruits as dewberries, blackberries, and wild strawberries which gradually diminish as staple foods at summer's end. Greens are important as food virtually year round. Before the large-scale production of cereal grains, seeds of weedy forbs such as ragweeds and wild sunflowers and wild rose hips were no doubt important winter foods for prairie-chickens.

During fall and winter, prairie-chickens flock in groups of as many as 50 or more, and roost in grassy cover or small grain stubble. Grasses, sedges, legumes, weeds, and even brush cover, or a combination of plant types that may be too tall and dense for nesting and rearing chicks, often serve as winter roosting cover. In winter, prairie-chickens also commonly use deep snow for roosting, digging 5 to 10 inches beneath the surface of the snow and then tunneling horizontally for a foot or so. This habit, plus the ability to digest woody buds, gives prairie-chickens an advantage of winter hardiness over quail and pheasants.

Prairie-chickens are known to range several miles in winter, apparently seeking food. Historical literature indicates that the species was once migratory, with movements of several hundred miles. The prairie-chicken's dark flesh contains a red pigment that combines with oxygen to provide sustained flight energy over long distances, consistent with that of migratory birds.

C.J. Henry, U.S. Fish and Wildlife Service

Nesting female prairie-chicken is well camouflaged in typical habitat. Predators nevertheless take perhaps 10 percent of nesting hens and 50 percent of the nests.

Thus, prairie-chickens have special needs for reproduction and survival. Although they can adapt to different or changing environments, their needs are largely fixed in their genes and there are limits to what they can tolerate.

The Pre-Columbian Environment and Early Settlement

The tallgrass prairies of the Midwest probably emerged as recognizable communities of grasses and forbs at least 25 million years ago, although the region's native plant life has continued to reflect unstable climates since the retreat of the last glacier 10,000 to 12,000 years ago.

Bison, together with fire, floods, drought, and insect plagues, were disturbing the prairies long before settlement by Europeans. Early explorers, fur traders, and the first pioneers wrote of prairies so heavily grazed by bison and sometimes so ravaged by grasshoppers that their horses starved. Early journals made little mention of prairie grouse or prairie ducks on such landscapes. Prairie-chickens did not even appear on much of the tallgrass and mixed grass prairies between the Dakotas and Texas in significant numbers until the great bison herds had been decimated by man and the grasslands had recovered from periodic overgrazing and drought. Bison did not occur on eastern prairies (today's Corn Belt) in the vast herds so typical of the Great Plains. There is little evidence, pro or con, as to whether prairie-chickens were widely abundant on the tallgrass eastern prairies before man introduced high-energy grains.

123

Before European settlement, booming grounds and associated sites for nesting, brooding, roosting, and feeding probably occurred on relatively small, scattered patches with particular kinds of plant life. These patches were colonized by perhaps 20 to 50 prairie-chickens. However, individual patches no doubt survived for only a relatively few years before advancing succession ("aging") or some form of natural or human disturbance made them at least temporarily useless to prairie-chickens. In time, a new series of plant successions would again bring them to an acceptable but again temporary condition. This temporary, ever-changing mosaic of patches suitable for the life functions of the prairie-chicken across the original landscape of the tallgrass prairie can be visualized as fireflies over an old field on a summer evening, glowing briefly, fading out, only to reappear nearby to glow and fade again.

Explorers, traders, and pioneers followed the same major river systems used by the Indians. The period of frontier settlement was a time of dispersed farmsteads and small villages along major streams that served as routes of commerce. By the early 1800's, Europeans had subdued the Midwest's Indians and settlement proceeded rapidly. The first areas chosen for settlement were primarily forestland or prairie edge because the extensive tallgrass prairies were too wet and too tough to plow. In addition, titles to prairie land were difficult to obtain, and many settlers believed then that because prairies had no trees, that they were infertile. Living on the prairie was also dangerous because of recurring fires, harsh winters and storms. Historical accounts are replete with tales of prairie-chickens moving in from prairies to cut-over forestland and becoming pests to farm crops.

The Agricultural Revolution

About 1830, pioneer agriculture began a shift from the simple, individualistic, labor-intensive, pioneer economy that led to today's scientific, capital- and equipment-intensive, computerized, business-managed, government-involved farm economy. Cyrus McCormick patented his reaper in 1834, and by 1851 he was reportedly turning out 1,000 steel plows annually from his plant in Chicago. John Deere by 1857 was producing over 10,000 steel plows annually from his plant in Moline, Illinois. Threshing machines were common after 1850. Attitudes prevailing at that time are reflected in a statement by Benjamin Johnson to the Illinois Agriculture Society in 1861: "The progress of improvement in this portion of Illinois is little less than wonderful. Ten years ago much of the country was wild open prairie; now there is scarcely a rood [one-quarter acre] of unenclosed land, except portions of the timber along the rivers and streams." That point of view in combination with rapid technological change made inevitable the destruction of the Midwestern tallgrass prairies. Improved farm machinery, the "farm it all" philosophy, and access to eastern markets made possible by canals and railroads, all led to a rapid conversion of prairies, forests, and wetlands to cropland. Mechanization allowed the farming of more acres by fewer people. The number of people on farms in several Midwestern States peaked in the 1870's and 1880's, and the farm population remained relatively stable until about 1910, when it began a decline that continues today.

During the period of rapid settlement and agricultural change, habitats also changed rapidly. Deer and wild turkey populations decreased and later almost vanished due to the clearing of forests and year-round hunting. Predatory animals were reduced by fur trapping as well as hunting. On the other hand, opening the prairie and forests to agriculture produced, at the time, an intermixed pattern of food and cover that was highly suitable for upland game.

Markets in Chicago used "cord" and "ton" as measures for shipments of harvested quail and prairie-chickens in 1853. As late as 1873, some 600,000 prairie-chickens were marketed in Chicago. H. Clay Merritt, a premier market hunter of chickens on the central Illinois prairies in the 1860's, noted, "I saw in October more birds rise out of a forty acre field than all the cities in the Union could consume in a month." Favorable habitats, perhaps along with low densities of predators, allowed upland species such as prairie-chickens, bobwhites, and cottontails to thrive. Prairie-chickens probably achieved peak abundance about 1860 in Illinois and about 1880 in Iowa. According to Professor Max Partch, Minnesota prairie-chickens expanded their range from the State's southeast corner where they were considered scarce in the 1830's to the northwest corner by 1884—about 500 miles in roughly 50 years. Similarly, wildlife historian John Beck provides evidence that as farming developed in various parts of Ohio, Indiana, Iowa, Kansas, and Nebraska, prairie-chickens *moved in* and became plentiful in areas where they had been absent or scarce.

A second stage in the agricultural revolution came with the internal combustion engine in the early 1900's, and the subsequent development of the farm tractor. As tractors improved, field size and farm size grew. By the mid-1930's, the plow horse and the hayfield had become obsolete in the Midwest. The gasoline engine also ushered in the dragline, which resulted in large-scale drainage of prairie wetlands and swamps.

The most famous drainage project relative to prairie-chickens was central Wisconsin's Buena Vista Marsh. Along with a lowered water table and ditchbanks came a dynamic patchwork of cropland (much of it marginal due to unpredictable summer frost), frequent patchy fires, the establishment and culture of bluegrass (a form of substitute prairie), and the removal of the remaining swamp evergreen stands. These changes created 50,000 acres of habitat on peat and sand soils into which prairie-chickens quickly moved. Their population peaked about 1912, but this area of Wisconsin continues to support one of the highest densities of the species—an ultimate testimony to the adaptability of the greater prairie-chicken and, as we will see, to the value of P-R supported research and management.

The Impact of Federal Farm Programs

Beginning in 1934, the Federal Government adopted various programs designed to strengthen farm markets through diversion of land away from crops, and to protect soil from erosion losses. These included the Cropland Adjustment Act of 1934 and 1935, the Agricultural Conservation Program of 1936 through 1942, the Soil Bank Program under which the Conservation Reserve phase lasted from 1956 to 1969, the Emergency Feed Grain Program of the 1960's and early 1970's, the Cropland Adjustment Program of 1966 to 1976, the Water Bank Program, and most recently the Payment in Kind Program. Some of these proved to be of major significance to wildlife.

During the 7 years 1936-1942, payments by the Agricultural Conservation Program were made for 252,410,000 acres of so-called "permanent" seedings to grasses and soil-restoring legumes, an average of 36,059,000 acres annually. The cropland diversions were greatest in the Corn Belt States, where payments were made for 153,060,000 acres, or about 60 percent of the U.S. total. Over the 7 years, payments in the Midwest were made annually for the diversion of the equivalent of almost 12.5 percent of the acreage of all crops harvested. The Conservation Reserve phase of the Soil Bank Program was almost as impressive over the 14 years 1956-69 with 215,900,000 acres of grass/legume seedings.

Although exceptions have occurred, the record indicates that since the successful introduction of pheasants into North America over 100 years ago, two major population booms and busts have occurred extensively across the mid-continental pheasant range—one in the early 1940's and another in the early 1960's. These booms, and the busts that followed, occurred at the times and in the places where cropland diversion programs had established long-term seedings of forage legumes and grasses, and where they were plowed up later. Programs based on mere annual diversions did not result in booming pheasant populations. In addition to pheasants, a wide variety of grassland wildlife benefited from long-term cropland diversions, most notably ducks, bobwhites, cottontails, prairie-chickens, and a number of songbird species. As we will see, the cropland diversion programs have proven a mixed blessing to the prairie-chickens.

Pheasant Boom and Prairie-Chicken Bust

The declines in prairie-chicken abundance that took place in the Midwest after World War I cannot be explained on the basis of land use change alone. For example, according to pioneering research on the species by Dr. Stephen A. Forbes, prairie-chickens persisted in 92 of Illinois' 102 counties as late as 1912, well after most of the native grasslands had been destroyed. Chicken populations, however, rapidly declined shortly thereafter in Illinois and in much of the Midwest coincident with large-scale releases and establishment of ring-necked pheasants. A report in 1941 by the Committee on Bird Protection, of which Professor Aldo Leopold was a member, was particularly perceptive, yet little appreciated even now:

In the United States, the main stronghold of the Pinnated Grouse [prairie-chicken] in the Lake States is fast shrinking, and for the same reasons as the Sharp-tail: the encroachment of aspen on

Don Schuhart, Soil Conservation Service, USDA

Beauty is in the eye of the beholder. This Illinois farm presents a picture of tidy, thrifty management to most viewers; but to wildlifers, *the absence of grassy cover, woods and water makes it a sterile scene indeed.*

126

marshes, and the encroachment of timber on the cutover land.
*Further south in the dairy belt grazing, drainage, and **pheasants***
are evicting remnants of Pinnated Grouse with exceptional
***rapidity.** Southern Wisconsin, northern Illinois, and northern*
Indiana may lose these grouse within a decade. . . . "Game-restora-
tion" efforts in many States are concentrated on raising and liber-
ating Ring-necked Pheasants, Hungarian Partridges and other ex-
*otic game birds. If long continued to excess, **this practice may***
not only replace but even exterminate some of our native
***game birds.** We believe that a larger percentage of available funds*
should be spent for research and for habitat improvement. More
emphasis should be placed on encouraging natural propagation
of native game birds. [The emphasis is ours.]

Thanks to Pittman-Robertson programs, studies on the life history, ecology, and management of prairie-chickens and other native game were undertaken in many States. Propagation of pheasants continued unabated, however. In Michigan, in a classic study on prairie grouse funded by P-R, Dr. Andy Ammann concluded that interactions with sharptails beginning in the late 1930's were responsible for losses of local prairie-chicken flocks when habitat was yet favorable for chickens. If sharptails, which are smaller than prairie-chickens, could rapidly replace chickens, why couldn't the much larger pheasant?

A long-term study begun in Illinois in 1962 has illuminated interactions between prairie-chickens and pheasants. Prairie-chickens responded positively and dramatically to the acquisition and management of scattered sanctuaries in Jasper County until pheasants became common there in the early 1970's. Harassment by pheasants of prairie-chickens on booming grounds was often observed, but research demonstrated that an even greater problem stemmed from pheasants using prairie-chicken nests to lay their eggs. This dual egg laying is called nest parasitism.

A pheasant hen commonly begins laying eggs before she has prepared a nest. These extra eggs may be left randomly on the ground or laid in the nests of other pheasants, as well as those of waterfowl and other ground-nesting birds, and even domestic chickens. Unfortunately, the adverse impacts of nest parasitism have not been generally recognized, although nest parasitism by brown-headed cowbirds is now well recognized as a principal factor in the current critical plight of the Kirtland's warbler. The common occurrence of pheasant eggs in the nests of other pheasants and other species indicates that parasitism is part of the innate reproductive stategy of pheasants, evidently giving them survival and competitive advantages. Pheasant chicks produced in prairie-chicken nests represent a "bonus" achieved at little expense to pheasants but at great cost to the parasitized prairie-chickens.

The incubation period of pheasant eggs is about 23 days compared with about 25 days for prairie-chickens. The prairie-chicken hen ceases incubation, begins brooding, and leaves her nest within about 24 hours after pipping starts, taking any hatched chicks with her. If the nest contained parasitic pheasant eggs, the hen prairie-chicken, failing to recognize the chicks as other than her own, leaves with the earlier-hatching pheasant chicks and abandons her own un-hatched eggs. By the early 1980's, parasitism along with more subtle interactions had reached such levels that the distribution and abundance of prairie-chickens in the Jasper County sanctuary had declined by at least 50 percent. In distinct contrast, chickens on a sanctuary system in Marion County continued to do well in the absence of pheasants. Both areas had similar soils, topography, and local agricultural land use and were under identical management programs supervised by the same manager (Westemeier). The only discernible difference was the presence of an increasing local pheasant population at the Jasper County sanctuary.

Findings to date strongly suggest that the loss of the native prairie-chicken, coinciding with the rapid establishment and spread of the exotic ringneck throughout the Midwest—particularly in the late 1930's and the 1940's—was not entirely a matter of habitat loss. "Exclusion" of prairie-chickens by reduced reproductive success due to parasitism (and perhaps other and more subtle behavior by pheasants as well) is a probable cause and is quite probably continuing to limit prairie-chicken numbers today in areas of South Dakota, Nebraska, Kansas, Illinois and elsewhere. As a recent example, in 1982 pheasants were implicated in the disappearance of Michigan's last prairie-chickens on a 1,000-acre refuge.

In contrast to intensively farmed areas, expansive native grasslands such as the Fort Pierre National Grasslands in South Dakota, the Sandhills in Nebraska, and the Flint Hills in Kansas, are apparently large enough to offer enough diverse habitat for pheasants and prairie-chickens to coexist, both in lower densities than on the Illinois sanctuaries. In areas of Missouri and Illinois where pheasants are not currently present, long-term P-R supported studies show the prairie-chicken's ability to persist with relatively little grassland, as long as there is some redtop, timothy, fescue, or degraded prairie remnants for prairie-chicken nesting and roosting. Currently, Missouri sustains several thrifty prairie-chicken populations (10 to 20 cock booming grounds) where wheat and red clover are essentially the only forms of "grassy" cover available; but none of these local areas contain any pheasants.

The Federal cropland diversion programs of the 1930's and the late 1950's and early 1960's were enormously beneficial to pheasants over most of the traditional midwestern prairie-chicken range. However, we know of no area in any State where *both* pheasants and prairie-chickens benefited simultaneously from Federal programs of cropland diversion to grassland; prairie-chickens enjoyed the benefits only in areas with few or no pheasants. This was certainly true in Illinois. The pheasant population booms prompted by cropland diversions of grass-legume cover would likely have been booms for prairie-chickens —had there been no pheasants.

The ways in which prairie-chickens, sharptails, and introduced pheasants interact make it complicated to determine just how much intensive land-use affects the abundance of prairie-chickens. In general, increasing land use intensity results in a more fragmented, island-like distribution of grassland habitat. Over time, these habitat "islands" have become smaller, fewer, farther apart, and lower in quality. Disease, weather, predation, and the poorly understood 10-year wildlife cycles all are additional complications. Today, habitat remnants tend to be occupied by fewer species at lower densities. These populations are increasingly unstable and produce fewer young to disperse and colonize other islands of habitat.

Current Status and Outlook

Among the six States with non-hunted populations of prairie-chickens, the greatest uncertainty of preserving remnant populations exists in Illinois, Colorado, and North Dakota. In Illinois, the spring census of 1985 indicated that only 153 cocks, among a total of possibly 300 birds, survived. These chickens were limited to two local flocks sustained by sanctuaries that total only 1,960 acres dispersed in 14 scattered tracts intensively managed by The Nature Conservancy, the Illinois Department of Conservation, and the Illinois Natural History Survey. As noted earlier, pheasants severely threaten the survival of the flock in Jasper County. However, a high density of about 100 cocks per square mile of managed grassland occurs in Marion County where pheasants are not present. Acquisition objectives call for an additional 1,000 acres in scattered tracts averaging 160 acres each and spaced about one mile apart.

Colorado currently has estimated spring populations of about 2,000 greater prairie-chickens, but all of these are on private range. Efforts are underway to transplant chickens to the State-owned 3,755-acre Tamarack Prairie in Yuma County; unfortunately, over a century of attempts to transplant prairie-chickens have been unsuccessful. North Dakota is more fortunate in having the Sheyenne National Grasslands (71,000 acres) as the current stronghold for prairie-chickens. Chickens on that public area have increased from about 100 males in 1972 to 300 to 400 males; however, numbers of chickens are again declining, primarily due to decreases in lowland burning over the past 4 to 5 years.

In Wisconsin, Drs. Fred and Fran Hamerstrom along with Os Mattson and sustained P-R funding, instituted "ecological patterning"—as opposed to administrative blocking or the single large refuge approach—as the basis for prairie-chicken management. The original scatter-pattern plan published in 1957 called for a dispersion of eighty 40-acre tracts of managed grassland *to supplement* the bluegrass seed harvesting industry on central Wisconsin's drained Buena Vista Marsh. Unfortunately, the bluegrass industry, which had provided extensive and effective "substitute prairies" for chickens, collapsed and refuges larger than 40 acres became essential.

Wisconsin's scattered refuge system, managed all or in part for prairie-chickens, now totals about 25,000 acres. From a low point of 250 males in 1969, the total census of booming males in those areas reached a cyclic high of about 1,100 in spring 1981—the highest in 30 years—and an excellent density of

Periodic controlled burning of brushy growth gives grasses a chance to come back, and thus is an important technique in prairie-chicken management.

about 30 cocks per square mile of managed grassland. As expected, by 1985 Wisconsin populations again showed a cyclic low. However, ongoing programs are aimed at controlling this and future cyclic lows as much as possible, by means of rotational prescribed burning, mowing, grazing, brush control, plowing and reseeding via sharecropping, in addition to well-distributed winter food patches.

Minnesota conservationists assumed a posture of positive resolve in 1973 with a special prairie-chicken conference. After a decade of cooperative efforts there now are 51,800 acres of scattered grasslands, mostly native prairie, which are managed at least in part for prairie-chickens in northwestern Minnesota. Despite losses of private grasslands, the managed grasslands were in large measure responsible for doubling prairie-chicken numbers in Minnesota to a peak of 1,648 cocks by the spring of 1982. Recent censuses (1985) show a reduced count of about 800 cocks, which probably reflects at least in part a cyclic trend.

Missouri has the highest abundance of prairie-chickens, about 6,000 birds in spring 1984, among the six States with nonhunted populations. Taberville Prairie in southwestern Missouri was purchased by the State in 1959 and is a long-standing success in prairie-chicken preservation, with densities up to 69 cocks per square mile. Charles W. Schwartz's classic research, funded by P-R, led to publication of *The Ecology of the Prairie-Chicken in Missouri* in 1945, the definitive foundation for the State's current programs involving at least 31 prairie preserves. In addition, a recent unique and successful program in Missouri involves annual seedings of several thousand acres of native warm-season grasses for pasture on private land. This prairie pasture program, similar to one in nearby Iowa, capitalizes on the need of cattlemen for a drought-resistant forage on which cattle can continue to gain weight through summer heat, but it also facilitates the establishment of quality grassland nest cover for wildlife on private land.

Among the four States in which prairie-chickens are hunted, current average harvests ranged from 4,000 or 5,000 in South Dakota and Oklahoma, 35,000 in Nebraska, and 68,000 (1978-84) in Kansas. In 1982 an estimated 109,000 prairie-chickens were taken by Kansas sportsmen. If the average harvest rate is about 10 percent of the total fall population, as some biologists suspect, the number of prairie-chickens in Kansas may have approached 1 million in 1982. Even if actual numbers were only half that high (hunter reports are notoriously biased), they would contrast greatly with reported scarcity in pre-settlement times, with the drastically reduced numbers reported during the drought of the mid-1930's, and with Dr. Maurice Baker's perhaps conservative estimate of 50,000 chickens in 1949.

Nebraska prairie-chickens are currently limited largely to the southern and eastern borders of the 20,000-square-mile Sandhills region which supports an estimated 150,000 to 200,000 prairie-chickens in fall. As elsewhere, the future of Nebraska's chickens is subject largely to private land management decisions, and to the prairie-chicken's interactions with pheasants and sharptails. As in Kansas, current populations and harvests in Nebraska are believed to compare favorably with those of pre-settlement times and the drought-stricken 1930's. Indications here, too, suggest that the "take half and leave half" (of forage) range management concept has become the accepted practice. However, pivot irrigation and excessive grain farming made ominous inroads into lands better suited for grouse and beef until 1984-85 when economics halted, at least temporarily, that adverse trend.

Thus, the current status of prairie-chickens varies greatly among States, and management programs must be tailored to local range and current economic conditions. Today's management programs, based on P-R research, do not stand as end points; rather, they only represent positive beginnings. Prairie-chicken populations can never be considered stable or secure because environments are never stable and because the economic rules by which the games of agriculture are played are constantly being rewritten with little input for natural resources. Through P-R we have learned much about how to manage prairie-chickens; however, we can not manage populations under tomorrow's rules if we must rely solely on yesterday's data. To answer tomorrow's questions we will need to continue long-term research efforts for tomorrow's answers.

One lesson above all others is to be learned from P-R research: the greater prairie-chicken is an adaptable, responsive, and challenging species. Given a reasonable chance, this boomer of the prairies will respond just as far as proper grassland management and pheasants will allow. Continued improvement in range and grassland management is vital. Federal programs of cropland diversion have excellent potential to benefit prairie-chickens whereever contracts are multi-year and specify perennial grasses and legumes and wherever pheasants do not present a potential problem. If the National Tallgrass Prairie Park becomes a reality in Osage County, Oklahoma, the future of greater prairie-chickens could well be secured in that State. These prospects, in concert with sustained efforts by The Nature Conservancy, the Prairie Grouse Technical Council, and the North American Prairie Conferences, offer hope for the future of greater prairie-chickens. P-R funding of research and management will be as essential in the future as it has been in the past.

Two males dispute territory on a booming ground.

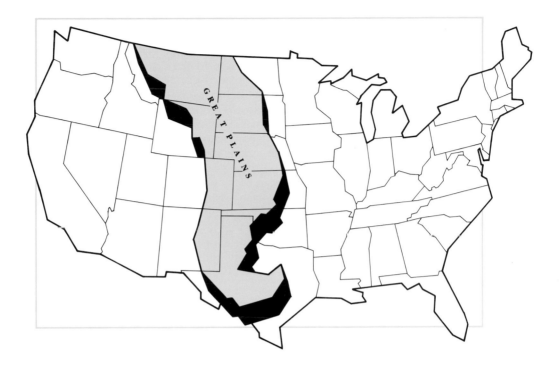

Pronghorn Antelope: Great Plains Rebound

by Charles L. Cadieux

Pronghorn antelope typify the Great Plains! More than any other animal, they are *American*. The pronghorn lives only in North America. Today, its range is centered in Wyoming, but reaches up into Saskatchewan and Alberta and all the way south to the middle of the Baja Peninsula in Mexico. Pronghorn range includes all the States from the Dakotas and Kansas to the Pacific with the surprising exception of Washington, where it has never done well.

The pronghorn is smaller than the white-tailed deer, a good buck weighing 100 to 130 pounds, and a doe at least 10 pounds less. Strikingly painted in reddish brown, black and white, it is surprisingly hard to see on the dun backgrounds of the Great Plains. Its eyesight is thought to equal ours—when

Mr. Cadieux, now a full-time freelance writer, earlier served North Dakota's wildlife agency as a game warden, editor of its magazine, and Assistant Director, followed by 28 years with the Fish and Wildlife Service and other Interior Department agencies. Author of nine books and more than 1,000 magazine articles, he is a former President of the Outdoor Writers Association of America.

ours is aided by eight-power binoculars. Easily the fastest running animal in North America, its lithe, slim-boned elegance belies its durability. Those slim bones are among the strongest of all mammals and the pronghorn almost never breaks a leg, although it dashes across rough terrain at speeds up to 50 miles per hour on short spurts. Its outer coat is composed of hollow hairs, insulating it against the wintry blasts of plains blizzards. Before plows and fences changed the face of the plains, pronghorn herds used to migrate considerable distances from summer to winter pastures. Today, they are essentially non-migratory, although they do shift from winter to summer ranges in search of the best forage. With the exception of adult bucks, the very gregarious pronghorn is seldom alone, and herds numbering more than 100 are common on prime pronghorn ranges.

It lives in some of the most shelter-less wildlife habitat to be found in America—yet blistering summer heat hasn't caused it to move out of Arizona and Texas, and blizzards and 30-below-zero temperatures haven't driven it out of Montana or North Dakota.

Wildlife scientists argue the question of pre-1942 pronghorn numbers. Some estimates put the North American population at 40 million, which would mean that the plains speedster was as numerous as the bison, and far more numerous than the elk.

Bison and pronghorn were sympatric species, mutually complementary in their forage needs and ability to combat the deep snows of the northern plains. Respected wildlifer Wendell Bever suggested that the antelope needed the bison to break a path through the drifts. Bever also felt that the bison, a grass eater, made the lower-growing forbs and browse plants more readily available to the pronghorn. In any event, the two lived side by side across a great slice of the continent, almost everywhere west of the forests dominating the eastern half of the land, all the way to the Great Basin and on to the Pacific Ocean in some areas. True, the pronghorn's range went into the southwestern deserts and the buffalo went into the forested lands farther east, but they existed together over a great hunk of America. The northern limit was somewhere in the middle of what is now Saskatchewan and the southern limit reached down into Mexico's mainland and to the southern tip of the Baja Peninsula.

Before the plow broke the Great Plains in the 1880-1910 period, this area was home to pronghorns and bison; mule deer were found over all of the area, while elk grazed on the lush grasses. Great Plains game herds could be matched only in East Africa.

But it wasn't only home to big game; sharp-tailed grouse were very numerous in the short grass prairies and in what we natives call "thornapple" clumps, which some of the experts call hawthorn and buffalo-berry; sage grouse boomed and strutted wherever sagebrush grew. White-tailed jackrabbits and cottontails were widespread, and prairie dog towns with populations numbering in the millions prospered from Texas to Canada. Probably most important of all, that part of the prairie which is now called eastern North and South Dakota, western Minnesota and most of northern Nebraska, and parts of Iowa, was the greatest producer of waterfowl that the continent has ever known. Canada geese nested across the northern part of this huge area, while puddle ducks populated the glaciated pothole regions of the Dakotas and into western Minnesota. Blue-winged teal were found in greater abundance in northwestern Iowa than has ever been recorded elsewhere. Snow and blue geese nested far to the north, but dawdled along across the plains on their southward migration. In some years, the Missouri River was the migration path for these geese from "beyond the north wind", forming concentrations of half a million birds in such traditional stopover spots as Forney's Lake in southwestern Iowa.

134

*Ensuring a good survival rate of fawns is a
major responsibility of wildlife managers.*

Predators large and small—wolves and mountain lions and coyotes and
badgers and raccoons and bobcats—took their share of game birds and animals
as they had for millennia past, and found plenty of rodents to round out their
diet. Until habitat destruction made their prey easily found, predators and prey
had successfully co-existed for millions of years.

The northern part of this immense area is drained by the Big Muddy—the
mighty Missouri River—and its tributaries. Along these watercourses cottonwoods and box elder provided some shelter for wildlife and, interspersed with
the taller trees, wild plums, thornapples, chokecherries and dozens of less
important shrubs provided food and escape cover.

At the eastern edges of the Great Plains, grass grew knee deep, waving in the
ever-present wind. It was upon these grassy pastures that many bison and elk
found their home, and to a lesser degree, so did the pronghorn antelope. Farther
west grew shorter grasses and a shrub more valuable, perhaps, than any other:
sagebrush. The gray-green foliage provided the staple food for the pronghorn.
The first green foliage in the spring was eagerly eaten by sage grouse, and its
leaves were relished in late summer by a host of birds and mammals. Too tough
to die in the droughts which hit the plains, tough enough to send its tap roots
down to find the vital moisture, the sagebrush was home and shelter to a vast
wildlife community. Sagebrush fawning grounds proved superior to other
habitats in protecting newborn fawns from the eyes and noses of predators.
Coyote, wolf and kit fox denned in the sagebrush, but the red fox had not yet
invaded the plains.

135

Sagebrush and prairie grasses were intermingled along a transitional belt which ran from north to south dividing the drier Great Plains—preferred home of the pronghorn—from the better-watered grass sea of the eastern half.

The face of the Great Plains had changed dramatically by the time I first saw it. The plow had done its work before 1920. Growing up on the North Dakota plains, I loved springtime the best, when the crocus poked through the dirt-streaked remnants of winter's snows and shallow creeks overflowed their banks. Skeins of Canada geese honked northward and the dapper pintail drakes chased sleek hens over the shallow waters of thousands of ponds. Although waterfowl numbers were greatly reduced, the Dakotas were still a waterfowler's paradise.

Summers were hot. June was life renewing itself—young birds everywhere, mule deer fawns hiding motionless in the brush, broods of Canada geese seeking protection by staying between their parents, and ducks everywhere. The sounds of springtime were the calling of waterfowl and the liquid notes of the western meadowlark, on a sun-drenched world of level plains unbroken by trees.

July was hotter, and brooding silent except for the first thunderstorms which marched—purple ramparted—from west to east across the endless plains. Thunderstorms increased in August, when billowing black clouds pre-saged cooling rain.

Fall was the bountiful time on the Great Plains. Unless hail had beaten him to it, the farmer harvested greater acreages of wheat every year. A very fortunate few enjoyed the Hunters Moon of October, when grouse were available in great numbers and swarms of waterfowl added to the winter meat supply.

Winter was another matter entirely. Blizzards howled across the Great Plains in insane fury, tearing the breath from a man's lungs. When the snows were followed by periods of thaw and refreezing, the pronghorns died from starvation because the preferred forage had been consumed by domestic live-stock or because fences barred them from moving to where forage was more available. During periods of heavy snows, the sharp-tailed grouse—the typical game bird of the plains—spent days motionless on a low branch of the thorn-apple-buckbrush complex, patiently waiting till the storm had spent its fury.

Despite the low rainfall which characterized the Great Plains, there were thousands of springs providing watering places for wildlife, due to the Ogalalla Aquifer, a huge pool of water which underlies a great part of the plains.

Weather patterns remain much the same, but wildlife's ability to withstand the ravages of weather has been greatly reduced. Many changes have taken place. First and foremost, of course, had been the settlement of the Great Plains by man. The plow and the mouldboard broke the plains, not always wisely. Near Glen Ullin, North Dakota, a statue commemorates the words of a Sioux chieftain about the plowed fields of the white man. "Wrong Side Up!" quoth the Indian, and all too often, he was right. As the plow reduced the habitat for the sharp-tailed and sage grouse, it improved habitat for the prairie-chicken, which prospered in the vicinity of grainfields. From 1920 until the onset of the Dust Bowl in 1933, the prairie-chicken increased in numbers, providing almost unbe-lievable hunting. Hunters in the Dakotas and Nebraska were able to flush fall concentrations of prairie-chickens numbering in the hundreds. Before the be-ginning of effective game law enforcement, in the 1930's, it was relatively simple to kill a wagon load of "chickens" on a morning's hunt. At the same time, the sharptail was finding his homeland growing smaller and smaller, until he count-ed only the unplowable rocky hills and brush-bordered watercourses in his domain. The plow drove out the white-tailed deer and moved the mule deer into a greatly restricted range.

By 1920, the plow had drastically reduced habitat for all wildlife species, and many wildlife populations showed an alarming drop. The bison was long gone, of course. Pronghorn numbers had shrunk from their pre-settlement high of perhaps 40 million to less than 25,000 for all of North America. Fenced away from their best range, their migrations stopped by sheep-tight fences that they never learned to master, overhunted for meat and for sport, their fawning grounds narrowed to the point where predators easily found the fawns, the pronghorn population had dropped catastrophically.

Man's drainage of shallow sloughs, to increase cropland acreage, cut waterfowl numbers by 60 percent in the Great Plains. North and South Dakota, which had exhibited the best puddle duck habitat in the world, found their water areas disappearing at an alarming rate. This continuing loss of waterfowl production areas has been a constant, from 1880 through today.

But everything that man had done to change the Great Plains paled into insignificance compared to what happened in the Dirty Thirties—the period from 1932 to the outbreak of World War II in Europe. Three happenings, two bad and one good, changed the Great Plains.

The Great Depression and the Dust Bowl drought were the bad things. The absence of rain during summers filled with searing winds extended over all of the Great Plains. I remember parking alongside U.S. Route 10 in eastern North Dakota because it was too dark to drive safely—at high noon. Winds picked up the dry topsoil of the Great Plains and carried it eastward, darkening the sky over the eastern half of the Nation, dramatically bringing the plight of the plains to the attention of the rest of the country. Dust sifted in around the windows of plains homes, and drifting soil buried entire buildings.

Light sandy loams of semi-arid Great Plains were well suited for native grasses and sagebrush, but when plowed for crops they blew apart in hot, dry 1930's windstorms.

White-tailed deer had almost disappeared from the eastern part of North Dakota. In 1936, a whitetail was seen north of Jamestown, North Dakota, and the event was important enought to be written up in the newspapers. Springs dried up and creeks failed to flow. Even the plains-toughened cottonwood trees died in the long dry spell. The Great Plains didn't grow much of a crop of grain, of cattle, or of wildlife, during the years from 1932 through 1936.

Even if the farmer was able to produce grain, he got very little money for it, for this was the Great Depression. What drought didn't do to the farmer, economic conditions did. Thousands of families abandoned their homesteads on the plains. The Okies' flight to California is well documented, but all the way from north Texas to Canada, homesteads were abandoned to the Dust Bowl.

When things were at their worst, the good things started to happen. The dry years forced our government to realize that something had to be done. Conservation giants, men like Hugh Bennett of the Soil Conservation Service, and Ding Darling of the U.S. Biological Survey (a forerunner of the U.S. Fish and Wildlife Service) rose to meet the emergencies. Under their leadership, with the cooperation of President Franklin Delano Roosevelt, a program of soil conservation was begun which coincided with the end of the drought period to produce spectacular results. The showpiece of soil conservation was the shelterbelt program, a boon to many a Great Plains farmer and to wildlife as well. Many in Congress who voted for the shelterbelt program thought of it then as a "make work" project, which enabled a man to feed his family by being paid for planting trees.

But the trees changed life on the Great Plains. Almost every farmstead was soon protected from north and west winds by a barrier of trees—shorter and denser-branched on the ouside rows, taller and longer-lived in the center rows. The shelterbelt diverted the bitter winds of winter, up and over the homestead. Of far more long-lasting importance, the shelterbelt slowed the winds of the plains and forced them to drop their snow load on fields which needed all the moisture they could get. The dense foliage of the shelterbelt proved to be a lifesaver for white-tailed deer, for sharp-tailed grouse, and for the newly arrived ring-necked pheasant, and became the number one nesting area for mourning doves and goldfinches. Cottontail rabbits inhabited the denser parts of the belts and the white-tailed jackrabbit sheltered himself in the lee of the bigger tree trunks.

As these shelterbelts matured, new species of birds came to the Great Plains, attracted by the nesting sites and food afforded by the trees. The fox squirrel, unknown there in the 1920's, became common in many parts of the plains, making their living in the shelterbelts and raiding the farmers' corn fields. At the same time, the red fox was extending its range westward to include all of the shelterbelt lands. Noting the improved conditions for wildlife afforded by the shelterbelts, many Great Plains States began systematic creation of other woody cover for wildlife.

However, woody cover did little to help the pronghorn, for he disdained stealth and never hid from his enemies. He preferred to outrun them. But another soil conservation program did him a lot of good. Stock water dams, built to spread grazing pressure by domestic livestock, enabled the pronghorn to repopulate areas from which he had been "dried" out.

At the same time, abandoned farms grew back into sagebrush and cactus, larkspur and loco weed, goldenrod, cocklebur, thread grass and yucca, rabbitbrush and fringed sage and saltbush and russian thistle. Globemallow and prickly pear and bunchgrass—native plants that had been plowed out by man's ill-advised ventures into dry-land farming—came back to cover the Dust Bowl lands, to tie down the soil, and gladden the heart and fill the stomach of the pronghorn.

Shelterbelts are still being planted for small game cover with P-R funds. Unfortunately, many older shelterbelts are dying out and not being replaced.

Pasturelands formerly fenced out of pronghorns' reach were again opened as untended fences sagged and disappeared, or were covered by drifted soil and mats of tumbleweeds.

By about 1942, many unwise irrigation projects had been abandoned, and thousands of acres which had suffered the indignities of "sagebrush removal" were reverting to nature's plan, greatly expanding the available range and forage for the pronghorn.

A major development of the 1930's was the passage of the Pittman-Robertson Federal Aid in Wildlife Restoration Act by the Congress and its signing into law in 1937 by President Roosevelt. Now, for the first time, State conservation agencies could afford to do a better job. For the first time, many States inventoried their wildlife resources. The amazing resurgence of the pronghorn, begun when man was forced to abandon lands he should never have farmed, accelerated as P-R funds were used to "census" antelope, to study new habitats and decide whether or not to restock them with antelope, to trap and transplant antelope—beginning with New Mexico's pioneer attempts and continuing to this day. No other big game animal has been the beneficiary of such a program of trapping and transplanting on such a large scale. The pronghorn's hardy vigor today is a result of P-R financed restocking programs. Inbreeding has not been a problem for pronghorn herds since restocking programs started.

The pronghorn response to bettered conditions, transplanting, and harvest management has been almost unbelievable, with continental populations approaching 1 million pronghorns, whereas 50 years ago we had less than 30,000! Because other mortality factors have been removed, man now happily substitutes hunting for the losses formerly caused by large predators. Regulated sport hunting is now an important tool of wildlife management.

P-R funds paid for basic research into the fundamental question of "what does a pronghorn eat?" The results of this research opened many new lands to the pronghorn, for it was found that their principal foods were forbs and weedy plants, unused or not preferred by cattle. The knowledge that antelope did not

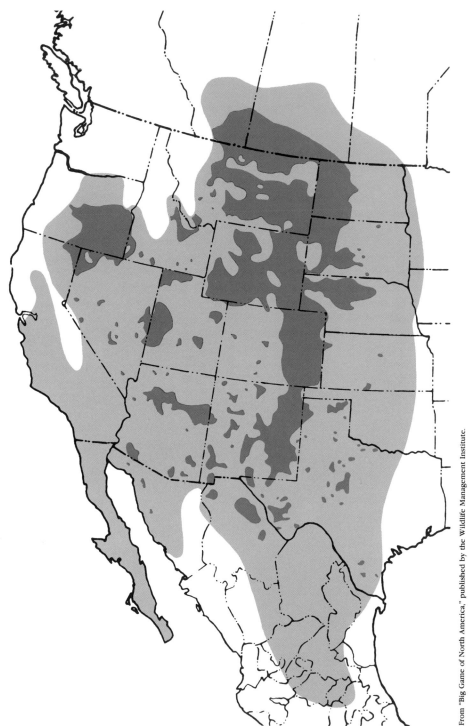

From "Big Game of North America," published by the Wildlife Management Institute.

Outer boundaries of the shaded areas indicate the outermost limits of the pronghorn antelope's original range (although not all this territory was occupied by pronghorn). The inner areas show pronghorn range as of 1970, indicating success of the continuing restoration effort.

compete with cattle changed the attitude of landowners who had considered the antelope a handicap to profitable livestock raising. P-R financed research into wildlife diseases proved to the world that the pronghorn was NOT a carrier of Bangs disease or brucellosis, as many cattlemen had thought. This research finding did much to make the pronghorn welcome across great parts of his range where he must coexist with livestock.

P-R funds paid for research projects which documented the loss of antelope fawns to coyote predation, lending support to livestockmen's pressure for State approval for greatly expanded programs aimed at reducing the numbers of coyotes. Compound 1080 was the most effective of all coyote control tools. Its use greatly reduced numbers of coyotes upon wide areas which then showed dramatic increases in newborn pronghorn survival. In all Western States, live-stock interests gladly paid the costs of coyote control programs using Compound 1080.

Results for pronghorns have been more dramatic than for any other species on the Great Plains. Where there once were less than 12,000 antelope in Wyoming, probably more than half a million pronghorns today range across the Cowboy State. Wyoming game managers actually feel that the pronghorn may now be overpopulating some parts of their range. Antelope have reclaimed some of their old ranges in Texas, New Mexico, Colorado, Montana, North and South Dakota, Kansas, Oklahoma and Nebraska, as well as over the mountains in Utah, Arizona, Nevada, and eastern Oregon. Ongoing P-R funded research is studying food habits of pronghorns, effects of different hunting season dates upon reproductive success, social relationships within antelope herds and many other facets. On the Great Plains today, and in the Great Basin to the west, the pronghorn is the best example of man's actions bringing about a great resurgence in big game numbers. P-R can take a lot of credit for that improvement.

But the pronghorn has not been the only beneficiary of P-R funded research. In 1985, hunters legally killed more whitetails in Texas alone than were found in all of the Great Plains in 1936. P-R projects have provided "gallinaceous guzzlers," concrete water catchments which provide life-giving water in near-desert habitats, benefiting Hungarian partridge and chukars, javelinas and mule deer, white-winged doves and Coues deer, bighorn sheep and cactus wrens. The 50 years of P-R work has been a boom period for Great Plains wildlife. In the 1980's, we find pronghorn populations at their highest point since 1870; mule and white-tailed deer are showing healthy numbers through periodic increases and decreases. Native Great Plains game birds, sharp-tailed grouse and mourning doves, are all showing good populations, adequate for regulated annual harvests by hunters. Research has shown the close relationship between the sagebrush and the well-being of game birds and mammals and has forestalled some sage-brush clearing projects before they began. P-R funds have been used by many States to buy lands which are then developed for wildlife production—produc-tion of ducks and geese, of grouse and elk, of rabbits and raccoons. Non-game species have benefited in almost every case, because well-managed land invari-ably produces better conditions for non-game birds and mammals as well as for the game species.

Introduced game birds, some of them the result of P-R research projects like the Hungarian partridge, have been experimentally stocked in suitable ecological niches, where they have prospered.

The great importance of woody cover to wildlife has been recognized, both as a result of the successful shelterbelt program and as a result of Pittman-Robertson financed tree planting programs. However, very little is being done to avert the silent calamity which now looms—not in the future, but right now—as

Geoff Tischbein, Colorado Division of Wildlife

*Helicopters and other aircraft are widely used
in pronghorn population surveys.*

most of the shelterbelts are maturing and dying without replacement. Evidently the lessons of the Dust Bowl are forgotten. It is very hard to convince a landowner that he should go to the trouble and expense to replant a shelterbelt, when he can remove the shelterbelt, plow up that land and grow another 200 bushels of wheat. The fact that the wildlife is needed and wanted, while the surplus grain is destined for government-financed storage, doesn't seem to tip the scales in the argument.

During the half century in which P-R funds have been made available to the States of the Great Plains area, there have been great changes in wildlife management. Decisions are no longer based upon educated guesses, but are more apt to be based upon hard facts gained through P-R financed research. The plains are dotted with State wildlife management areas, dedicated to wise conservation of natural resources—which includes game bird and mammal hunting as one of its tools—as a result of P-R financed land purchases. The real value of wetlands to wildlife has been recognized as a result of P-R research, although we are still losing the fight to prevent the loss of wetlands.

During that half century, the pronghorn has been the greatest success story of plains wildlife. But there have been many pluses to which we may point, and rejoice in the fact that the far-seeing legislation of 1937, sponsored by hunters, has played a big part in those successes. White-tailed deer and, to a lesser degree, mule deer, have made a tremendous comeback in numbers. The whitetail has made a spectacular recovery, up from less than 1 million to 14 million or more across the continent. That gaudy import, the ring-necked pheasant, is well established in the Dakotas, Nebraska, Kansas, Oklahoma and even extends his range into Montana, Wyoming, Colorado and New Mexico, as well as moving east all the way to Pennsylvania and Ohio, and west to join earlier stockings in Oregon. Not all things are rosy, but the States of the Great Plains now have the tools to "know" the proper course of wildlife management across their vast area. "Knowing" is a far cry from "doing," unfortunately. The greatest problem is that of influencing land use practices, where dollars speak so much louder than words. If drainage of wetlands to produce still more surplus grain is continued, we cannot arrest what could become a catastrophic slide in waterfowl numbers. The failure of wildlife managers to stablilize the population of ducks, in my opinion, has been our greatest failure in the past 50 years.

If the shelterbelts, which changed living conditions on the Great Plains for both humans and wildlife, are not replaced, there will be significant losses in populations of songbirds, rabbits, pheasants, grouse, deer and squirrels—for they will be without nesting cover for birds and without winter escape cover for both birds and mammals.

The Ogalalla Aquifer, that vast underground freshwater sea, is being depleted by 50 years of over-use, with insufficient recharge. If this trend continues, great portions of the southern Great Plains will no longer be able to support irrigated agriculture by the end of the century. This could be a tragedy for man, but a boon for some wildlife species. Much of this irrigated land, without Ogalalla Aquifer waters, may revert to its natural state and provide much improved wildlife habitat for those species which can exist with scant water supplies.

1937 to 1987, a glorious half century for most wildlife, has had its ups and downs, but the trend is definitely upward. P-R has helped to discover the needs of wildlife, and to find answers to problems. It has provided lands upon which crops of wildlife are being grown, has enabled the State conservation agencies to do a far better job than they were doing prior to 1937 . . . and don't forget, the sport hunter pays for practically all of it! The money comes from the Pittman-Robertson excise tax upon archery equipment and firearms and ammunition.

Biologists supplement aircraft by using "spotting scope" to help estimate pronghorn herd characteristics.

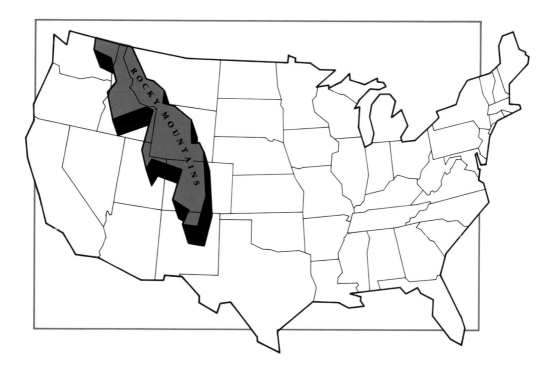

Elk: Rocky Mountain Majesty

by L. Jack Lyon and Jack Ward Thomas

For many years, the Boone and Crockett world record bull elk trophy was a pair of antlers (circa 1890) discovered in an abandoned ranch building in Wyoming. When a new record was discovered, in 1961, it turned out to be another 19th century elk—this time from Colorado. Clearly, the "good old days" dominate the records. Or do they? The third largest trophy antlers came from a bull killed in Alberta, Canada, in 1977—and those antlers displaced to fourth position a bull that was killed in Montana in 1958.

Drs. Lyon and Thomas, senior wildlife research biologists for the U.S. Forest Service, have devoted decades to studies of the Rocky Mountain elk. Dr. Lyon has been a Research Project Leader at the Intermountain Research Station, Missoula, Montana, for over 20 years; authored more than 60 papers on wildlife habitat ecology; and recently completed work on the Final Report of the Montana Cooperative Elk-Logging Study 1970-1985. Dr. Thomas, Chief Wildlife Research Biologist stationed at La Grande, Oregon, was one of the two compiler-editors of the award-winning book, The Elk of North America—Ecology and Management, *and has authored more than 200 articles on elk, white-tailed and mule deer, wild turkeys, and other species; he is a past President of The Wildlife Society and a fellow of the Society of American Foresters.*

145

The record book only adds to the magic, and the mystery, of a species many consider the premier North American big game animal. Every hunter, in every State where elk are important, believes in the possibility of a massive bull—and the records confirm this belief. If there is a single species of wildlife that seems to characterize the wild and open spaces of the mountains, it is the Rocky Mountain elk. When we recognize that the 19th Century giants from Colorado and Wyoming could easily have represented a requiem for the species in North America, the mystique grows even larger. The recovery of elk populations that had nearly disappeared in 1900-1910 represents one of the great success stories of wildlife management in North America. The fact that magnificent trophy animals continue to be a part of that success makes it even more remarkable.

When European settlement of North America began, six subspecies of elk occupied what is now the United States. By 1910, only two existed in a truly wild state, the Roosevelt elk, native to the areas between the Cascade Range and the Pacific Ocean, and the Rocky Mountain elk, surviving in remote areas of Idaho, Montana, Wyoming and Colorado. By 1920, three of the six original subspecies were completely gone and the tule elk had been reduced to scattered populations in California. It has been estimated that before settlement, there were as many as 10 million elk in North America. Early in this century, there were perhaps fewer than 50,000.

Between 1910 and 1980, the turnaround and recovery were almost as dramatic as the original decline. Yellowstone National Park, created in 1872, in part to protect a spectacular elk herd, provided a nucleus. South of Yellowstone, near Jackson, Wyoming, as many as 20,000 elk wintered annually during the period 1887-1911 in an area which eventually became the National Elk Refuge. At the time, this was about 40 percent of all the elk in the U.S. Montana began trapping and hauling elk from Yellowstone Park in 1910, and Colorado began transplanting elk from Jackson Hole in 1912. The Forest Service estimated Colorado elk in 1910 at somewhere between 500 and 1000 animals in 10 small herds scattered in terrain rough enough to offer sanctuary. By 1976, Colorado elk populations were estimated to total 98,000; and by 1985 there were 135,000.

Other Western States had similarly successful programs. Throughout the Rockies, public support, initiated by concerned big game hunters, contributed to the success of elk restoration efforts, aided by the dedicated work of the State game departments and Federal agencies, particularly the U.S. Forest Service and the U.S. Fish and Wildlife Service. Some measure of that success is indicated by elk populations rising to 90,000 animals in 1922 and over 422,000 by 1976. The annual harvest grew steadily from 30,000 in the late 1940's to over 65,000 in the 1970's, and the current annual sale of elk hunting licenses exceeds 400,000 in five Rocky Mountain States.

In retrospect, the characteristics that nearly led to the demise of the Rocky Mountain elk are the same characteristics that made restoration so desirable. The elk is prized for its trophy value, majestic size, and palatable meat. The antler mainbeams of a dominant herd bull sweep back nearly five feet and weigh 30 or more pounds. Bulls over 3 years old are likely to weigh more than 700 pounds, three times the weight of a large white-tailed deer. In the wild, and in an appropriate setting, an elk herd is a magnificent sight. Even the sounds made by elk, the shrill bugle and resonating grunts of a bull in rut, are completely unique in the deer family. The species also receives much attention from the non-hunting public and is a prime attraction in Yellowstone, Grand Teton, Rocky Mountain and Glacier National Parks. For the outdoorsman and city dweller alike, the elk is a symbol of wilderness, open space, and freedom.

As desirable as it seems to be, can the Rocky Mountain elk survive in our modern world? An elk is a big animal, requiring plenty of space and food. Is there a place for it? Do elk compete with other uses of the land and vegetation? In short, can we afford elk? There are a number of reasons that make it possible to answer in the affirmative. An animal that stimulates the imagination of so many people will certainly continue to receive the management attention it needs to survive in good numbers. The elk is adaptable to many kinds of habitats and conditions, and current indications are that available habitat will be managed to support substantial herds. The welfare of the elk is inextricably tied to management of the land. Let us examine the Rocky Mountain elk as it is today and the habitat in which it lives—as it once was, and as it is now.

Elk are gregarious, which means that they normally congregate in groups or herds. A group may consist of as few as two to five in the summer or as many as several thousand on the winter range. Herding, however, is not just an evidence that elk like each other. Throughout the year, group size and structure are evidence of behavioral characteristics not seen in other members of the deer family. Presumably, these characteristics also promote the survival of the species. During the fall breeding season, the larger, most dominant and successful bulls attempt to gather harems of cows and keep them segregated from other bulls. A bull in rut takes every possible action to intimidate competitors and advertise his own availability. The spine-tingling bugling that begins in September is both a challenge to other males and an invitation to females. This challenge is intensified by wallowing about in mud and urine and thrashing small trees. Posturing and intimidation settle most encounters, but fighting leading to serious injury has been recorded.

Yearling cows rarely breed, but the pregnancy rate in older cows usually exceeds 90 percent. Between conception and birth, the fate of the unborn calf is closely tied to the condition of the habitat. Elk generally move from summer range areas in the high country to lower-elevation winter ranges where herds can number in the thousands. Pregnant cows going onto winter range in good condition and finding adequate forage are almost 100 percent successful in delivering calves. As habitat quality declines, however, calves may be born smaller and have notably reduced chances for survival.

Calves, averaging about 32 pounds, are born sometime in May or June. Cow elk seek seclusion when giving birth, but as soon as the calves can travel, bands of cows and calves gather in nursery herds. The large number of adult animals in this herd aids the cow in protecting her small, vulnerable offspring. As summer progresses, however, the nursery bands break up, and elk are often seen in relatively small groups until the beginning of the fall rut.

Food habits of elk are extremely varied. Elk are able to feed on a much wider variety of plant material, and use it more effectively, than other North American members of the deer family. The Rocky Mountain elk, throughout its entire range, reportedly consumes 142 species of forbs, ferns and lichens; 77 species of grasses and grass-like species; and 111 species of shrubs and trees. Elk seem to prefer grazing, particularly on native bunchgrasses, but they also thrive where shrubby browse plants make up a substantial portion of the available food. The fact that elk prefer grasses establishes an obvious potential for direct competition with livestock, especially on the national forests where livestock grazing is a traditional use.

Most Rocky Mountain elk herds are migratory, moving down from high country when snow accumulates in autumn or early winter. When snow depths recede in spring, elk move from lower elevation winter ranges (often on private lands) to higher summer ranges (usually on the national forests). Elk that winter

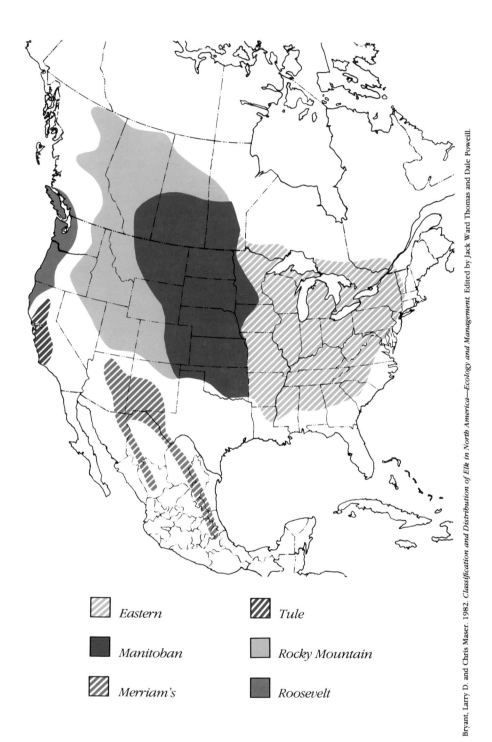

Bryant, Larry D. and Chris Maser. 1982. *Classification and Distribution of Elk in North America—Ecology and Management.* Edited by Jack Ward Thomas and Dale Powell.

Eastern	Tule
Manitoban	Rocky Mountain
Merriam's	Roosevelt

Original distribution of North American elk, by species

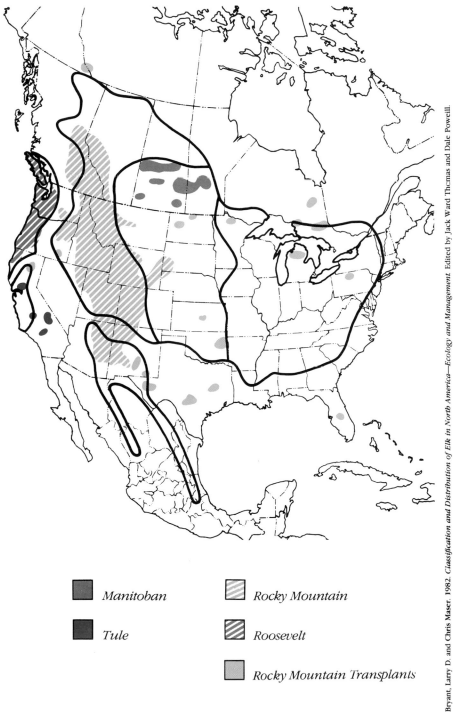

	Manitoban		Rocky Mountain
	Tule		Roosevelt
			Rocky Mountain Transplants

Present distribution of North American elk, by species

on private land sometimes damage haystacks and fences. The presence of elk on private lands sometimes causes conflict so severe that the limiting factor on many elk herds is the level of tolerance of private landowners.

Elk, with few exceptions, are associated with trees. The forests and mountains inhabited by elk are also primary habitat for most other North American big game species. Mule deer, white-tailed deer, moose, and black bears are often found where elk are found; and not too distant are the habitats of mountain goats and bighorn sheep. In the "lower 48" United States, habitats for grizzly bears are limited chiefly to the forested mountains of Montana, Wyoming and Idaho; and woodland caribou to Idaho and Washington. Small mammals, birds, and fish are also important, but the Rocky Mountains hold a unique significance as the epicenter for big game in the lower 48 States.

Rocky Mountain Wildlife Habitat

The mountains were the long-term refuge that enabled many North American wildlife species to survive the cross-Continental march of civilization. The "unlimited" bison herds have been gone from the Great Plains for 100 years, but the Rockies still support a variety and abundance of big game animals. Other regions have more upland birds, or more waterfowl, but there are few other places where the condition of big game animals serves as a reliable index or barometer for the well-being of all wildlife populations.

Every mountain range is potentially significant to wildlife because mountains represent great habitat diversity. In the mountains, each change of slope, aspect, and elevation produces a change in the diversity and abundance of the plant community. These changes may be so great that a totally different combination of wildlife species can be supported. The Rocky Mountains are particularly diverse because they consist of many smaller, sometimes disconnected ranges. The Bitterroot Mountains, the Bighorns, the Tetons and the Sangre de Cristo are more than specifically named high points—they also represent unique wildlife habitats that support unique combinations of wildlife populations.

Trees and elk just naturally go together. Nearly all Rocky Mountain elk spend their lives in or near national forests.

Gene Brehm

150

Wildlife habitats in the Rocky Mountains include a great diversity of vegetation, ranging from grasslands, sagebrush, and chaparral through lowland cottonwood and sidehill Gambel oak to aspens, alpine meadows, and rocky peaks. And the factor that ties it all together, from the foothills to the peaks, is the coniferous forest. The Rocky Mountains rise through elevational belts of ponderosa pine and Douglas fir upward to lodgepole pine, subalpine fir, and Englemann spruce. Other conifers, including western larch and white pine, or blue spruce, or cedar and hemlock, provide local diversity, but there is an underlying similarity and continuity of the first five named evergreen tree species throughout the Rocky Mountain forests.

A second common factor of similarity and continuity is provided by forest fires. In varying degrees, all the conifer forests of the Rockies have burned sometime in the past. From time immemorial, lightning or primitive man has started fires that burned beneath the trees—and very often burned the tree crowns as well. These fires are important to wildlife because they assure a continuous rejuvenation of forest vegetation. Forest recovery following fire proceeds through a succession of plant communities, each with unique values for some kind of wildlife. Thus, repeated burning and recovery of wildlife habitats in the Rocky Mountains is a part of the constant change that produces habitat diversity and wildlife productivity.

A third common factor, one that further increases natural continuity, is the very high percentage of public land in the Rocky Mountains. The region includes over 140 million acres of forest land, much of it designated as national forests. It also includes four of the largest and most scenic national parks and a very substantial proportion of the existing National Wilderness Preservation System. The existence of national forests and national parks, and the ready accessibility of these lands to the public, is of extreme importance to wildlife.

Wildlife History in the Rocky Mountains

It has always been assumed that before the coming of whites, man had little direct influence on wildlife populations. This assumption is probably not true, but it is clear that the American Indians were only rarely responsible for local extermination of wildlife populations.

Early explorers were impressed by the wealth of beaver and the fierce intolerance of the grizzly bear, but they also reported with awe the numbers of bighorn sheep and other game in the Rocky Mountains. Grouse, deer and elk were generally plentiful, mountain goats were seen on the peaks, and mountain lions, porcupines, and caribou were at least locally abundant. The magic of the mountains, however, was the beaver. In 1805-1806, Lewis and Clark found the Montana Rockies teeming with beaver and beaver dams. Zebulon Pike was less perceptive about the Colorado Rockies of 1806, but it made little difference. Within a few years of these early historic explorations, the mountains were invaded by an army of trappers—the "mountain men." The effects on the beaver are partially demonstrated by the brief life span of the fur trade. The last Fur Rendezvous was held on the Green River in 1840, but the numbers of beaver pelts sold had declined for several years before that. The mountain men lived much as the Indians did, and while the pressures they exerted on other wildlife were greater because they were better armed, they posed no major threat to big game populations.

Between 1840 and 1870, more than a quarter million people crossed the North American Continent. Many of these pioneers passed through the Rockies in southern Wyoming without having any influence on wildlife except in the immediate vicinity of the Oregon Trail. The Rockies were a dark and fearsome obstacle to wagon traffic, and since there was little impetus for settlement, few people stayed. This pattern changed, however, when gold was discovered in Colorado in 1859, in Idaho in 1861, and in Montana in 1862. Interestingly, the discovery at Chicago Creek in Colorado was made by an elk hunter.

Primitive tent and log cities burgeoned throughout the mountains. Lumber camps sprang up. The Mullan Road from Walla Walla, Washington, to Fort Benton, Montana, a distance of 624 miles, was started in 1859 and completed in only one year. By 1865, there were steamboats on the Yellowstone and the Missouri Rivers and 120,000 new people in Montana—at least during the summer. The first trail herd from Texas reached the northern plains in 1866, and the Union Pacific Railroad crossed southern Wyoming only two years later. By 1870, Colorado had replaced California as the leading U.S. gold producer, and Denver was a developing railroad center.

The pressures on wildlife in the mountains began to grow during this period. Transient fur trappers and wandering prospectors had killed game for food when it was convenient, but as the numbers of people increased, wild game became a staple food source. And, especially in areas near towns, mines, and railroads, market hunting became a widespread and lucrative profession. Wildlife habitat was also affected, but generally in concentrated areas. Wherever people congregated, valley bottoms and forest lands were cleared for crop and pastureland, and logging in some localized areas devastated the forests to provide timber for railroads, mines, and ore smelting.

This rapacious cutting of forests in the West prompted the establishment of the first Forest Reserves. Between 1891 and the end of the century, Presidents Harrison and Cleveland designated 40 million acres of public domain as Forest Reserves. The resulting preservation of habitat may have balanced some of the localized habitat changes related to logging and destructive fires, but the immediate habitat changes were not particularly important to wildlife populations. The most significant thing happening to wildlife in the period before 1900 was that it was being killed.

Some of the Territories enacted game protection laws as early as 1850, but such restrictions were mostly ignored by residents and unenforced by the government. The historical record shows that in a relatively short period prior to 1900, many species of North American wildlife were vanishing in a universal and systematic slaughter. The bison were gone from the plains by 1883, and for at least three decades market hunting inflicted severe pressures on wildlife in the mountains. Bighorn sheep were subjected to intensive market hunting pressure; many herds disappeared, and in Montana, the Audubon subspecies was driven to extinction. Trumpeter swan skins were an important trade commodity in the late 1800's, and the number of swans surviving dropped to fewer than 100 in the early 1900's. Like many other endangered species, the few remaining survivors held out in the Rocky Mountains.

By 1900, most of the large predators and many of the big game animals had virtually disappeared. Except for animals in Yellowstone National Park and a few scattered local herds, elk were considered to be nearly extinct, there were no wolves, bighorn sheep and mountain goats were rare, and even deer were considered uncommon. Public concern was developing during this period, but for some species it was too late, and for others it appeared that time was running out.

In the early years of the 20th Century, several important events combined to alter the course of history for wildlife in the Rocky Mountains. By 1900, law enforcement was receiving strong emphasis in wildlife conservation programs,

This is a Montana State wildlife research area, set up to calculate the effects of logging on elk populations. Because logging practices are a crucial factor affecting elk today, much P-R funding has been directed toward such inquiries.

and within a few years, the States were mounting substantial efforts to restore the major big-game animals by trapping and transplanting. Elk from Yellowstone National Park were transplanted to many areas of the Rocky Mountain West. One of the significant wildlife conservation victories of the period was the dedication of Red Rocks Lake Wildlife Refuge in Montana for the protection of the trumpeter swan. Other refuges were established by both State and Federal governments.

Along with these evidences of progressive management, there were also major defeats for wildlife conservation. At least 500 bull elk were killed for their teeth in Yellowstone National Park in 1915, and a major market for elk hides, and for bison meat and robes, existed in the communities surrounding the Park as late as 1920. One of the sorry chapters of wildlife history in this period was an all-out effort by the Bureau of Biological Survey to rid the West of wolves, grizzly bears, mountain lions, bobcats, coyotes—and anything else that might conceivably kill domestic sheep or cattle. There is little evidence that the welfare of wildlife was given any consideration in this effort—although there is an ironic possibility that some big game species benefited.

While the primary technique of wildlife conservation during this period was increasingly effective law enforcement, other changes, of both political and biological significance to wildlife, were taking place. In 1906, Theodore Roosevelt designated additional large acreages in the Rocky Mountains for Forest Reserves that eventually became the region's national forests. At the time, the primary concern was to protect the timber resource, but the influence of these reserves in providing habitat for big game animals and other wildlife was very important, and has grown in importance over the years.

Also of major significance in the early decades of this century was a general drought accompanied by wildfires throughout the Rocky Mountain West. In the

153

10 years prior to 1920, more than 5 million acres of forest burned in Montana and Idaho alone. There were smaller, but significant long-term modifications of wildlife habitat by fire throughout the Rockies. Areas that had been covered with mature trees were partially or totally burned. In the newspapers of the day, these areas were mostly reported as devastated. There was little recognition that forest fires clear the way for natural development of early successional vegetation that is highly productive for wildlife—or that habitat diversity was far greater in many parts of the Rockies because of past burns.

Thus, before the 20th Century was one-third gone, a fortunate series of planned and unplanned events created favorable conditions for widespread transplanting of game animals in the Rocky Mountains at the very time when wildlife law enforcement was receiving more emphasis, when a government-protected habitat base had just been established, and when forest habitats were undergoing changes of a type most likely to increase their productivitity for wildlife. In retrospect, it might appear that wildlife managers could hardly have failed—except that there were few wildlife managers and only the beginnings of a wildlife management profession. Aldo Leopold did not publish his classic text on game management until 1933.

Professional wildlife management received major impetus with the passage of the Pittman-Robertson Act in 1937. This new law proposed to distribute money generated by a tax on firearms and ammunition among the States for wildlife work; but first, State funds had to be secured against diversion to other uses. Every State had to pass legislation guaranteeing that fees received from hunting licenses could only be used for the operation of the State fish and wildlife management agency. For the first time, fees paid by sportsmen were universally being channeled back into restoration and management of wildlife. Many States began to hire biologists and to view game management as a science based on facts rather than gimmicks and guesswork.

In the Rocky Mountain States, some of the earliest game surveys and much of the initial research effort under Pittman-Robertson concentrated on the important big game species. Early research on moose, for example, demonstrated an unexpected adaptability to upland habitats, and as a result management was modified to encourage expansion of moose populations. Although elk had been pretty well re-established in most forest habitats, Pittman-Robertson research provided the impetus for actually gathering facts about the biology and life history of the species. Out of this research came information on food habits, breeding rates, and methods for determining the ages of animals by examining tooth wear.

In the period after World War II, State game departments continued to shift their emphasis from law enforcement to professional game management. Universities developed programs to train biologists, and large numbers of returning veterans entered the wildlife profession. Wildlife research under Pittman-Robertson expanded substantially, and facilities such as the Sybille Wildlife Research Unit and the Wildlife Diseases Research Laboratory at the University of Wyoming were developed. At these and other laboratories, significant progress has been made in understanding wildlife diseases, nutritional status, and physiology of big game animals.

During this same period, the forest habitats that had burned 30 years earlier began to reach a productive peak for big game, and substantial investments of Pittman-Robertson funds went into the purchase by States of big game winter ranges from private landowners. In Montana, the famous Sun River Elk Range, and in Colorado, the Mount Evans Elk Management Unit, made the survival of two great elk herds possible. Land purchased with Pittman-Robertson funds has been extremely significant in most of the Rocky Mountain States for both winter range values and for providing public access to hunting and fishing.

The expansion of mule deer populations that had started in the 1940's continued to new highs in the 1950's. Throughout the west, mule deer populations reached levels never before recorded or even imagined. This was the period in which death on the winter range became a major consideration and emphasis in big game management. Winter range damage became the measure of declining habitat quality for whole herds of big game animals. The contributions made by P-R assisted acquisition of winter ranges to big game survival became evident in many areas. Colorado hunters will recognize such names of important winter range areas as Piceance and Little Hills, just as Pinedale and Whiskey Basin are recognized in Wyoming, Sand Creek and Boise River in Idaho, and the Gallatin and Blackfoot-Clearwater in Montana.

During the 1950's and 1960's, biological information gathered by State game departments with Pittman-Robertson funding increasingly affected management decisions. Research biologists collected information on deer and elk migrations, food habits, and population dynamics of many herds. The growth of knowledge about carrying capacities of winter ranges, and about the reproductive potential of certain herds, translated into management actions of great importance. It was during this period that several States pioneered either-sex elk and deer hunting seasons that were justified by biological discoveries made under Pittman-Robertson-supported research.

While big game management and research were making giant strides in the Rocky Mountain West, some important political decisions were being made in Washington, D.C. Increasing pressures to intensify timber harvest on national forest lands were of much concern, and Congress passed the Multiple-Use Sustained-Yield Act of 1960 to ensure that all resources would be properly

Picking up signals from radio-collared elk via antenna. This is typical elk country—rugged and forested with plenty of open space.

These elk in a Wyoming enclosure will be transplanted elsewhere. Elk may be easily captured in winter by setting out feed atop the snow cover; the animals eat their way into a penned area.

recognized in management. Wilderness was formally recognized by Congress as a dedicated land use in 1964. Between 1962 and 1977, nearly 7 million acres of timberland on the national forests in the Rocky Mountains were reclassified from commercial timberland to Wilderness or Wilderness Study status.

By 1970, clearcutting on the national forests had created a strong negative public response and drawn complaints ranging from watershed damage to destruction of wildlife habitat. Several independent studies of forest management on the national forests were conducted, and eventually the Forest and Rangeland Renewable Resources Planning Act of 1974 and the National Forest Management Act of 1976 became law. In both of these Acts, evaluation of existing wildlife habitat and of the influences of commodity production on habitat values were recognized as important considerations in land management. Similar recognition of these factors on acreages administered by the Bureau of Land Management came with passage of the 1976 Federal Land Management and Policy Act. This act also mandated major studies of BLM lands for possible designation as wilderness.

For the past 20 years, both habitat quality and wildlife populations have continued to change. Habitat modification has mostly been accomplished through logging, although some fairly large forest fires have burned. Elk populations levels have not been notable for sudden changes; and yet, virtually throughout the Rocky Mountain States, elk populations have continued to rise steadily. In some areas, it is believed that the numbers of elk in current herds may be as great as ever recorded.

Management of this resource and all other big game species has changed drastically. Today, there are more hunters, and management of the harvest has become more sophisticated as well as more complicated. Few State wildlife agencies set a statewide general hunting season for any big game animal, and for most big game species other than deer and elk, the majority of hunting licenses must be issued through drawings. Limitations on license sales, if required, are determined by projections of big game population levels, reproductive rates and expected hunter harvest. In many States, these projections are based on sophisticated population models produced by Pittman-Robertson research. Another sign of more sophisticated big game management is a greater recognition of the influence of year-around habitats on herd health and productivity. Today, the condition of the summer range is viewed just as critically as the condition of the winter range, and cover is considered to be as important as forage in judging habitat quality.

Significant changes are also occurring in the wildlife profession. The World War II veterans who graduated in the wildlife management classes of the late 1940's have reached retirement age, and a whole new generation of wildlife professionals is moving into positions of responsibility. In addition, we are seeing shifts in relative numbers of practicing wildlife professionals in the State game departments and the Federal agencies. States retain full responsibility for the management of hunted populations and enforcement of wildlife laws, but the welfare of wildlife is becoming a shared responsibility with Federal biologists. Some States now employ fewer professional wildlife biologists than the Federal agencies that manage wildlife habitat on lands within the State borders.

These ongoing trends have dramatic implications for elk and elk hunting. In the late 1970's, about 93 percent of all the elk in the United States spent at least part of each year on national forests. However, very little of this land can be devoted solely to elk habitat. Approximately 89 percent of the national forest land occupied by elk will likely be assigned to multiple-use management to produce wood, water, recreation, wildlife, and grazing. The Rocky Mountain elk is inextricably tied to the management of the national forests and adjacent lands—and, fortunately, this fact has already become widely recognized. Joint research by P-R funded State wildlife agencies and Forest Service Research Stations in Montana, Oregon, and Wyoming have resulted in the development of elk habitat-timber management guidelines that are widely used on public and private land throughout the West. Elk are certain to receive more consideration than many other species in forest land management because so much recent research has gone into the development of these coordination guidelines.

If past history is a measure of probability, wildlife habitats in the Rocky Mountains seem less subject to change and modification than habitats outside the mountains. Yet substantial changes continue, and many of the expected developments cannot be considered desirable from the standpoint of wildlife. Habitat will continue to loom large as a problem for elk managers and land managers. Management of the national forests and adjoining private lands holds the key to the welfare of most elk in North America. It is particularly critical that the concerns of landowners about the impacts of elk on private lands be addressed.

Regulation of sport hunting will almost inevitably increase, and the management problems will continue to grow. Currently, for example, several States are concerned that overharvest of mature bulls could have long-term detrimental results; young bulls, although capable of breeding, are suspected of being less effective. As human populations rise, the demand for elk hunting will also increase even though elk numbers remain static or even decrease. These trends lead inevitably to more and more rationing of elk hunting opportunities over the long term. At the same time, the ever-increasing numbers of roads being built into previously unroaded or lightly roaded areas of the national forests mean that more and more people will have access to these areas for work and recrea-

Erwin and Peggy Bauer/Outdoor Life Magazine

"During fall breeding seasons the larger, most dominant and successful bulls attempt to gather harems of cows and keep them segregated from other bulls," say the authors.

tion. This in turn will call for increased road and people management and law enforcement if elk numbers are to be maintained at current levels.

Livestock grazing and timber harvest are expected to remain fairly constant although some downward trend in the acreage identified for logging seems inevitable. In the northern Rocky Mountains, nearly one-fourth of the forest land cannot produce the minimum considered to represent "commercial" timberland—20 cubic feet of wood per acre per year. Less than half the forest land in Montana and Idaho is capable of producing more than 50 cubic feet of wood per year; Colorado and Wyoming forests mostly have lower capabilities. Many of these areas, however, are renowned as elk population centers. It is clear that the limited capability of these lands will decree less emphasis on commodity production and greater emphasis on other values of the national forests in the future.

At any level, however, timber harvest is likely to continue as the most important influence on wildlife habitat quality in the Rockies. A slight downtrend in timber harvest reflects the high costs of extracting timber in previously unroaded and mountainous areas, as well as the constraints imposed by laws emphasizing protection of the environment and multiple use. Management guidelines for elk habitat do not directly constrain forestry practice in the Rockies, but better planning is required when the guidelines are followed. Guidelines for less adaptable wildlife species, however, might eventually prove to be constraining. The grizzly bear is today found in only three Rocky Mountain States, and the caribou only in northern Idaho. It is expected that cutting methods will eventually be modified to allow habitat manipulation for bears and caribou.

Grazing is also a pervasive influence on wildlife habitats throughout the Rockies, but there is little convincing evidence to demonstrate the effect this has had on wildlife. Grazing has been going on for so long at such high levels in most of the West that managers cannot judge what the vegetation might look like in the absence of livestock. The few exceptions, places like Yellowstone National Park and the Elk Refuge at Jackson Hole, are different only because overgrazing is caused by wildlife rather than livestock.

Recreational development, specifically ski areas, condominiums and residential housing, will produce some of the greatest long-term undesirable impacts on wildlife habitat. Winter range areas in some parts of the Rockies are already gone—and so are the deer and elk originally supported by those ranges. On forest lands with less potential for development, fire control has become more effective than ever before. There has been some loss of habitat diversity although large fires still occur. At the same time, land managers' attitudes toward fire and the role fire plays in ecosystem function have changed. Fire can be expected to play a greater role in habitat manipulation.

Establishing a link between these management trends and impacts on wildlife habitat is somewhat more complicated than simple increases or decreases. Habitat requirements are different for each wildlife species, which will mean that prime habitat conditions for any species are likely to be less than prime for some other species. The future of forest wildlife on Federal lands will be governed by law and by the effectiveness of multiple-use management of the land. National Forest Plans completed under the Resources Planning Act, along with State conservation plans developed with Pittman-Robertson funding, now provide management direction that can assure the future for elk.

State and Federal elk managers in the Rocky Mountain region are generally optimistic about the future of elk and elk hunting. Those of us in the wildlife profession believe we can maintain elk numbers in the Rocky Mountain West, but none think it will be certain, simple, or cheap. Some herds will increase, but others will decrease; and in some areas hard decisions will require tradeoffs between elk and other resource values. Continued substantial research and increasingly intensive management will be essential—and continued Pittman-Robertson funding will be important in both functions, as it has been for the past 50 years.

In looking back on the effort that returned the species from the brink of oblivion, there is every reason to believe that the continuation of a magic combination of public support, dedicated wildlife managers, adequate technical knowledge, and adequate resources will assure a future for the Rocky Mountain elk.

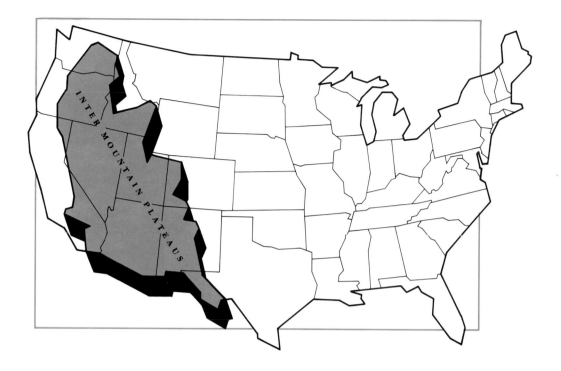

Bighorn Sheep: Desert Cliff-Hanger

by George Tsukamoto

The bighorn sheep has fascinated humans since antiquity. It was celebrated in Indian rock art long before the Spanish set sail for what turned out to be the Americas. Archaelogists have discovered bighorn sheep bones and horns in so many places in the West that it is evident the animal was widely distributed and, in some places, abundant. It also was revered by Native Americans—perhaps because it was so difficult to hunt successfully—and it appears that some tribes developed hunting magic rituals to ensure that this animal deity would continue to abound.

Early European explorers in the Southwest sighted bighorn sheep and noted the encounters in their journals, remarking on the magnificence of the rams' large, curling horns. In 1567, Spanish officers and missionaries wrote of a

Mr. Tsukamoto, Chief of the Game Management Division of the Nevada Department of Wildlife, has spent his entire career there specializing in big game management and research. He has had extensive experience with desert bighorn trapping and transplanting programs and helicopter census techniques. Author of Hunting the Desert Ram, *he was the project leader for research leading to Nevada's comprehensive 1978 bulletin on that species.*

161

town called Tusonimon, so named because of a great heap of wild sheep horns there. Two centuries later, Father Escalante reported bighorn sheep were abundant along the Colorado River, and wrote that the frequency of their tracks compared with large flocks of domestic sheep.

Interestingly enough, many early explorers remarked about the abundance of wild sheep and antelope, while taking special note of the general absence of deer. Today, deer are numerous and widely distributed through the West, pronghorn antelope are coming back strongly in many localities after a long absence . . . but bighorn sheep are seldom seen except in rather remote, craggy areas, chiefly within the vast region we call the Intermountain Plateaus which lie between the high Rockies and the Sierra Nevada and Cascade mountain ranges.

There are two distinct species of wild sheep in North America. The thinhorn or Dall sheep, *(Ovis dalli)* has its center of distribution in Alaska. The bighorn sheep, *(Ovis canadensis)* occupies a broad area of the West from Canada to Mexico. There are at least five races of bighorn and these are further separated into two general groups, the Rocky Mountain and the desert races. Even experts sometimes find it difficult to distinguish between the bighorn races, because of so many variations. Desert bighorn are surprisingly small, standing only 30 to 39 inches tall at the shoulders. Adult males, called rams, average about 160 pounds and females or ewes, about 105 pounds. Their general appearance is blocky and short-legged. The massive curling horns of the rams makes them appear much larger. Ewes also have horns, which are much smaller and slender. The feet of bighorn are especially adapted for clinging to narrow ledges and traversing rough, mountainous terrain.

The breeding season, or rut, peaks in late August and early September. During this period, rams actively engage in horn butting to establish dominance in the social order of the herd. Usually the largest-horned rams are the dominant individuals and most successful breeders.

Most lambs are born in February and March. Ordinarily a single lamb is born in a secluded rocky outcropping or other area that affords protection from predators. Within hours of birth, lambs are able to stand and walk.

Bighorn rams ségregate into "bachelor" herds or remain as solitary individuals after the rut, unless they are yearlings. This segregation of age and sex classes in the herd is very distinct. While ewes, lambs and yearling rams are quite predictable in their selection of favorite haunts, rams are much less so.

Desert bighorn foods vary greatly, depending on availability, season, and even individual preferences. Three classes of vegetation are important to bighorn: grasses, forbs (herbs and weeds) and shrubs. Shrubby species are used extensively during drought periods, but in the spring and shortly after summer showers, when new growth of forbs and grasses occur, these plants are eaten with relish.

This Intermountain desert region is the dryest part of the United States, where water is usually scarce. Generations of desert bighorn have come to rely on a few permanent sources of water. Often these waterholes can be easily spotted from the air as the telltale trails, like spokes on a wheel, lead to the axis where the liquid of life is available. Understandably, but with fateful results, these same waterholes were relied upon by the early settlers, their livestock and even miners and prospectors. The latter often built their shacks near these sites to take advantage of the water, but also for the easily obtainable supply of fresh meat from animals that came to drink. It is no wonder that bighorn were decimated in many of their historic haunts.

Desert bighorn populations undoubtedly occupied most of the suitable mountain ranges before the arrival of white men, notably the isolated desert

Desert bighorn sheep blend almost magically into their surrounding crags. See if you can count how many are in this photo. (Answer: 8)

mountain ranges of Nevada, California, Arizona, New Mexico, southern Utah, southern Colorado and west Texas. When settlers arrived to stay, they at first relied on native game for food, and the bighorn sheep, among other wildlife, was readily available. The demand for red meat expanded with the discovery of precious metals, and before long, wild game could no longer satisfy the appetites of booming mining camps. As the region developed and railroads accelerated the influx of people, cattle and sheep were driven west to graze the open ranges. Competition for forage between domestic livestock and wild sheep became severe. Livestock grazing had a dramatic impact, with severe consequences to the environment and wildlife. Competition was not limited to food but also included water and even living space. H.K. Buechner, in 1960, suggested that bighorn sheep were damaged not only by livestock grazing and over-hunting, but perhaps even more by large die-offs from the parasitic infestations of the scabies mite. Scabies apparently was unknown to the native Indians prior to the invasion of white people and their livestock.

The most drastic bighorn decline occurred primarily between 1850 and 1900. More recent estimates indicate some further local reductions have occurred since the mid-20th Century. However, the overall population has shown an increasing trend since 1975.

While some recent bighorn populations have declined because of increased human disturbances, the general trend was up during the early and mid-1980's in California, Nevada, Arizona and Utah. In all the desert bighorn States of Arizona, California, Colorado, Nevada, New Mexico, Utah and Texas, it is estimated that there were approximately 15,645 in 1985 compared to 9,212 in 1974.

Improved census techniques are probably most responsible for the increased animal numbers in California, Arizona and Nevada, where early esti-

163

mates were made. Still, there are areas where significant populations are presently confirmed, compared to none or a very few before.

Although these numbers may seem pitifully small, they represent progress through heroic human efforts to restore the desert bighorn. Without the active support of sport hunters, the Pittman-Robertson program, and individual States' initiatives, the species might be little more than a memory today.

Hunters consider the desert bighorn one of the most prized trophy animals in the world. Certainly, it ranks as the top trophy of North America, if for no other reason than the very limited opportunity to hunt it legally. During the 1984 season, only 188 permits to hunt desert rams were authorized in the United States. In addition, the Mexican government allows a few permits each year.

There were 5,027 applications for those 188 desert bighorn hunting permits available in the United States in 1984. Only 20 of the permits were issued to nonresidents of the respective States. This limited supply also tends to inflate the economic value, as is typical for most commodities.

In Nevada, the desert bighorn was opened again to hunting in 1952, after having been closed since 1864. A total of 1,168 desert rams had been harvested in Nevada by 1984, and Arizona was a close second with 1,037. In addition, Utah has taken 85 and New Mexico, 74. In all the U.S., only 2,364 desert bighorns were harvested legally between 1952 and 1984. Currently, only Arizona, Nevada and Utah maintain annual hunting seasons. California has been closed to bighorn hunting since 1883.

Arizona, Nevada and New Mexico first opened desert bighorn sheep hunting to gather biological data and to determine if hunting the desert bighorn would result in any adverse impacts. The initial hunts were closely supervised and monitored. Arizona initiated the first comprehensive research project on desert bighorn hunting and life history, using Pittman-Robertson Federal Aid in Wildlife Restoration funds. John P. Russo, project leader, recorded some significant findings in the 1956 Arizona Game and Fish Department Bulletin entitled, "The Desert Bighorn Sheep in Arizona." This research incorporated an experimental hunting program as an integral part of the overall project. The primary objectives of the bighorn hunt were: (1) to examine animals for disease and parasites; (2) to lower the excessively high ram:ewe ratio gradually; (3) to evaluate the reproduction trend; and (4) to give sportsmen an opportunity to remove a number of old trophy animals, thereby generating public interest in the species.

A recent survey conducted in Nevada by Fenton Kay and several associates confirmed the high monetary value associated with hunting the desert ram. During the 1984 hunting season, 102 hunters who were polled said they spent $237,902 for their hunts. The "net willingness to pay" value, which is the additional willingness to pay over and above what was actually spent, was calculated to be $140 per day and $1,638 per tag.

Another indication of the value placed on a bighorn permit by hunters is the astronomically high bids that have been made in recent years at auctions for single permits. During the annual meeting of the Foundation for North American Wild Sheep held in San Diego in 1984, the highest bid for a Nevada desert bighorn sheep tag was $67,500. During this same auction, an Arizona desert bighorn sheep tag was sold for $64,000.

Auction tags are a recent innovation used by State wildlife agencies to raise funds for special projects in bighorn sheep management and research. Arizona, Nevada, Utah and Wyoming offer bighorn sheep tags to be auctioned as fund raising for those purposes.

Grancel Fitz, a member of the Boone & Crockett Club, coined a phrase, "The Grand Slam," that has had a profound affect on hunting the North American varieties of sheep. Fitz defined it as the feat of collecting four varieties of sheep trophies—the Stone, Dall, Rocky Mountain and desert bighorn. The most difficult of the four prizes to obtain is the desert bighorn, which helps explain the high interest and the exclusive nature of the Grand Slam achievers.

The desert bighorn sheep hunting program is a classic example of how a well-managed, biologically sound approach to sport hunting can enhance a wildlife resource without jeopardy to it. For the past 30 years, hunting of the desert bighorn in Arizona and Nevada has shown no evidence of damage to the overall population. In fact, during this period the populations have generally responded with some sharp increases in numbers and distribution. As John Russo stated in his 1956 report, "The hunting program has generated interest in the bighorn sheep with increased emphasis for research, development of habitat, monitoring of populations and factors influencing their survival." Unfortunately, bighorn hunting opportunity is unlikely to ever meet the future demand, and bagging a desert ram will remain the exclusive experience of a relatively few people.

One of the most successful programs in sheep management is trapping and transplanting to restore wild sheep to historic ranges. This work was initiated in the 1950's, but success was not immediate because of the general lack of technology and understanding of how to accomplish the job. There were many trials and errors to overcome; one of the biggest problems was the misconception that desert sheep were too fragile to trap and translocate without great risk and difficulty, and that therefore it was better to leave them alone.

Some of the initial capture methods were crude and ineffective. One such idea was the strategic placement of padded steel leghold traps on well-used bighorn trails. Although a few sheep were captured using this technique, injuries were common and escapes frequent. The labor intensity of this method also proved too costly.

Biologists at a check station gather data on size, age, sex, physical condition and location where animals were shot.

165

Tranquilizer drugs, delivered through numerous darting systems, were used in Arizona with some success during the 1970's. This technique required "darting" selected animals from a hovering helicopter and following through until the drug took effect. The technique required fast-working drugs and well-trained personnel. Unfortunately, although it was used successfully in cap turing bighorn in Arizona, sometimes the drugs used where lethal to bighorn sheep because of their narrow tolerances, the low-level flying was extremely dangerous, and the method was almost always very stressful to bighorn. As a result, captured animals were often released in either poor or questionable condition.

During the quarter century between 1954 and 1978, only 153 desert sheep were successfully trapped and transplanted. But from 1979 to 1985, 1,355 desert sheep were captured and transplanted. The difference between early failures and recent successes was twofold: improved trapping techniques and larger populations of wild sheep. The most significant advances in desert sheep trapping were (1) the development of the drop net and drive net traps (2) the discovery and successful use of apple pulp bait and (3) the improved handling and hauling techniques employed. All of these methods were developed through P-R supported research and development programs.

In 1984, a one-year record of 297 desert sheep were successfully captured and transplanted in six States. Nevada enjoyed phenomenal success with 112 animals captured and transplanted to five sites within the State.

Although it is still premature to label all transplants successful, the prospects look excellent for a high percentage. The success of a transplant can be determined by whether it leads to establishing a self-sustaining population. Some transplanted populations may remain relatively small in size, and never support a hunting program. However, it is hoped a majority will establish huntable populations for more sportsmen and women to enjoy.

Drawn by bait, desert bighorn throng a drop-net site.

The net drops and biologist runs to complete the capture.

With the enthusiastic support and financial assistance of sportsmen and the general public as a whole, bighorn trapping and transplanting programs have been greatly accelerated. Groups such as the Foundation for North American Wild Sheep, Arizona Desert Bighorn Sheep Society, the Society for the Conservation of Bighorn Sheep, The Fraternity of the Desert Bighorn, Bighorns Unlimited and many other groups and individuals have contributed to the success of this effort. The financial contributions by these groups provide thousands of dollars annually to carry on State wildlife agency research and development projects for desert bighorn. These funds are often matched with Pittman-Robertson Federal Aid funds to further enhance the program. The success of the transplant programs can be attributed, in large measure, to the financial commitment of the concerned public.

Research is a continuing requirement of wise management in any field of endeavor and this is no less true of wildlife management, where the knowledge gained through carefully planned and executed research has been put to work. In 1985, with the assistance of Pittman-Robertson funds, Arizona, California, Colorado, Nevada, New Mexico and Texas were involved in desert bighorn research.

The Region and Its Wildlife Habitats

The Intermountain Plateau Region of the West has a rich diversity of habitat and wildlife. This region is commonly lumped together and described as the American Desert, evoking an impression of hot, dry, sparsely vegetated landscape—in short, barren wasteland. But the truth is more complicated. The region contains a great variety of landscapes, climates, altitudes, and plant and animal life. Even its deserts differ distinctly from one another.

The Intermountain deserts are characterized by plants that are adapted to survive an extended period of drought. Mesquite, brittle brush, creosote and numerous varieties of cacti are typical examples. When conditions are poor, the desert plants look dead and withered. However, with ample moisture, they can quickly rejuvenate and produce a lush and colorful bloom. When this happens,

167

the wildlife are greatly benefited and the desert bustles with life. Sometimes large expanses are vegetated by one dominant plant to the exclusion of others, but elsewhere the right combination of soil, climate and water provides a rich diversity of plant life, supporting a diverse animal community.

Some other mammals that live with the desert bighorn include the mule deer, ring-tailed cat, kit fox and the ever-present coyote. A surprising number of birds live in the desert; the road runner is a commonly observed favorite. Many of the migratory birds, such as the mourning dove, congregate in the region during their annual migrations. Desert tortoises are common residents of the valleys and benchlands of the desert, and are often in company of a great variety of snakes and lizards.

For the most part, wildlife are adapted to the desert environment and that is why bighorn sheep can survive for several days in scorching heat without water to drink. Other desert animals have the ability to obtain sufficient water from the vegetation they eat, and some survive by limiting their activity to the cooler night hours, or only at dawn or dusk.

When habitat conditions change markedly from one year to the next and from season to season because of climatic differences, all wildlife and plants are affected either beneficially or adversely, resulting sometimes in wide fluctuations of wildlife populations.

All wildlife species require their own unique habitats. Some species are a little more tolerant than others of change in their environment, especially those brought about by man's activities. While animals like the desert bighorn are highly sensitive to human disturbances, they do have an ability to tolerate them just as long as the basic requirements of food, water and space are not significantly altered.

Before the arrival of Europeans, the land, wildlife and man were in a rough sort of harmony. Except for natural forces, there was little or no air pollution, and no systematic efforts to control predators. Harvesting of wildlife by native Indians was a part of the natural scheme of things. But hunting underwent a dramatic change with the introduction of firearms to the Native Americans. A "fire stick" in the hands of skilled stalker resulted in much larger bags of game. All hunters became extremely adept with firearms, harvesting game for personal use and for a growing commercial market. Wildlife therefore was greatly impacted during the settling of the West.

With the arrival and settlement of the region by white people, the stage was set for major and more permanent change, reflected in the character of the land. Perhaps at no time in history did man's influence inflict such major and rapid change on wildlife and its habitats.

The vast majority of the lands in the Intermountain Plateau Region are Federally owned, administered by the Forest Service, Bureau of Land Management, U.S. Fish and Wildlife Service and National Park Service. These lands have undergone enormous change in little more than a century and the pace has quickened with man's ever-increasing desire to develop and use the natural resources. Despite its aridity, this region contains some of America's fastest growing cities, including Phoenix, Tucson, and Las Vegas, to name a few—a tribute to human cleverness in diverting scarce water supplies. These water developments affect habitats and wildlife directly—and indirectly, too, because they encourage more urban growth.

The American life style has changed drastically as well. The advancements in human comforts and conveniences have led to pressures for maximum use and development of natural resources. Mineral extraction continues to be a major industry in this region, and the appetite of well-fed Americans for red meat

Dave Daughtry, Arizona Game and Fish Department

Bighorn hooves are especially adapted for rugged, tricky footing.

still sustains a vigorous livestock economy. A constantly increasing demand for energy resources has dammed rivers and laid a cris-crossed pattern of power line transmission corridors over the face of the land. Rapid transportation has resulted in superhighway systems that traverse even the most formidable mountain ranges. The highway systems, like the water projects, are truly a testament to man's engineering skills. Where roads do not exist, four-wheel drive, all-terrain, and various other off-road vehicles have appeared in increasing numbers. No challenge is too great, so most of the land is subject to mechanized, wheeled travel; the more difficult the challenge, the greater the effort expended in off-road vehicular recreation. All these factors, and more, are affecting wildlife and habitats.

Perhaps the greatest change to the western environment occurred during the 1870-1970 century. Livestock grazing, mining, and increased urbanization radically changed habitats. No area was immune to livestock grazing. Much vegetation was trampled and overgrazed, and when the grass ran out, the remaining vegetation was burned, sprayed, plowed or bulldozed, in an attempt to quickly restore more grass. Timber was removed rapidly to meet the demands of new industry and unprecedented urban growth. Sometimes whole landscapes were denuded of trees to meet the demand for lumber.

Cattle were first introduced by the Spaniards to the New World in the 16th Century and, by 1700, they had spread throughout Mexico and into Texas, Arizona and California. Hundreds of thousands of cattle, sheep, and horses, and lesser numbers of goats, burros and other grazing animals, were using the open western rangelands by 1900.

At first livestock grazing was limited and somewhat controlled by the natural elements, just as wildlife was held in check by drought or bad winters. The tremendous growth in the free-ranging livestock operations carried with it a major weakness that destroyed many rangelands and almost ended ranching. G. Stewart in 1936 described the problem thus: "It (open rangeland grazing) was based on a husbandry transplanted from Mexico, which brought to English-speaking people for the first time in history the practice of rearing cattle in great droves without fences, corrals, feeding ... The very newness of it all as well as the immensity of the outfits left Americans without guide or standard by which to gauge either the security of the cattle as they roamed at large or the ability of the forage to stand up under continual intense utilization." He concluded that livestock instead of grass came to be regarded as the basic resource.

The impacts of livestock grazing on the environment of the West have gone largely unnoticed by the general public. Sometimes the magnitude of the problem cannot fully be appreciated even as seen by one's own eyes.

Aldo Leopold, founder of the modern science of wildlife management, said it well:

> *The damage done to game by overgrazing is little appreciated by the public in comparison with its appreciation of damage by fire and drainage. This is because the deterioration of game food and coverts by overgrazing is qualitative rather than quantitative. Especially in semi-arid climates, overgrazing eliminates the palatable food plants without apparent reduction in the amount of plant cover. Worthless plants promptly fill in the gaps left by the valuable one, and the layman sees no difference. He suffers no pain over the invisible but fundamental deterioration which his own industries have inflicted.*

The feral horse and burro populations, descended from domestic animals turned loose by their owners, have had major impacts on the western environment. Feral horses and burros have been protected on BLM and Forest Service land since the passage of legislation in 1971, requiring that excess animals be rounded up, cared for in a humane fashion, and disposed of through an adoption program. Unfortunately, there are more captured horses than adopters, so the Federal government is saddled with feeding and caring for animals nobody wants.

Meanwhile, the free-roaming feral horse and burro populations continue to expand, destroying valuable habitats and costing the taxpayer huge sums of money to pay for removal programs and an unworkable disposal plan. On BLM lands, the total spent for this purpose was expected to cost $5 million more in 1986 than the agency budgeted to manage all native fish and wildlife habitat under its care.

When the early settlers homesteaded in this region, they invariably selected the lands adjacent to available water. Where water was appropriated, existing wildlife uses were usually affected, sometimes severely, as in the case of Winne-mucca Lake, in northwestern Nevada.

Winnemucca Dry Lake, a former wetland haven for wildlife, is nestled between two desert ranges. The Newlands Project, initiated in 1903, was the first Federal Reclamation project of its kind in the United States. The plan was to divert Truckee River water to be combined with Carson River water to reclaim desert wasteland for agriculture in Lahontan Valley. The diversion of the Truckee River was accomplished in 1905 with the completion of Derby Dam, miles of canals, and Lahontan Dam and Reservoir on the Carson River drainage. Only a few short years later, Pyramid Lake, dependent on Truckee River flows, began lowering and the overflow to Winnemucca Lake ceased. The loss of water to Winnemucca Lake resulted in a relatively quick death to the lake by 1938. Today, it is a barren desert completely devoid of any wildlife. Ironically, Winnemucca Lake had been selected and designated a national wildlife refuge until the wildlife disappeared.

Even more ironically, this happened at a time when wildlife conservation was becoming popular. Most of the impetus came from the East, where organized sportsmen were concerned over the need to conserve and manage a dwindling wildlife resource. In the Intermountain Plateau region, the early wildlife conservation movement came in the form of more stringent hunting laws and regulations. For example, desert bighorn sheep hunting was closed indefinitely in all States; big game regulations to protect young of the year and females of the species, and more restrictive bag limits and shorter season lengths were commonly accepted practices during the early 20th Century.

One of the earliest wildlife management experiments in the region took place on the Kaibab Plateau of Arizona. President Theodore Roosevelt estab-

Livestock grazing has impacted many dry-land areas, sometimes to wildlife's loss.

lished the Grand Canyon National Game Preserve on November 28, 1906, providing full protection to mule deer. The establishment of a game refuge was a popular answer to saving and managing wildlife during that era.

Livestock grazing on the Kaibab had already left its mark when in 1893 the Grand Canyon National Forest Reserve was established in the area and, at least 200,000 sheep, 20,000 cattle and 20,000 horses grazed the plateau. After the preserve was established, sheep numbers were reduced but cattle and horses still grazed the area.

To further protect the mule deer, the Kaibab area was closed to all hunting, and predator control was initiated with a fervor. Between 1906 and 1931, government hunters, using poison, traps, and guns, removed 781 cougars, 20 gray wolves, 4,889 coyotes and 554 bobcats.

The early success of this misguided effort was phenomenal, with the Kaibab mule deer population doubling and then tripling to a record of approximately 30,000 animals by 1923.

Range damage became increasingly evident as the deer herd increased and as cattle began competing directly with the deer for forage. By 1920, there was already a growing concern for the great number of deer and the impacts of too many animals on the range. By now the deer were dying of starvation by the thousands, and the key browse species utilized by both deer and livestock were dying too.

This classic example of an early failure in wildlife management was an expensive mistake. The range suffered severe damage and the mule deer resource suffered a needless waste through wholesale starvation. A valuable lesson was learned. Wildlife preserves, sanctuaries or refuges in themselves are not a sensible or effective wildlife management program; the key to maintaining a healthy wildlife population is through proper habitat management.

The Pittman-Robertson Federal Aid in Wildlife Restoration Act of 1937 enabled State wildlife agencies to embark on an aggressive program of wildlife management and research surpassing any previous efforts in history. Development and restoration of wildlife habitat was a high priority consideration in the Intermountain region. One of the most successful P-R wildlife habitat restoration and development programs was initiated in California.

In the Mohave desert, many areas were not inhabited by Gambel's quail even though all essential requirements of food and cover were present. The one crucial item lacking was water. In 1942, the California Fish & Game Department constructed an experimental water collection and storage device following the design of Ben Glading.

The "Glading Gallinaceous Guzzler" collected rainwater from an artificial apron and stored in in an underground tank. A small opening provided access to the water for use by a variety of animals including quail. The guzzlers tested so successfully that by June 1947, 29 units had been installed and the following year the total number had risen to 123. California took the lead and has built a total of 2,201 gallinaceous guzzlers, creating thousands of acres of quail habitat which was formerly unusable. In addition, many other birds, small mammals and reptiles have benefited from these water developments in California and other States as well.

More recently, water developments for big game have met with great success. Bighorn sheep have benefited most from such water development, but mule deer, elk and pronghorn antelope have also been aided.

In California, Arizona and Nevada, the wildlife departments and an enthusiastic force of volunteers, led by The Society for the Conservation of Bighorn, The Arizona Desert Bighorn Sheep Society, and The Fraternity of the Desert Bighorn,

A desert guzzler. The blue patch is a collection apron, catching rainwater which drains down to roofed-over cistern; from there, under-ground pipe supplies small trough at center. Fence excludes livestock but not wildlife.

have constructed numerous water developments which have expanded the area of usable habitat for bighorn.

The value of a guzzler can be determined quite readily by simply observing use by wildlife. However, to evaluate the long-term benefits and costs involved in guzzler development, State agencies try to measure the economic returns.

In Nevada, it has been found that guzzlers are a very effective and economically beneficial means of expending wildlife funds for quick return on the sportsmen's investment. One study estimated that a chukar partridge population that was developed through well-placed guzzlers paid for the investment in 3.48 years, based on a value of $4.50 per bird produced.

Another example of the value of water developments for wildlife can be found in the River Mountains near Boulder City, Nevada. Development of permanent water, where there was none previously, has established a resident population that fluctuates between 250 and 350 bighorn. Prior to 1965, the 35 square miles of habitat on the River Mountains provided only seasonal and transient use of the area by bighorn. This population has now developed into one of the most productive herds in the Southwest, all as a result of water development. Since the population was established, it has sustained the highest removal rate of any wild sheep population in the United States. Between 1969 and 1984, 279 sheep were trapped and transplanted from the River Mountains. Removal programs have not reduced the population; quite the contrary, higher birth rates have more than made up for any removal losses. The value of animals removed for transplant from the River Mountains is estimated at more than $139,500, based on an estimated value of $500 per sheep.

Wildlife restoration programs are expensive and time-consuming efforts. Unfortunately, when wildlife populations are found to be in jeopardy, it is now usually because of some major problem with habitat or disease.

One of the most valiant efforts in wildlife management occurred in new Mexico. During the 1978 bighorn sheep hunting season, all five desert rams

As one worker attaches a radio collar to a captive bighorn, another applies oxygen; together with hood, oxygen speeds recovery from stress of capture and handling.

harvested were infested with the parasitic psoroptic mite *(Psoroptes ovis)* which causes the dreaded scabies disease. A population inventory of the San Andreas bighorn herd prior to the hunt had led to an estimate of 200 to 250 animals, a healthy number for the area. By April 1979, the number of animals was estimated at 100 to 200 and by June, 1979, only 85 to 95. A count in September revealed only 60 to 70 bighorn left.

The New Mexico Department of Game and Fish, realizing it had a crisis on its hands, acted swiftly to combat the mite infestation, and to save a precious herd of rare desert bighorn sheep from almost certain extinction.

In early October, 1979 plans were begun for a major wildlife salvage operation. State wildlife biologists teamed with entomologists, veterinarians, helicopter pilots, military personnel from the White Sands Missile Range, the U.S. Fish & Wildlife Service and U.S. Department of Agriculture, and experts from the academic community—all joined in the fight to save the herd. The capture operation began on November 17 and continued through November 24. A total of 49 animals were captured through the use of various techniques, all of which required very dangerous low-level flying, and drive nets, tranquilizing dart guns and net guns. Although several animals were lost to accident and stress, 27 were successfully treated and relocated to the Red Rock Experimental Wildlife Area to be held until it was safe to reintroduce them back into their native habitat. In January, 1981, the bighorns were returned. It is still too early to tell if this herd will make a permanent recovery, but the feeling is one of cautious optimism.

This operation was expensive, costing well over $100,000. The entire effort was made possible by modern advances in wildlife management, dedicated workers, public support and Pittman-Robertson funds.

Future Prospects

Wildlife has held the interest of man from the beginning of time. Initially, man's dependence upon wildlife was for food, clothing and indeed his very existence. The importance of wildlife to man is less obvious now, but no less significant.

Despite all the years of exploitation and habitat destruction, wildlife still persists and even thrives—a reflection of the resilience of some species and their powers to adapt and survive man's ever-greater presence. It is also testimony to the effectiveness of the conservation ethic and the principles of wildlife management.

The Pittman-Robertson Federal Aid in Wildlife Restoration Act was born in step with the conservation movement. Aided by the enthusiastic supporters of this program, acting in enlightened self-interest, a measure of harmony with the land has been achieved over the past 50 years—a little here and a bit there. By no means has there been a total conversion to the conservation ethic, but steps, small as they might appear, have nevertheless moved us forward.

If wildlife is to survive the next century, more people must understand and practice the conservation ethic. Aldo Leopold wrote, "Conservation is a state of harmony between men and land. Harmony with land is like harmony with a friend; you cannot cherish his right hand and chop off his left."

Leopold described the outstanding scientific discovery of our era to be the complexity of the land organism. "Only those who know the most about it can appreciate how little we know about it," he said, adding:

The last word in ignorance is the man who says of an animal or plant: "What good is it?" If the land mechanism as a whole is good, then every part is good, whether we understand it or not. If the biota, in the course of aeons, has built something we like but do not understand, then who but a fool would discard seemingly useless parts? To keep every cog and wheel is the first precaution of intelligent tinkering.

The challenge remains unchanged—maintain harmony with the land. Only now, new thoughts, tools and a renewed dedication clear the way to solving even greater tasks. The incentive for and reward to man is priceless. The alternative thought of a land desolate and devoid of wildlife is intolerable.

Aldo Leopold, 1886-1948, was a forester, ecologist, pioneering wildlife management professor, and gifted writer.

175

Mountain Lion: Pacific Coast Predator

by Maurice Hornocker and Howard Quigley

The mountain lion is becoming a true success story of wildlife management, one in which Americans can take pride. It is a success story for several reasons: its unrestrained persecution by humans has stopped, its numbers appear to be stable or increasing, we better understand its role in the ecosystem now, and we are learning to manage the mountain lion as a desirable big game species. But one feature makes the story stand out world-wide: the mountain lion is a large predator. Rarely in this world today is a predator "allowed" to exist in such close proximity to people, especially one the size of this cat. Even in much less-developed areas of the world, predators, large and small, have long

Dr. Hornocker, now Director of the Wildlife Research Institute headquartered at Moscow, Idaho, has spent 25 years studying the carnivores of the West. Best known for his work on mountain lions, he also has published some 40 scientific papers on other cats, bears, and smaller mammals. His popular articles and films have helped communicate to the public the true relationship of predators and their prey. Dr. Quigley has researched the black bear in California and Tennessee, the jaguar in Brazil, other animals in China, and the mountain lion (with Dr. Hornocker) in Idaho.

been destroyed. In Asia, the tiger, largest of the cats, has been relegated to isolated sanctuaries. The same could be the fate of the jaguar in South America before the end of this century. The African lion, "king of beasts," has been pushed into reserves or banished to yet-undeveloped forests where, for the time being, it can live in a sort of hiding. The mountain lion is *our* big cat; but in contrast to the others, the mountain lion still roams a large area of North America. We confidently believe the results of our research on the mountain lion, together with other early studies on predators, opened a new realm for wildlife science and uncovered facts which have helped this big cat to live in relative peace with man and his endeavors.

The mountain lion, also known as the puma, cougar, or panther, once had the widest distribution of any mammal in the Western Hemisphere, from northern British Columbia, south through the tropics, to the tip of South America. Its home has been reduced substantially, and to this day thousands of acres of its habitat are lost each year. In the United States, the mountain lion has been eliminated from over two-thirds of its former range. East of the Mississippi, aside from a few scattered sightings in the Appalachians, it clings only to a small clawhold in the Big Cypress-Everglades region of southern Florida, classified as an endangered species there. Northward from south Texas, through the Plains States to the border of Canada, a few isolated populations still hide. But the West is the stronghold of this cat. From the rim-rock of west Texas, through New Mexico, along the Rocky Mountains to the Canadian border marks the eastern boundary of lion country. States harboring "good" populations of lions are Arizona and New Mexico in the Southwest, Utah, Nevada, and Colorado in the central Mountain West, and Idaho and Montana farther north in the Rocky Mountain chain. California, our most populous State, has mountain lions in many areas, sometimes in high densities, as do Oregon and Washington.

Although it lives in a wide variety of habitats, the mountain lion's basic appearance varies little. Its tawny coat, dark-framed white muzzle, long dark-tipped tail, and sleek, powerful body are easily recognized. Though some record specimens have weighed over 200 pounds, male mountain lions generally weigh from 140 to 180 pounds and females 30 to 60 pounds less.

The cat family as a whole is uniquely adapted to the quick capture and kill of its prey. They have sharp, recurved claws for gripping, short jaws with long canine teeth for the killing bite, and a flexible, but muscular frame for pouncing. The mountain lion applies these tools to the capture of a large range of different prey, from ground squirrels and armadillos to moose. Most commonly, however, over most of the United States, mule deer and white-tailed deer are the prime food of this cat. On our study area in central Idaho, however, elk are preyed upon as commonly as are mule deer. Unlike bears, which are "opportunist" feeders and derive much of their nourishment from plant life, mountain lions are true carnivores. Their dependence on meat can require them to range widely, depending on the density and movements of their prey. Movements into grazing land, where they occasionally learn to recognize cattle and sheep as prey, have made them extremely unpopular with livestock raisers. Thus, there are constraints—both natural and man-made—to the capacity of any given land area to support mountain lions.

The North American Indian reserved great respect for the mountain lion, calling it "greatest of hunters" and "lord of the game animals." But the settlers of early America were strangers in a strange land, determined to carve out a safe, comfortable, and profitable home for themselves. Land was cleared for agriculture, Indians were cleared out or subdued, and wildlife species considered to be dangerous were eliminated whenever possible. The most visible target was the

The mountain lion, unlike the black bear, feeds almost solely on meat, and domestic livestock are not always exempt—which is why moun- *tain lions are still unpopular in some rural areas.*

wolf, first to meet the wrath of the colonists. Late in the 18th Century, Colonies legislated bounties for the more secretive mountain lion. To our forefathers, and until relatively recently, hunting mountain lions and other predators was not a sport, but a chore. Professional hunters and trappers normally carried out the task. The hide of the mountain lion was not particularly prized in comparison to the wolf or the black bear, but the added incentive of bounty money heightened its allure. In addition, it presented a badge of courage for the successful hunter.

As settlement swept across the coastal plains, eastern mountains, and interior plains, the mountain lion was swept out along the way. From the West, a similar picture was developing, at a slower pace. With the Spanish mission system on the Pacific Coast came the same systematic elimination of the mountain lion from developing areas. Thus, civilization drove out the mountain lion, at an ever-increasing pace, through the 1800's.

Hard times continued for this great cat into the 1900's. Reflecting the attitude of the time, even if sheep or cattle had not been bothered, trackers were quick to search out mountain lions when signs of their presence were encountered. Great reputations were built around these men of the mountains. Every area of the West had its famous "lion killer" who plied his trade for the government or for private ranchers. In Arizona and New Mexico, it was Ben Lilly, in the Northwest, Cecil Smith, in California, Carl Hert. Hert estimated that during his years as County Predatory Animal Control Officer (in the 1920's and 30's) in San Bernardino County, east of Los Angeles, he killed more than 10,000 animals, including bobcats, raccoons, and foxes. He collected bounty on 109 mountain lions and killed "many other mountain lions—so many, in fact, that I came to be known as the 'County Lion Killer', a title of which I am justly proud, for through my efforts the predatory lions have been practically eliminated from San Bernardino County." Interestingly, Hert felt this had made more "quail, pigeons, doves, and deer" available to farmers and sport hunters.

Poisons became popular in predator control during the late 1800's. In 1878, Charles Hallock, a writer and travelling sportsman, wrote "use of poison against carnivorous animals of all kinds has become so general in the West within the past few years, that they are rapidly becoming exterminated in all districts within reach of the settlements ... each shepherd and herder is provided as a matter of course with a certain amount of strychnine." Commonly, a poisoned carcass of a domestic or game animal in an area frequented by coyotes, mountain lions, or wolves took care of the problem. The method was effective but other, "non-target," animals were also killed. Though predator control efforts continue into the current period, with coyotes as their prime target, poisons have become much more selectively used. The reduced use of poisons since the early 1970's may have contributed to the mountain lion's recovery in many areas.

Population levels of the mountain lion probably reached all-time lows in the 1950's and 60's, even in their western strongholds. But as with many of our most menaced wildlife species, those which can inhabit areas least hospitable and accessible to humans have the best chance for survival. From the western wildlands, the mountain lion crouched, poised to bound back when the time was right.

It was in this darkest hour for the mountain lion that a changing public attitude presented a ray of hope. A more comprehensive approach to the management of wildlife was being called for, one in which endangered species, songbirds, and even predators could be included. At the same time, the "ecosystem" approach—a more systematic view of how plants and animals interact —was bringing an appreciation of the important role which every species plays in the web of nature. But some of the least understood species in the system were predators. Without information, how could anyone develop effective plans for their management?

Biologist uses antenna to locate a mountain lion wearing a radio collar. His dog waits in the pickup for a closer encounter.

Claire Guimond Dobert, U.S. Fish and Wildlife Service

Fortunately, about this time, new field equipment and techniques were developed by researchers which made the study of these secretive animals possible. Radio-telemetry equipment and methods for injection of immobilizing drugs from a distance also made these studies safer. Work began on wolves, bears, mountain lions, and smaller predators.

But no methodology of capture and marking was available to us when we began our lion research in the 1960's, working for the Idaho Cooperative Wildlife Research Unit, with funding from private sources and the Idaho Fish and Game Department. No research such as this had ever been done, so we had to start from scratch. We worked with houndsmen—trail hounds were the proven method of hunting lions—to capture lions alive and unhurt. But the mountain lion is a powerful and potentially dangerous animal; we needed proven, efficient drugs to handle them. Veterinarians, drug companies, and other researchers were consulted on constraint techniques. Then we learned from the best teacher—experience.

The cats have successfully evolved a "flight" rather than "fight" behavior, we found, and most of them are not aggressive toward man. We did, however, have some tense moments. In one case, Wilbur Wiles, who was involved in our 10-year research effort (beginning in 1964) from start to finish, was pursuing a male lion which had sought refuge on a narrow ledge, but then disappeared from view. Wiles, thinking the lion had gone around the bluff, climbed the ledge to see where he had gone and suddenly found himself face to face with the cat. Wiles crouched instinctively on the ledge; the lion had nowhere to go but toward Wiles. With a mighty effort, the lion leaped directly over Wiles' head and was gone, leaving the shaking lion hunter without a scratch.

In another incident, Wiles and I (Hornocker) were tracking two lions, a male and female. We passed under a small fir tree where the lions had slept. Glancing up, I saw the male lion sitting in the tree about 10 feet above Wiles' head, calmly gazing down at the situation. But the lion didn't attack. Time after time the misleading image of the mountain lion as a bloodthirsty killer was disproven as we carried out our work.

We found complicated social systems at work in these animal societies, maintained through intricate behaviors and communication. Individual animals were forming dominance relationships—or "status levels"—which assured such essentials as a place to live, or a place to raise young. We learned that predators were not always so successful at capturing prey as we previously believed. In addition, they were not killing all animals at equal rates, but did best in weeding out the unprotected, the unwary, and the unhealthy. For example, on our Idaho study area, the healthiest elk have the least chance of being killed by mountain lions. In reality, predators were helping create healthy prey populations!

Western States began to respond to this new information and to the new public attitude. The mountain lion finally became a beneficiary in the healing process already underway for more "desirable" species. Long classified as "vermin," the mountain lion could be killed legally at any time of the year, under almost any circumstances, and the killer might even be paid for his action; it was a degradation of a noble species and a degradation of the natural fabric of which the lion was a part. Colorado, in 1965, led the way toward reform by reclassifying the mountain lion to the status of game animal, with set hunting seasons and monitoring. By 1972, all of the Western States had reclassified the lion to game animal. California went one step further and instituted a temporary moratorium on mountain lion hunting which continued until 1985. Banished by 1970, bounties became a relic of the past. The pursuit of mountain lions could finally be controlled. Most States limit the bag to one lion per hunter per season, with

*Dog has mountain lion treed, making the
predator easier to tranquilize.*

season length varying from region to region. There is no question that lion
populations have responded by increasing throughout most of their range in the
Western U.S. Another factor, undoubtedly, has been better management of
ungulate (hoofed mammal) populations by State agencies, resulting in healthy
populations of deer and elk (major lion prey), in most areas.

The number of deer and elk available, along with topography, cover, and
other factors determine how large an area individual mountain lions need to
live. Researchers in Utah found that a male mountain lion used an area larger
than 300 square miles, while biologists in California found that their male
mountain lions barely used over 20 square miles. On our Idaho study area, home
range size for a male may be as much as 150 square miles—50 square miles for a
female. Females always appear to use less area than their male counterparts.
Young dispersing males have been known to travel more than 100 miles in
search of a home area. A young male marked in Wyoming was later killed at a
spot in Colorado that was more than 300 miles distant.

Even with these long forays taking place, many people have lived and
worked most of their lives in lion country and have never seen one. Lions are
active both night and day, but in most areas it appears most of their hunting is

182

done in darkness. In the warmer climates and during summer in the northern latitudes, they routinely "lay up" during daylight hours in a cave, thicket, or other secure cover.

Some degree of conflict between wild animals and humans is inevitable. Urban sprawl, road building, and canal or pipeline systems chew up present and potential mountain lion habitat and can reduce the number of prey available for them. In addition, logging roads and second home developments have brought humans into formerly little-visited areas. Recent research findings have shown that permanent or even temporary use of an area by humans makes the area less desirable to mountain lions and can alter their movement and activity patterns. Aside from this indirect influence on the cats, we sometimes tempt direct conflict with mountain lions with our domestic animals, especially when the latter roam freely and unattended. Most livestock, except for healthy adult cattle, are easy prey for a fine-tuned predator like the mountain lion. Some areas of the country, such as the Southwestern States, report more conflicts than others. Now, however, if conflicts arise between the cats and livestock, trouble-making lions are dealt with on an individual case basis rather than a continuing blanket effort aimed against all. This approach has worked well in most cases. Also, various herding strategies and the use of guard dogs with livestock have shown some promising results in preventing heavy losses.

In some rare instances, wildlife managers may be justified in seeking reductions of mountain lion populations over large areas. With good management and prudent use of available monies such as Pittman-Robertson funds, thriving populations of deer, elk, and mountain lions can be achieved and maintained. However, there are times and places when prey populations can be drastically diminished by a number of causes, such as over-hunting by man, catastrophic loss of habitat, or disease. When prey species are decimated, reductions of all factors leading to loss of life among prey—including reduction of predators such as mountain lions—may be warranted. When the prey population has recovered sufficiently, this temporary control can and should be stopped.

The popularity of the lion has soared with hunters and non-hunters alike. For hunters, it has been the thrill of the chase, targeted on a large, possibly dangerous animal, and venturing into remote areas they had not experienced before. For others, it is the thrill of a rare sighting, just the sight of a pug-mark, or simply hearing about some one else's experience and knowing that this once-lost component of the land is on its way back. The "lord of the game," "greatest of hunters," is back!

But compared to management of some other wildlife species, intensive mountain lion management is in its infancy. Practically no objective information on the lion existed as recently as 20 years ago. Though we now have information on the natural history of the mountain lion, we know little about how its populations respond to hunting pressure. Even so basic a method as how to count this species is still lacking. The animals are so secretive it is impossible to "census" them with methods used for most other species. Short of intensive research in each area, we must utilize different strategies. Track counts are used in some areas, systematic observations of tracks, droppings, and other signs observed by experienced persons, harvest figures over a period of time, age and sex structure of the cat harvest taken by hunters—all these are utilized in arriving at population estimates.

The survival of this big cat, under continued pressure from humans, is a result, in part, of its resiliency. But it is not only the "nature of the beast," but also the "nature of the land" which allowed it to survive the long arm of humans. Mountain lions thrive in wilderness where man's impact is minimal. The large tracts of unpopulated or sparsely populated wilds—mainly on Federally-owned lands that occupy so much of the West—provided refuge when the animal was being heavily persecuted. But this is a most adaptable species, as evidenced by its huge and varied historic range; and its adaptable, secretive ways enable it also to thrive in close proximity to man, provided adequate habitat is available and it is not killed at every opportunity. The time is fast approaching—with our improved management techniques, the proven desirability of the mountain lion, and its ability to live peacefully with humans—when the eastern wilderness areas could become a part of the restoration process for this cat. Burgeoning deer populations in many areas could certainly support the effort and benefit from the lion's presence.

The mountain lion, like the grizzly and the timber wolf, is associated with wilderness. But in comparison to these other carnivores, the cat was less threatening, less visible to humans, and, moreover, more flexible, melting into the hidden crags of the West. Perhaps if the Western States had been settled first, the results would have been different; maybe the over-exploitation of wildlife, logging-off, and overgrazing would have reached farther, even eliminating the mountain lion. But we think not. The land is too big, too expansive, and early methods were too crude. The West is a land of big mountains, big valleys, and sharp, jagged contrasts.

The youthful character of the Pacific Mountain System, formed by the Cascade and Sierra Mountain Ranges on its eastern border and the Pacific Ocean on the west, governs all the plant and animal life it supports. Fifty million years ago, the Appalachians had already completed most of their building and were being eroded down; the Rocky Mountains were spreading, lifting and shaping the interior of the continent; but most of the land which forms the Pacific mountains and valleys had not yet risen from the sea. Since that time, one of the most diverse and fruitful areas in the world has been forced above the surface by colliding land masses, then forged by the elements. The new rock made not only the peaks which form the region's borders, but also the fertile soils which support and sustain its life. Hot springs, volcanic explosions, and earthquakes all testify that the process continues and the shaping is still taking place.

The barrier formed by the north-south formation of the Sierra Nevada and Cascade mountain ranges is not as long nor as broad as the Rocky Mountains, broken in spots and barely 60 miles wide over some of the highest crests. But it is this sharpness which gives these mountains their character.

The coastal mountains, at the region's western edge, sweep up from the Pacific with less of the sharpness or majesty of the Sierra Nevada and Cascades, but with a character of their own, drenched in the fog and breezes of the ocean. Like the Sierra-Cascade chain, they are not an uninterrupted barrier. In reality, the Coast Range is a family of smaller ranges, cut by streams and rivers in their inevitable journey to the sea, born also from the forces of colliding land masses.

To the adjectives youthful or new for the Pacific Mountain Region, let us add varied and contrasting. The mountains, valleys, and the long north-south extension of the region serve to separate dramatically different climates and differing native forms of life. The rain forests of the Olympic Peninsula, in Washington State's northwest corner, receive more than 200 inches of precipitation per year, much in the form of snow; 10 inches of rain in the San Bernardino Mountains, in California's southwest corner, is a wet year. From the top of the Sierra's Mount Whitney, the highest point in the lower 48 States, the viewer can survey the boundaries of Death Valley, the lowest point in the U.S. The moss-enshrouded brook which flows into Oregon's Willamette Valley seems as from another world compared to the dry sagebrush country on the low eastern slopes

A tranquilized mountain lion lets biologists readjust its radio-tracking collar prior to release.

of the Cascades, hardly 60 air-miles away. Alpine chill to scorching sand dunes, glacier-polished granite to brackish bogs, the Pacific mountains form contrasting worlds, isolated from one another by steep barriers. As would be expected, these characteristics shaped the plants and animals which live there.

The life forms are as different as the towering coast redwood, tallest of all trees, and the miniscule, but robust desert Joshua tree; the moisture-dependent Douglas fir and the dry-adapted ponderosa pine found their places. Woody shrubs also adapted, from the sun-loving chamise and manzanita to the shaded rhododendron. On and amid these varied plant types lives a mix of animal types whose diversity is equally impressive. The region supports two or more types of bighorn sheep, elk, and deer, and a number of native reptile, amphibian, and bird species. The mosaic of types overall may not match the complexity of the eastern forests, but in the newness of the West, it is only a beginning. Man's thriving cities have encroached into almost every different landscape, spreading their constructed uniformity, linking areas of separate identities. The effects of this on the various forms of plants and wildlife, including the mountain lion, are obvious.

In the late 1700's, the Spanish and the Russians became the first outsiders to settle along the Pacific Coast—the former from south to north with their mission system and domestic livestock, and the latter from north to south with their sea otter and seal harvesting operations. Neither ever gained the hold they needed to extend their fragile existence. But both made a notable impact on wildlife and wildlife habitats. As Spanish cattle grazed the virgin rangeland and the Russians depleted the native stocks of coast-dwelling fur bearers, trappers from the United States and Canada moved in to take the beaver, river otters, and other forest dwellers, with devastating results for those species.

Early explorers and settlers sent back word of the amazing wildlife spectacle. They saw hundreds of elk in a single vista. And deer, also! In the sky flew waterfowl flocks the size of which they had never imagined; ducks, geese, and swans filled the skies with their winged migrations. Life—in great abundance—was literally everywhere.

Starting with the California Gold Rush, there began a boom for human development in the West—and one of the bleakest chapters ever written for wildlife anywhere, characterized by a wanton commercial slaughter seldom if ever equaled in North America. In Oregon and Washington, the destruction began slowly. The farmers, loggers, and fishermen of the Willamette Valley and Puget Sound areas were few and far between for a long period. An elk killed and properly cared for could supply a family of four for weeks; supplemented with small game, it went even further. But the congregations of people and their dispersion over California made another situation entirely. When the rush for gold began, the herds of cattle built up earlier from Spanish ranching endeavors had already declined to a low ebb. The exploding human population could not survive on domestic stock alone. In 1849, dried beef in San Francisco went for as high as $2 per pound, a lot of money then. Wild game was soon commonly preferred over stringy, range-fed beef, a simple preference of the palate, if not the pocketbook. Especially during the winters, idle miners and other entrepreneurs supplied urban centers with more than enough wild game to feed their customers. Their quarry included elk, deer, antelope, geese, ducks, and swans. It was not uncommon to find quail and even grizzly bear on restaurant menus in the Sierra foothills. The abundance of wild game on the market brought the price of eating meat down substantially. One black powder merchant said that game was "in the greatest profusion, and the man who cannot afford them must be 'flat broke' indeed. I can safely say that [San Francisco] is the greatest game market in the world."

No doubt, many more animals were killed than were utilized. Some entire herds of elk were wiped out. As William Hornaday, one of the early American conservationists, wrote in 1914, "Wherever killable wild life is found, greed and ignorance are quite as deadly as shotguns . . . abundance is the only word with which to describe the original supply of animal life that stocked our country only a short half century ago . . . let it be remembered for all time that no wild species of mammal or bird can withstand systematic slaughter for commercial purposes."

Agriculture and forestry also ran largely unchecked in the 1800's. The best soils available for crops lay in valley bottoms or flats and were flooded for at least part of the western winter and spring. The development of these lands for agriculture meant the loss of prime big game wintering ranges, and the drainage of land which had been home to waterfowl and wading birds. Logging first leaped into a big swing with the construction of the railroads; thousands of tons of ties had to be milled. Hydraulic mining (which caused gaping erosion scars) required wood for the channeling of water; deep-mining required wood for supports; urban centers increased their share of the demand as they grew.

The first few decades of the 20th Century framed a time of resource partitioning and policy changes. In the Pacific Mountain Region, most of the Federally owned public domain was placed under the jurisdiction of the Forest Service, National Park Service, and, later, the Bureau of Land Management. Policies were born and evolved which would govern the level of resource development. Though crude in those early beginnings, there grew a realization that there could be different approaches to resources. Out of the "age of extinction," which the second half of the 1800's is often called, people began to notice

186

the effects of over-utilization, and found them unacceptable. Awareness of wildlife's plight developed after the turn of the century, deepening gradually into serious concern.

In comparison to what had been, only a few generations earlier, the contrast was shocking; and the region's growth and development had barely begun. Climate, fertile soils, and new water projects attracted millions of visitors who became permanent residents. Americans had become more mobile; the car was quickly changing from the great American luxury to the great American necessity, and the West's "wide open spaces" beckoned. By the eve of World War II, conditions were ripe for a new wave of massive roadbuilding, giant agribusiness enterprises, and industrial growth—all of which consumed more wildlife habitat.

The injection of Pittman-Robertson Federal Aid in Wildlife Restoration funds came at a critical time for wildlife in the Pacific Mountain System. Many species had been exterminated in some areas and were barely holding on in others. Some had vanished altogether from the entire region. The grizzly was essentially gone from the Pacific States, save for a few strays in the North Cascades. The pronghorn antelope was all but eliminated from the native grasslands west of the Sierra-Cascade crest, a victim of market hunting, introduced diseases, and fences erected by ranchers who feared competition with their livestock. By 1915, bighorn sheep had disappeared from the Oregon Cascades, also victims of overhunting, competition from domestic stock, and disease; by 1925, the same was true of bighorn in the Washington Cascades; a few remnant herds clung to life in the highest summits of the Sierra Nevada. What portion survived of the once-great flocks of waterfowl can only be speculated.

State game agencies were never flush with funds; they struggled to maintain even the status quo, at a time when the list of needs was expanding. Because

Rugged, almost inaccessible habitat has enabled the mountain lion to survive generations of bounty hunting in the West.

Maurice Hornocker

187

prime wildlife habitat was being swallowed up by agriculture and urban development, one of the most important needs on the list was the purchase and protection of land. The Pacific States stepped in with large amounts of the first Pittman-Robertson money allotments and bought land for State wildlife management areas. These areas have been expanded over the years and now offer a wide variety of public recreational opportunities which otherwise could have been lost. More importantly for wildlife, in a number of areas, the purchase and management of the land was critical to the survival of particular species. Each year hundreds of thousands of P-R dollars are used to maintain wildlife management areas; this is one of the most consistent functions of P-R money over the years. By managing habitats, they benefit many forms of wildlife.

Buying land was simple in comparison to the basic priority of the agencies: the increase of game stocks. Little was known about even the most essential needs of many animals; this made satisfying their requirements difficult. To deal with this, Pittman-Robertson funds were directed toward research on "high priority" species, notably, deer, elk, and other game animals. As management of big game species, based upon this research, became more effective, some of the benefits spilled over to help the predators who rely on them for food. Restoration of prey populations and habitats undoubtedly was P-R's biggest *management* contribution to restoration of mountain lions and of all predators.

One of the beauties of the P-R program is its flexibility. States can largely determine where the money goes, depending on their specific needs. California, for instance, with its enormous agriculture industry, chose to direct P-R dollars toward a long-term investigation into the effects of pesticides and other farm-based chemicals on fish and wildlife. Oregon, at about the same time, put even more money into developing a comprehensive 10-year plan for management of both game and nongame species, including predators. In Washington, where some of the best upland game habitat is on private lands, a program was developed to increase hunter access and to improve the accessed land. In a noteworthy effort, the State of Washington also carried out a long-term evaluation and research project on its native cats, the bobcat, lynx, and mountain lion, with P-R funding. The effort produced some first-ever research results on the lynx and a valuable review of the distributions, biology, and regulations pertaining to all three cats.

Pacific States have also put large efforts into restoring native species to areas where they had been eliminated. This can be an expensive process, requiring large numbers of personnel, costly equipment, and lots of time. In the end, though, the benefits of such restoration efforts prove their worth when the animals become established and begin to disperse once again on their own. Oregon, Washington, and California have all worked on re-introductions of bighorn sheep and pronghorn antelope. P-R funds have brought in sea otters once again to their native offshore home. After a long absence from all but the most remote localities, beaver are again plentiful in most drainages because of restoration programs and protective regulations, thanks in large part to P-R funding. The beaver's role in forest ecology still is not fully understood, but its water impoundments clearly have improved habitats for many birds and mammals of the Pacific Mountain System.

Potentially the biggest success story of re-introduction has been the tule elk, a small subspecies uniquely adapted to the low valleys of California. Thought to have been exterminated at one time, a small population has been nursed back to health and dispersed on State and Federal lands. Some of the most thriving populations are on wildlife management areas bought and maintained with P-R funds.

A little-noticed, but highly important P-R contribution has been in providing funds which enable State wildlife managers to coordinate their activities with the Federal agencies controlling fully 45 percent of the land area of California, 52 percent of Oregon, 28 percent of Washington, and even higher percentages in some other Western States. Major modifications proposed for these national forest, national park, BLM, military, or other Federal lands are carefully scrutinized by State biologists for potential impacts on wildlife habitats, populations, and management plans.

Possibly the greatest P-R contribution, overall, has been the reliability of funding to enable State wildlife agencies to employ professionals in every aspect of wildlife management. During recent years, the State agencies have tended more and more to plan their research and management comprehensively, taking an overall approach to both game and nongame wildlife. This systematic approach derives from the maxim that everything in the natural world is linked to everything else, whether or not the linkage is readily apparent. It is one of the most promising developments of all.

The successes are encouraging and easy to point to, but the road to wildlife restoration in the Pacific Mountain Region will be a long one. The wise use of funds, both P-R and otherwise, is important, and must be done with a feel for the past, a vision of the future, and a finger on the pulse of the public. With every reinstated piece, the public's view of that restored landscape becomes more clear and enthusiasm for the effort mounts. Money has made possible the scientific means, a worthy goal has supplied the enthusiasm, and the successes have built growing support. Through well-directed research, careful planning, cautious implementation, and critical evaluation, the future looks bright for our wildlife heritage in the region.

This is all the more remarkable when one considers the region's 50-year record of spectacular human growth, urbanization, and consumption of natural resources. The mountain lion may be regarded as a key indicator of wildlife's success in this region and throughout the West. Its future prospects are not unlimited, even in so huge and rugged a land; people and their activities will continue to press in on this predator and its prey. But coexistence of man and mountain lion has been shown to be both possible and desirable, despite the odds. Continued public support can make this a story we are proud to tell our grandchildren.

Mountain lions are well adapted to their solitary, predatory existence.

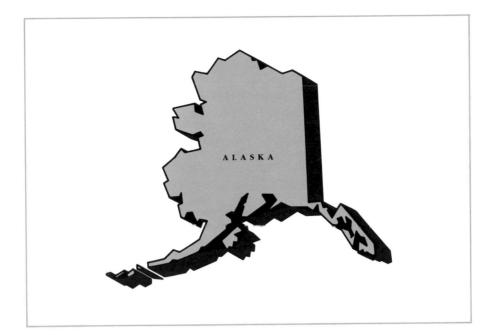

Caribou: Alaska's Wilderness Nomads

by David R. Klein

Back in 1920, a young biologist named Olaus Murie was assigned by the Biological Survey, forerunner of the Fish and Wildlife Service, to survey and describe the movements of caribou in the Territory of Alaska. Dr. Murie studied caribou during the 1920's and wrote the first comprehensive monograph on the species in Alaska. He went on to a distinguished career as author of several books on wildlife and served as president of the Wilderness Society.

On a crisp day in late April of 1923, Olaus Murie sat on a hillside in the mountains north of Fairbanks and counted caribou streaming by in migration. The long-legged, deer-like animals moved easily over the broad expanses of snow and occasional patches of bare ground. Their broad hooves kept them from sinking deeply into the thawing snow; during the previous winter the wide fore hooves had been used as "shovels" to dig through the snow to obtain food.

Dr. Klein, Leader of the Alaska Cooperative Wildlife Research Unit, has carried out research on Caribou and other Alaska ungulates for more than 30 years. He has also done research and published on caribou in Canada and Greenland, and on wild reindeer in Scandinavia and the Soviet Union.

Most of the migrating caribou that Olaus Murie counted that day were adult females, heavy with calves, on their way to the calving grounds and their traditional summer range. These females weighed well over 200 pounds. Unlike other female members of the deer family, they had antlers, and most would retain them until the time of calving in late May and early June. Most bulls had shed their larger antlers in early winter following the rutting season, and their migration from winter to summer ranges would be later than that of the females.

Caribou are protected from the extreme cold of winter by a coat of long hollow hairs with an underlayer of fine wool that provides excellent insulation. The winter hair is shed in early summer. The new, brownish hair of summer and autumn becomes bleached to a light gray by spring from long hours of exposure.

Olaus Murie estimated that the caribou flowing by him during that day in 1923 on their way to the calving grounds numbered 3,000. In 1920, on the basis of reports from a number of observers during the migration of this herd, he had estimated the size of this same Fortymile Caribou Herd to be more than 500,000, an estimate now believed to have been unrealistically high. Experience has shown that accurate counts of large concentrations of milling and migrating caribou are nearly impossible to obtain from the ground. Observers tend to overestimate, rather than underestimate, the numbers present.

Techniques for accurate "censusing" of caribou populations have been developed and refined since the 1960's with the support of Pittman-Robertson funds. Current methods involve intensive aerial surveys along flight transects during the post-calving period to obtain direct counts, as well as aerial photographs of concentrations of caribou. In addition, movement patterns of caribou are now being plotted with the aid of the latest space technology. Recently caribou in the remote northeastern corner of Alaska were captured, fitted with radio transmitting collars and released to join the rest of the herd. Mercury switches in the collars record activity of the caribou and the information is stored via microchips. When a polar orbiting satellite passes overhead, radios in the collars transmit bursts of information to the satellite. The satellite stores the information until it can be retransmitted to a ground station, from which it is sent by telephone to a computer in the office of a biologist in Fairbanks. The information is then decoded to give the precise location of the animal and the pattern of its activity during the interval between satellite passes. Migration routes, rates of movement and activity patterns of caribou can now be automatically recorded on a regular basis regardless of weather conditions that might ground airplanes or intimidate pilots. Caribou management in Alaska has advanced a long way since Olaus Murie sat on that hillside north of Fairbanks.

Historically, caribou were found throughout much of the Alaska mainland, except the coastal forests of southeastern and south-central Alaska (habitat of the Sitka black-tailed deer and the Alaska brown bear) and the low-lying delta country of the lower Yukon and Kuskokwim rivers in western Alaska (which is one of North America's major goose, duck and brant breeding areas and the site of the 20-million-acre Yukon Delta National Wildlife Refuge, largest of all national wildlife refuges). Caribou also are seldom found in the broad, low-lying and forested valleys of the Yukon and Tanana rivers of Interior Alaska that provide habitat for large numbers of moose.

In summer, caribou are typically found in tundra areas, either north of the tree line or in the alpine zone. Their summer diet consists mainly of grass-like sedges, leaves of dwarf willow, and herbaceous plants. The mountains where some of Alaska's caribou spend their summers are also the home of the white Dall sheep. In winter, caribou usually move into open spruce forests south of the tree line, to the foothills of mountain ranges, or to sub-alpine highlands.

Lichens, often called reindeer moss, make up the major portion of the winter diet. Lichens are high in carbohydrates and are therefore a good source of energy in winter. The availability of ground lichens depends largely upon the depth and hardness of the snow cover through which the caribou must dig to obtain them. Caribou also feed on lichens that grow on trees but these are more common in the pine and fir forests of Canada than in the spruce forests of Alaska. Caribou winter distribution and movements are related to the distribution and abundance of lichens as well as to snow conditions.

Winter forage appears to be the limiting bottleneck in the annual caribou food cycle. Not only does snow cover the forage, requiring the animals to expend energy in digging through it, but lichens are very slow growing. Overgrazing of lichens, or wildfire, can reduce the availability of winter food for long periods. But lichen production may also decline in forests that have not burned for hundreds of years. Thus forest fires, although destructive to lichens on a short-term basis, appear necessary for the long-term cycling of forests and associated growth of lichens. Current fire control policies in Alaska vary with the classification of lands for their value to wildlife; important winter ranges for caribou are among the highest priorities for fire control, in contrast to moose habitat, which requires more frequent burning to create the best availability of deciduous shrubs that are important moose forage.

The species *Rangifer tarandus,* which includes both caribou and reindeer, is present throughout the world's northernmost land areas, including Greenland, the Canadian Arctic Islands and Canadian mainland, Alaska, Siberia,

These caribou are closely bunched because they all want the same thing—to catch a breeze that can give them relief from Alaska's notorious mosquitos and flies.

David R. Klein, Alaska Cooperative Wildlife Research Unit

northern Russia, Scandinavia, and Spitzbergen. Historically caribou lived in many of the northern tier of States from Maine to Washington, but in the contiguous 48 States they are now limited to a few dozen mountain caribou along the Canadian border in Idaho and northeastern Washington. There are some physical differences among subspecies, but most are not readily apparent.

In North America, the native species has been traditionally known as caribou, while in the Old World, both the wild and domesticated forms are called reindeer. Domestic reindeer that were introduced to Alaska from Siberia apparently will interbreed with the native caribou if given the opportunity, and caribou bulls have been used in the past to add "new blood" and to increase the body size of Alaska reindeer.

The approximately 25,000 reindeer in western Alaska and 4,000 in Canada near the Mackenzie River delta are the result of imports from Siberia to Alaska around the turn of the last century. The original introductions were authorized by the U.S. Congress in the hope of alleviating food shortages among Eskimos in northwestern Alaska, associated with scarcity of caribou throughout that region. Large fluctuations in population size are characteristic of caribou, and they remain vitally important as food for many Eskimos and Indians.

Alaska's large caribou herds have been looked upon by Alaskans and other Americans as safely distant from most human activity. This may have been true two decades ago, but no longer; the land is being partitioned for a variety of uses, and portions of the once-remote caribou rangelands are the scene of intensive oil exploration and development. Recent changes in land use categories that have occurred in Alaska are the product of several Congressional Acts. This legislation was stimulated chiefly by the discovery of huge oil reserves at Prudhoe Bay, requiring a clarification of the legal status of Alaska lands before an oil pipeline could be built. The Alaska Native Claims Settlement Act of 1971 and the Alaska National Interest Lands Conservation Act of 1980 brought about major changes in land status all across the State. These laws accelerated the partitioning of Alaskan lands—equal in area to one-fifth of the rest of the United States and until recent years almost all Federally owned—among Native, State and Federal agencies, with proposed uses ranging from mining and oil development to national parks with wilderness status. Under terms of the Alaska Statehood Act of 1959 the new State had already been granted the right to select for its own uses some 104 million acres, nearly 28 percent of the total land area.

Coincident with accelerated oil and gas exploration and development in northern Alaska during the 1970's was the rapid decline of the Western Arctic Caribou Herd, which in 1970 had numbered approximately 240,000 and occupied a vast area of 140,000 square miles in the northwestern corner of the State. This herd, at the time the largest on the continent, dwindled to 50,000 to 60,000 animals by 1976. Several other Alaskan caribou herds also experienced declines during this same period.

Prior to 1976, the Western Arctic Herd had supplied over 20,000 caribou annually to nearly 10,000 residents in 30 Alaska Native villages from Barrow to Kotzebue. Traditionally many of these Eskimos and Indians depended upon caribou as a basis of their subsistence life style, and there were virtually no regulations restricting their hunting. On the basis of aerial censuses conducted by the Alaska Department of Fish and Game with P-R funding and involvement of Natives in the survey flights, the harvest of caribou from the Western Arctic Herd was curtailed during the winter of 1976-77. The Alaska Board of Game established strict quotas and allotted harvests to villages on the basis of need. Restrictions on the Natives' traditional way of life by an impersonal governmental agency 1,800 miles away in the State capital in Juneau were viewed with hostility

U.S. Bureau of Land Management

A herder moves his domesticated reindeer across a tundra area. Winter range is in foreground, summer range in background.

Reindeer and caribou will interbreed, but reindeer herds can deprive caribou of needed forage.

in the atmosphere of renewed cultural pride that characterized the era following passage of the Native Claims Settlement Act in 1971. However, involvement of the local Natives in survey flights and in the allocation of harvest quotas among the villages helped to resolve this management problem.

The Western Arctic Herd recovered rapidly from its alarming decline and is currently sustaining an annual hunter harvest of well over 10,000 animals. It now numbers approximately 170,000 and has resumed its importance to the well-being of the Indians and Eskimos of northwestern Alaska. The recovery of this herd to its former productivity stands as an example of how wildlife management in Alaska has matured along with the dynamic changes that have overtaken the State in the past two decades. Thanks to the support provided by P-R funds, intensive investigations of the Western Arctic Herd were carried out, and Native peoples were involved directly in the management decisions that led to the herd's recovery.

The decline of the Western Arctic Herd, as well as several other Alaskan and Canadian caribou herds in the 1970's, was alarming but the causes were not well understood. In some cases, poor calf survival as a result of bad weather seemed to be involved, while other herds suffered from over-hunting and heavy losses to predators. Most often several factors, acting jointly, tipped the scales against the caribou and started the declines. Although Indian and Eskimo hunters, joined by people who were unfamiliar with the facts, were inclined to blame the decline of the Western Arctic Caribou Herd on North Slope oil development and the construction of the Trans-Alaska Pipeline, there is no evidence to support this view. Fortunately Prudhoe Bay, where the major oil development activity occurred, as well as the pipeline route, lie east of the range of the Western Arctic Herd and west of the range of the Porcupine Caribou Herd, Alaska's second largest.

Considerable research has been carried out with both P-R funding and oil industry support on the relatively small Central Arctic Herd of about 15,000 animals on the North Slope in the vicinity of the Trans-Alaska Pipeline and its parallel haul road. This research has shown that oil field development and the Pipeline Corridor have altered caribou movements and caused a local decrease in use of their rangelands. Females accompanied by young show the strongest reaction and tend to avoid the roads, pipelines, and oil field structures. Nevertheless, the Central Arctic Herd has continued to increase. But it should be recognized that the influence of petroleum development on the herd is extremely difficult to assess; the situation is complicated by a simultaneous reduction of wolf numbers in the area through trapping and shooting adjacent to the pipeline haul road, and by lack of historical data on the status of the herd. The long-term effects of oil development on these caribou remain to be assessed.

The Porcupine Herd, of approximately 150,000 caribou, migrates between Alaska and Canada, and occupies rangelands in the Arctic National Wildlife Refuge to the east of the Trans-Alaska Pipeline Corridor. The Porcupine Herd (which gets its peculiar name from a major river it crosses in its annual migration) was one of the few Alaskan caribou herds that remained large and productive during the 1970's when many other herds were declining. This herd, however, may be threatened by future oil and gas development. Exploratory drilling on the coastal plain of the Arctic National Wildlife Refuge may be authorized by Congress under the terms of the 1980 Alaska National Interest Lands Conservation Act. And the Dempster Highway, extending from Dawson in the Yukon Territory to Inuvik on the MacKenzie River delta in Canada's Northwest Territories, cuts across portions of the Porcupine Herd's winter range and

This caribou herd is being "censused" by airborne photography as it migrates.

Alaska Department of Fish and Game

migratory routes. This transportation corridor may be used in the future for pipelines to transport Beaufort Sea oil and gas. Harbor facilities and oil field staging areas are also being planned for the coastal plain of northern Yukon Territory, an important summer grazing area for Porcupine Herd caribou.

This caribou herd is hunted by Eskimos from the village of Kaktovik on Alaska's north coast and by Indians from Arctic Village south of the Brooks Range. In adjacent Canada, Indians from Old Crow on the upper Porcupine River have traditionally hunted this herd. In addition, several Native villages on the lower Mackenzie River, as well as mining communities in the Yukon, have access to the herd via the Dempster Highway, and hunting of caribou by these people is expected to increase.

Research into the ecology and population dynamics of the Porcupine Caribou Herd has been jointly carried out in both Alaska and adjacent Yukon Territory through close cooperation of the Alaska Department of Fish and Game, the U.S. Fish and Wildlife Service, the Yukon Wildlife Branch and the Canadian Wildlife Service. This work has been guided and coordinated by an ad hoc technical committee, whose members include biologists from all of the cooperating agencies and the University of Alaska. The close international cooperation that has characterized the collection of data necessary for proper management of the Porcupine Caribou Herd has been a voluntary effort on the part of biologists working on a common wildlife resource. There is need, however, for an international treaty between the United States and Canada to assure the continued well-being of the herd. A treaty is necessary to ensure the protection of critical habitats, such as the calving grounds, insect relief areas on the summer range, and the winter lichen ranges. A treaty is also necessary to provide a basis for allocation of hunting quotas between the two countries. Native groups in both Alaska and Canada have recently pledged their support for a treaty, and negotiations have now been initiated by the two countries to develop specific terms and conditions.

Five major caribou herds in Alaska have each exceeded 25,000 animals in the past three decades, and all but the Porcupine Herd have experienced wide population fluctuations. The Nelchina Herd, which numbered 70,000 in the 1960's, has been the most heavily hunted herd in the State. It declined in the late 1960's and early 1970's after reaching a very high density. Studies of range vegetation, especially of lichens, were begun in the 1950's through P-R funding. Permanent enclosures, plots and transects have enabled long-term studies of vegetation changes. These have shown that the high density of caribou coincided with a reduction in lichens. The decline of this herd was accelerated by heavy hunting pressure with a high annual loss of wounded animals. Unfortunately, the magnitude of the decline was not promptly recognized by biologists of the Alaska Department of Fish and Game. Predators are also believed to be a factor in the herd's decline. When the herd had fallen to about 10,000 animals, very restrictive hunting regulations were adopted and more intensive study of the effects of wolf predation was undertaken with P-R funding. The decline was halted and the herd has now increased to nearly 30,000 animals.

Several other Alaskan caribou herds that declined to low levels in the 1970's have again begun to increase. The size of the Fortymile Herd, although overestimated by Olaus Murie a half century earlier, undoubtedly was very large and may well have numbered over 200,000. By the early 1950's this herd had declined to an estimated 50,000 animals, and by the mid-1970's to 5,000. Because of its reduced size it was particularly vulnerable to predation by wolves and by grizzly bears on the calving grounds. Hunting restrictions, an apparently concurrent decline in wolf numbers, and favorable winters all probably com-

Source: Davis, J.L., *Status of Rangifer in the U.S.A.*, a paper presented at the second Caribou-Reindeer Symposium in Røros, Norway, 1979.

1) Adak
2) Alaska Peninsula
3) Andreofsky
4) Beaver
5) Central Arctic
6) Chisana
7) Delta
8) Fortymile
9) Granite Mountains
10) Kenai
11) Kilbuck Mountains
12) Macomb
13) Denali
14) Metasta
15) Mulchatna
16) Nelchina
17) Rainy Pass
18) Ray Mountains
19) Sunshine-Cloudy Mountain
20) Teshekpuk
21) Porcupine
22) Western Arctic

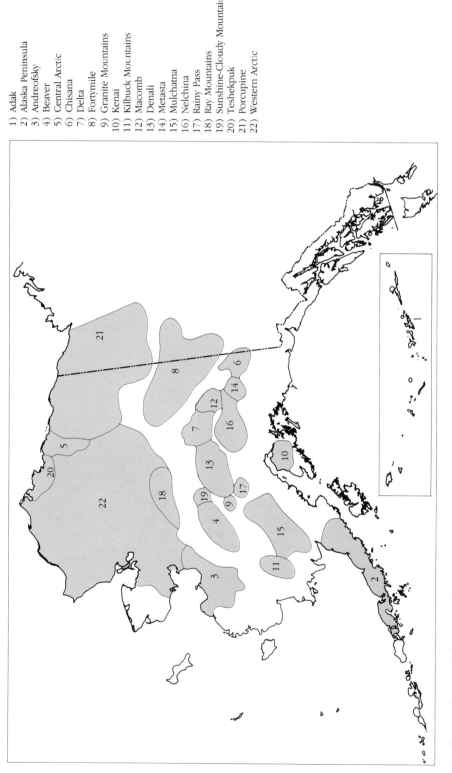

Distribution of major Alaska caribou herds

Source: U.S. Fish and Wildlife Service

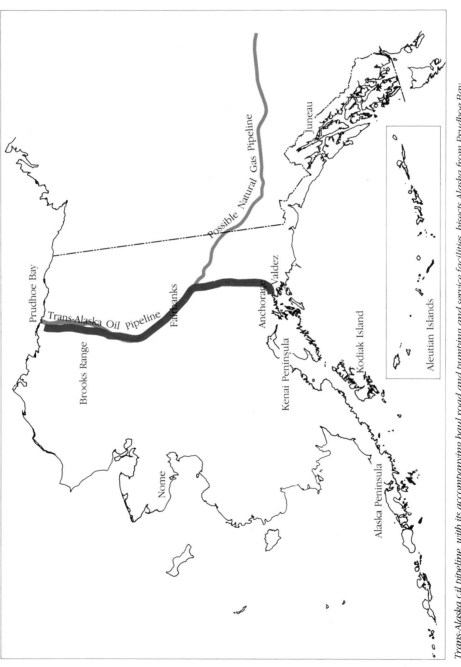

Trans-Alaska oil pipeline, with its accompanying haul road and pumping and service facilities, bisects Alaska from Prudhoe Bay south to Valdez. Possible future natural gas pipeline would branch off southeastward into Canada and "Lower 48."

Caribou pass beneath a raised segment of Trans-Alaska Pipeline north of the Brooks Range. Some caribou, notably females with their young, tend to avoid pipelines, roads, and oil field structures.

bined to enable a recent recovery of the herd to about 14,000. The extremely large size of this herd 60 years ago was apparently an abnormal high; overgrazing and fracturing of the herd may have contributed to its decline.

The Denali Herd, occupying rangelands mostly within Denali National Park (formerly Mt. McKinley National Park) numbered 25,000 to 30,000 in the 1930's and 1940's. Adolf Murie, brother of Olaus, made the counts and studied the ecology of this herd while he was a biologist for the National Park Service. The herd declined to 15,000 in the mid-1960's and continued a steady decline to an alarmingly low level of 1,000 animals in the late 1970's. The causes of this decline are more obscure than those for the other herds; like the others, however, this herd appears to be once again on the increase, and by 1985 it had reached 2,400 animals.

The historically smaller Alaskan herds, for the most part, have remained stable or increased slowly during the past few decades. The Alaska Peninsula herd, which is believed to have been derived from a mixing of caribou with abandoned reindeer, recovered from an extremely low level in the 1940's and is now thought to number approximately 30,000, including 5,000 on Unimak Island. Caribou introduced to the Kenai Peninsula and Adak Island in the 1960's through P-R support have been expanding and now number approximately 450 and 300, respectively. Caribou had occurred on the Kenai Peninsula until just before the turn of the last century when extensive fires burned over much of their range, destroying lichens in the wintering areas. Overhunting by miners apparently eliminated the remaining caribou. The forest fires transformed the spruce forests into second-growth stands of willow, birch, and aspen that provided excellent winter food for moose. The subsequent expansion of the moose population on the Kenai Peninsula made it famous throughout North America for its abundant and very large moose, thus attracting the first major influx of trophy hunters to Alaska in the early 1900's.

The large size of some caribou herds in the past in relation to their available range may have caused the subsequent declines through overgrazing of the highest quality forage. If lichens on the winter range are removed more rapidly than they can be replaced by annual growth, caribou in winter concentration areas may be forced to compete with one another for the remaining lichens. This may weaken the caribou, resulting in lower rates of reproduction and survival. The inflated populations of caribou in the past may have been the result of a series of favorable winters as well as reduced wolf predation during the era when wolves were hunted extensively from aircraft. Overgrazing and heightened competition for available food may have been intensified in some areas by forest fires, which forced the animals to concentrate during winter. Periods of caribou scarcity and abundance are not peculiar to recent times; they also occurred before the advent of firearms, mechanized equipment, wolf control programs, and human-caused forest fires.

When a caribou herd is declining because of a food shortage, the decline gains a momentum that is not easily stopped. Sustained hunting and predation tend to accelerate the decline. Moderate levels of hunting and predation may have had little effect on a large, expanding population, but these same levels of mortality may bring a declining herd to very low levels within a few years. In the extreme case, recovery may require virtual total protection from both hunting and wolves.

The killing of wolves is an issue that fires people with emotion. In the concern over the well-being of the wolf, the importance of caribou to the wolf is frequently forgotten. If caribou populations decline, the wolves that prey upon them also face a corresponding decline because caribou are a primary food of the wolf. Recovery of caribou from population lows is limited by their relatively low breeding potential. Female caribou bear only one calf per year under the best of circumstances, while wolves at their best average six to eight young in a litter. Wolf populations do tend to fluctuate with changing abundance of their prey. However, it is possible for wolf numbers to remain high locally when caribou herds decline if moose or other wildlife are available as alternative prey. Wolf populations in Alaska today, unlike those in most other States, remain healthy and relatively stable with no threat of extinction. Their habitat and prey populations have not as yet been greatly influenced by human activities, and wolves generate little conflict with Alaska's domestic livestock.

Wolves, however, are not the only predators of caribou. Through P-R funding, studies of the causes of death of caribou calves have been carried out using special radio-transmitting collars that alter their signal when an animal is no longer active. This has enabled biologists to determine that grizzly bears are the most serious predators on some calving grounds. Golden eagles also tend to congregate on caribou calving grounds and prey on very young calves.

Often overlooked in the concern for existing herds of caribou in Alaska are the numerous local extinctions of caribou herds that occurred around the turn of the century. Extinctions occurred on the Seward and Kenai Peninsulas, as well as in the Kilbuk and Kuskokwim Mountains, the Nulato Hills, and on Nunivak Island. The widespread introduction of firearms among the Natives and the demand for meat by whalers, prospectors, and miners were important, if not the primary factors in these local extinctions. Reindeer were ultimately introduced to many of these areas and, in some instances, their presence contributed to the local decline of caribou and prevented the natural re-establishment of caribou from adjacent areas.

In recent years, caribou have dispersed back into the Kuskokwim Mountains and have been successfully re-introduced to the Kenai Peninsula.

Caribou remain absent from several other areas they formerly inhabited even though reindeer herding has declined greatly since the early 1930's. During the deep decline of the Western Arctic Caribou Herd in the 1970's, Eskimos in northwestern Alaska showed a renewed interest in reindeer as an alternative meat source and as a basis for expanding their cash economy. There was a major effort to expand the reindeer industry into rangelands of the Western Arctic Caribou Herd with both Federal and State support. The prospect of using reindeer as an interim source of meat to lessen human impact on the recovering caribou herd appeared superficially to be an ideal solution to an awkward problem. This solution, however, had a "Catch 22" clause. Reindeer and caribou eat the same foods; therefore, successful expansion of the reindeer industry into caribou ranges would ultimately force caribou out. Reindeer and caribou not only compete for the same foods, but the presence of caribou around domestic reindeer makes herding extremely difficult. Also, wolves may follow the caribou and quickly learn to prey on reindeer. Reindeer herders are quite familiar with these problems and work hard to keep caribou away from their herds, often by shooting them. In the Soviet Union, wild reindeer have been systematically eliminated from areas where intensive reindeer herding is practiced.

Establishing reindeer on caribou range is therefore not a satisfactory solution to problems of caribou shortage. Instead, it tends to result in permanent loss of caribou as a natural part of the environment and as the basis of a traditional subsistence economy and culture. In fact, the proposed use of caribou rangelands for reindeer husbandry in northwestern Alaska totally loses its appeal when one realizes that the Western Arctic Caribou Herd provides a subsistence base for people in 30 communities over a 140,000-square-mile area, while reindeer husbandry under the most optimistic projections could only meet the needs of a few of these villages.

When the future of caribou is viewed within the context of present-day Alaska, with the prospect of continued widespread energy development, changing land status, changing rural life styles, and an increasing human population, there is clearly cause for concern. The habitat of caribou in Alaska, at least up to now, has remained virtually intact, and past population declines have been reversed. But it is not at all clear whether extensive tracts of unaltered land can be maintained for caribou in the future. Caribou are a "wilderness species" that require large expanses of unaltered natural habitat, free of obstructions to their movements and without excessive human disturbance.

Caribou in North America have declined with the advancing frontiers of human development, in contrast to certain other, more adaptable wildlife. For example, white-tailed deer thrive in second-growth forests and the forest-field edge, and have increased their numbers and range with the cutting of forests and development of agriculture. But caribou, formerly present in 11 of the Northern Tier States, have virtually disappeared from the "lower 48." In winter, the few survivors depend on tree lichens of the subalpine forest, which are increasingly being logged. Although in the Canadian North caribou have increased dramatically in recent years, they have been eliminated from extensive areas in the southern portions of the provinces through habitat alteration and through parasitism by the brain worm carried by white-tailed deer which are relatively resistant to its presence.

A similar but more extensive pattern of reduction of wild reindeer has occurred in Scandinavia and the Soviet Union, but with competition from domestic reindeer husbandry playing a more important role. In Norway, the few remaining populations of wild reindeer are threatened by extensive hydroelectric developments that are flooding their rangelands and blocking migrations. In

202

Caribou often must travel long, demanding distances for food in winter. They need to locate lichens on the ground beneath the *snow—which must be soft and shallow enough so caribou can dig through with their shovel-like front hooves.*

the Soviet Union, an above-ground gas pipeline in north-central Siberia has altered the migratory patterns of the largest remaining herd of wild reindeer, and a railroad constructed to a northern coal field has restricted the migrations of one of the few remaining populations of wild reindeer west of the Ural Mountains.

A view of a map of Alaska showing recent changes in land ownership and political jurisdiction quickly demolishes the naive assumption that Alaskan caribou rangelands are secure in their remoteness from human influence. Such legal boundaries bear little or no resemblance to the natural features or condition of the land. The recent and continuing carving up of the land among a multitude of State and Federal agencies and native corporations has already brought about changes in land use. Plans for large-scale development, including hydroelectric projects, large mines with connecting roads, and additional oil fields, are on the drawing board for many of these areas. These new land uses are bound to change the ecosystems, and inevitably will affect the caribou which are inseparable elements of these systems.

The new national parks and wildlife refuges set up under the 1980 Alaska National Interest Lands Conservation Act are large compared to those in other States, and they protect important components of caribou habitat in Alaska. However, such protective status will not guarantee the survival of the major caribou herds. Although the Gates of the Arctic National Park, Kobuk Valley National Park, Selawik National Wildlife Refuge, and Noatak National Preserve all offer protection to important components of the range of the Western Arctic Caribou Herd, they collectively fall far short of providing protection for the entire land area used by this herd.

Source: U.S. Bureau of Land Management and Alaska Department of Natural Resources

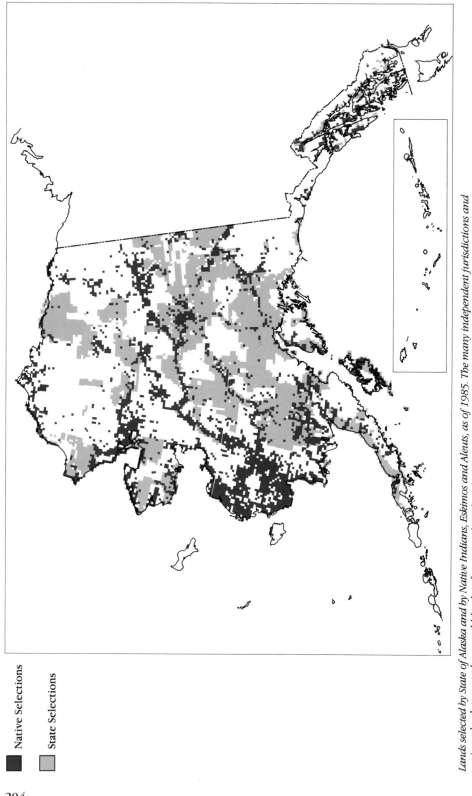

Native Selections

State Selections

Lands selected by State of Alaska and by Native Indians, Eskimos and Aleuts, as of 1985. The many independent jurisdictions and various development plans could lead to fragmented caribou herds unless cooperative land use agreements are adopted and observed.

Source: University of Alaska, Institute of Social and Economic Research

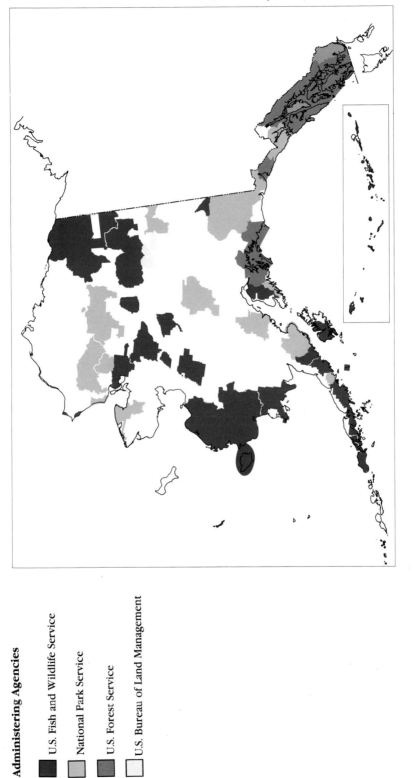

Administering Agencies

- ■ U.S. Fish and Wildlife Service
- ▨ National Park Service
- ▨ U.S. Forest Service
- □ U.S. Bureau of Land Management

Areas designated by 1980 Alaska National Interest Lands Conservation Act as parts of National Park, Forest, and Wildlife Refuge Systems and as special recreation/conservation areas to be administered by Bureau of Land Management.

The great herds of caribou are "a unique resource unparalleled except in the grasslands of East Africa," in the author's words.

The land classification process resulting from the Alaska Native Claims Settlement Act and the Alaska National Interest Lands Conservation Act has resulted in the protection of extensive areas of wildlife habitat. At the same time, however, these laws and the Alaska Statehood Act also provide for mining and petroleum development, reindeer herding, development of transportation corridors, and other activities on intervening lands. Caribou recognize no boundaries of land use or of administrative authority. Their annual travels of hundreds of miles take them through different ecosystems, from wintering grounds to specific calving areas, summer grazing land, and coastal or mountain areas where cool, windy conditions provide relief from insects. In the process, they may graze and travel across national park and wildlife refuge lands, but other important components of the rangelands they use may not be protected.

Experience with the Trans-Alaska Oil Pipeline as well as knowledge of pipelines, highways, and railroads in other northern regions of the world indicate that transportation corridors may interfere with the free movements of caribou. Extensive development of additional transportation corridors in Alaska may ultimately lead to major disruptions of caribou range use patterns or migrations. Similarly, other land use activities such as reindeer herding and certain types of mining and oil exploration and development may work to the serious detriment of caribou.

It has been suggested that migratory disruptions may merely fracture the large caribou herds, leading to more small herds of a non-migratory nature. Relatively small herds do exist in the mountainous regions of central and southern Alaska where winter range occurs in close proximity to alpine summer range; but for the large Porcupine and Western Arctic herds, the primary winter ranges lie in the open spruce forests and shrublands south of the Brooks Range, while calving grounds and summering areas are hundreds of miles north on the tundra beyond the Brooks Range. If these great herds cannot move freely between essential components of their range, their populations can survive only as mere fractions of their previous size, and we will have lost a unique resource unparalleled except in the grasslands of East Africa.

A possible solution to the problem of caribou management under the complex land ownership pattern that is emerging in Alaska is to establish a procedure of cooperative management involving all land owners. Such a system could also help in managing other wildlife where habitat units extend across administrative boundaries, or where the animals themselves readily travel across these boundaries.

Only a small percentage of caribou habitat in Alaska is State-owned; most is under the jurisdiction of agencies of the Department of the Interior or Native village or regional corporations. However, the Alaska Department of Fish and Game, using P-R funds, has designated critical wildlife habitat areas for caribou and most other wildlife species throughout Alaska. This classification of lands serves to focus attention on special wildlife values inherent in the specific areas involved. It is used by both State and Federal agencies in evaluating permit requests for proposed land use activities. The designation of critical habitats by the Alaska Department of Fish and Game, however, places no legal constraints on land use practices if the lands involved are not in State ownership.

Effective wildlife management that will guarantee the continued welfare and productivity of animal populations must ensure that the habitat is protected. If the majestic herds of caribou that have been so much a part of the Alaskan landscape in the past are to remain as dynamic elements of our northern ecosystems, provision must be made for the cooperative management of caribou range lands both within the State and in adjacent Canada. Only in that way can caribou, and other living resources that transcend artificial boundaries we impose upon the land, escape being forfeited in favor of development schemes or localized management objectives. Within natural systems, the value of the whole invariably exceeds the sum of the parts.

Summertime and the livin' is easy for this caribou, silhouetted against one of Alaska's many magnificent mountains.

A public target range constructed and operated with help from P-R funds.

Hunter Education: Safety and Responsibility

by Jim Jones, F.E. "Bud" Eyman, Frank Disbrow and Homer Moe

Young Doug Hunter, on a cool and crisp autumn day, carefully removed a lightweight 20 gauge double-barreled shotgun from the gun rack and eagerly moved toward the front door. With ammunition in his hunting jacket, blaze orange cap and vest, Doug was an impressive sight to his parents and younger brothers on this, his first unsupervised hunting experience. Although Doug's thoughts were on the cottontail rabbits and ring-necked pheasants and a day in the field, his parents were very concerned about his personal safety. Will he be injured or injure someone else? Will he violate the law? Will he damage property or livestock? No, Doug returned home after a successful hunt with a couple of rabbits and one pheasant. Actually, he limited out with four rabbits and two pheasants; however, he shared his harvest with the landowner where he hunted. Oh yes, Doug also helped the landowner return several cows that had strayed from the farm, thanks to a thoughtless hunter who had left a gate open. As Doug completed his story of the day's hunt to his father, he concluded with, "The hunter who left the gate open sure could use the hunter education course I took last month."

Hunting is one of the most time-honored activities of the human species. Pictorial accounts of hunting expeditions are found on the walls of caves inhabited by our prehistoric ancestors. Early written accounts of hunting activites are found in the historical writings of the ancient Babylonians and Egyptians, and in the Old Testament. Hunting, both for food and recreation, played a major part in the lives of American Indians and the European settlers who moved in on their territory, leaving indelible imprints on the cultures of both. Avoidable accidents occurred frequently, too, but life itself was a dangerous gamble at best—especially at the edges of human settlement. Only after the frontier disappeared, and wild game became scarce, did attitudes about hunting begin to undergo change.

First came a revulsion against hunting for profit—market hunting—because it clearly menaced the wild game that remained. State laws, followed by the Federal Lacy Act, outlawed it. States also adopted bag limits and hunting seasons, but enforcement was spotty and weak; wildlife did not recover. Genuine sportsmen began to be outraged by the behavior of hunters they called "meat hogs" and "slobs." At the 1906 meeting of the parent organization of the present International Association of Fish and Wildlife Agencies (IAFWA), Charles Joslyn of Michigan voiced alarm over greedy hunters who killed hundreds of ducks daily without concern for the future of the species. Irresponsible hunter behavior prompted Seth Gordon to develop a code of ethics that was published by the

Mr. Jones, chairman of the group which wrote this chapter, is Hunter Education Specialist for the U.S. Fish and Wildlife Service's Region 5, covering the Northeast and Mid-Atlantic States. Messrs. Eyman, Disbrow, and Moe are the Hunter Education Coordinators for the State wildlife agencies of Missouri, Connecticut, and Wisconsin, respectively. Editorial assistance was contributed by Eugene C. Stephenson and Robert G. Nelson, who head up hunter education activities for USFWS' Federal Aid Division.

Izaak Walton League in 1928, emphasizing safety, respect for others, respect for property rights, and respect for wildlife. Good sportsmen applauded and were impressed. Others went on doing whatever they could get away with. Eventually, it was concern for human safety that led to serious action by the States toward the twin goals of safety and sportsmanship.

During the post-World War II period, when millions of new hunters were going afield, a sharp increase in hunting accidents led several States to initiate firearms safety courses. In New York, a sportsmen's organization, alarmed at the rising number of accidents, prompted passage of the first hunter safety law in 1948. This law required that all first-time hunters be trained in the safe handling of firearms to obtain a hunting permit. Other States were to follow New York's lead. Although progress was slow at first, nearly 18 million men and women nationwide had, by the mid-1980's, received State-sponsored training in hunter safety and ethics.

Invaluable assistance came during the early years from the National Rifle Association (NRA) which supplied New York and other States, at their own request, with instructors and training materials. The NRA Uniform Hunter Casualty Report, established early in 1948, was designed to collect information about the causes of hunting accidents. It became the base upon which NRA, in cooperation with the National Education Association, developed the first standardized hunter safety course offered by the States in 1948-49. The NRA also provided program recordkeeping services and recruited volunteer instructors from among its membership.

Other States soon recognized the need to train hunters and eliminate problems associated with hunting. By 1970, 33 States had developed and implemented a hunter safety course that was funded and operated entirely by State resources. With the increased ability of the States to manage their programs, the role of the NRA as administrator and recordkeeper diminished.

Meanwhile, it became apparent that something more than safe firearms handling was needed. States began developing their own specifically targeted educational materials and new subject areas were added to their programs,

A hunter education classroom. Sessions may be held in schools, meeting halls, or any other suitable facility. Volunteer instructors are the program's backbone.

Claire Guimond Dobert, U.S. Fish and Wildlife Service

Why Call Them Sportsmen?

As usual, Cartoonist "Ding" Darling expressed better than anyone the ethical hunter's contempt for game hogs, and others who unfairly exploited wildlife and spoiled the outdoor experience for genuine sportsmen. The cartoon dates to 1937.

Tennessee Wildlife Resources Agency

Outdoor archery class conducted by a hunter education instructor.

including hunter responsibility, the hunter's role in conservation, survival, wildlife management, bowhunting, muzzleloading, wildlife identification and first aid. In 1966, the NRA led the way toward an expanded national program by sponsoring the first Hunter Safety/Education Coordinators Workshop, an annual event that continues today.

Prior to 1970, as we have noted, all training of hunters was funded by the States without Federal assistance. However, on October 23, 1970, President Richard Nixon signed Public Law 91-503 amending the Pittman-Robertson (P-R) Act to provide funds to the States for hunter safety programs and for the construction, operation and maintenance of public target ranges. These new monies were generated through a 10 percent manufacturer's excise tax on handguns and, in 1973, an 11 percent excise tax was added to archery equipment, split 50-50 between wildlife restoration and hunter training. These newfound dollars provided the opportunity to strengthen the States' hunter training programs.

Nationwide, hunter education has progressed from basic firearms safety to a more inclusive course covering almost all aspects of hunter responsibility. Now there is strong emphasis on hunting-related problems and their solutions, starting with the fundamentals of safety, knowledge and understanding of hunting equipment, and the responsibilities of the hunter. All States are encouraged to develop hunter training programs based on identified needs so that the maximum benefits of that training effort can be realized.

P-R funds are used to purchase student textbooks, instructor teaching aids, firearms and archery equipment for safe handling and live practice firing experience, films, portable target ranges, boats, motor vehicles and numerous other items necessary to develop safe and proficient hunters.

Hunter education classes are conducted in homes, schools, fire stations, churches, meeting halls or wherever space exists. Where the P-R assisted course is offered, it is required to be available to everyone regardless of race, creed, religion, color, sex, or physical handicap. Courses are taught in urban areas as well as rural regions.

The backbone of hunter education is the cadre of more than 45,000 volunteer instructors throughout the Nation. Each has his or her own personal reasons for devoting countless hours to this unpaid work. Volunteers may be male or female, young or old, even a husband-wife team, where hunting is a family-oriented activity. Volunteers have diverse backgrounds which include every conceivable occupation and trade, such as doctors, teachers, lawyers, skilled and unskilled workers, and retired individuals. Each devotes an average of more than a week's work each year to hunter education. Together they contribute nearly $25 million worth of volunteer services annually nationwide.

It is the responsibility of the State to recruit and certify qualified instructors and provide them with adequate materials and equipment. Since instructors must demonstrate their knowledge and proficiency, they may be provided training in effective teaching techniques, use and care of audio-visual materials, classroom management, and, if necessary, the safe and proper use of hunting equipment. Although they are volunteers, they do represent the State wildlife agency.

During the early years of Federal participation, the States' offerings varied from 4 to 16 hours of classroom activities. To assist the States' efforts to expand training, the Federal Aid Division of the U.S. Fish and Wildlife Service set a requirement of at least 6 classroom hours, beginning in 1973. With greater emphasis on the need to heighten awareness and knowledge of hunter responsibility, supported by a study of hunter education by the International Association of Fish and wildlife Agencies in 1981, the Federal Aid requirement was increased from 6 hours to 10 hours of training beginning October 1, 1985.

Instructor shows young students a safe way to get through a fence while carrying weapon. Some States have cut their hunting accident rates by more than 50 percent in the past 10 years, thanks in part to "hunter ed" with P-R aid.

Hunter education emphasizes the need for students to increase their sense of individual responsiblity as well as their knowledge about hunting. Students are provided an opportunity to develop a deep appreciation for our natural resources in addition to training in how to deal with emergency situations in the field, knowledge of the game being hunted, species identification, and the proper care and processing of the animal after it is taken.

Several States offer advanced hunter education to address specific problems or needs. Missouri is currently presenting a series of special turkey hunting seminars to stem the rising accident rate among turkey hunters. Colorado is using a series of big game seminars to improve hunter behavior and hunter-landowner relationships. Several Northeastern States include waterfowl hunting seminars to curtail the decline of the black duck. Finally, special advanced training programs are used to introduce new regulations designed to minimize a hunting problem either locally or statewide.

Hunter educators cite psychologists' findings that their best results are with young students. This youngster is learning some fundamentals from an instructor only a few years older.

Tennessee Wildlife Resources Agency

A major task of hunter education is to teach hunters to continually police their ranks in an effort to eliminate unsafe practices and such unsportsmanlike behavior as spotlighting, hunting without a license, disregard for game laws or bag limits, and trespassing, among the most common violations.

Despite the accomplishments that have already been made in hunter education, we have a long way to go. Psychologists note that to make a significant impact on the attitudes and behavior patterns of hunters, they must be educated at a very early age, with periodic retraining as they grow and mature into adulthood. At elementary grade levels, students should: (1) be taught the fundamentals of wildlife management; (2) begin to appreciate the meaning of wildlife conservation; and (3) become aware of the need always to exhibit good outdoor ethics. The new and the seasoned hunter alike must learn that sustaining substantial wildlife populations depends on preserving and maintaining adequate amounts of prime habitat in a good clean environment.

The well-informed hunter knows about wildlife management, woodsmanship and woodcraft, and wildlife signs. He or she also has the best chance of being successful and will probably continue to hunt.

The 1970 amendment to P-R which provided funding for hunter education also authorized Federal assistance in the development of target ranges. Congress recognized that in order to train safe, responsible, knowledgeable and involved hunters, demonstration of one's ability with firearms would require live practice firing and hands-on experience. To reach this goal would require safe shooting facilities. Since the number of existing shooting ranges appeared to be inadequate, States were encouraged to develop suitable facilities.

Today, with the assistance of P-R, public shooting facilities are becoming an integral part of the States' hunter education programs. They vary from indoor small-bore rifle and pellet gun facilities to large multi-use shooting/training complexes. In many cases, however, a range will simply consist of a safe shooting site in some remote area. In addition to development, ranges are often leased or rented from sportsmen's clubs. Aside from requiring a safe place to practice with firearms or archery equipment, the law stipulates that the facility be available for hunter training and open to the public.

Hunter education has clearly proved itself in the area of safety. Accident statistics are analyzed and disseminated so that problem areas may be identified and addressed without delay. Research is often performed to find ways to solve specific hunting problems. The use of "blaze orange" caps, vests, and coats is one of many improvements in hunting equipment that grew out of the need to reduce accidents. In addition to the handling of firearms, safety includes such areas as how to handle boats used by hunters, the use of black powder and bowhunting equipment, survival, home firearms safety, handling and reloading of ammunition, terrain conditions, and first aid. Further, many States are attempting to reduce the number of heart attacks and other disabling ailments by focusing on the physical condition of hunters. They are also addressing the hunter's ability to use a map and compass and to deal with hearing and visual impairments when afield.

Under the current program, more than 700,000 hunters are trained each year. By the mid-1980's, successful completion of the course was a requirement for obtaining a hunting license in 36 States, and available for voluntary participation in the other 14 States.

Considering the number of hunters afield, hunting is no longer the dangerous sport it used to be, and it continues to become safer. For example, Wisconsin reports that during the first half of the 1980's, fatal deer hunting accidents decreased by 60 percent compared to the same period in the 1970's.

215

The following chart compares the number of hunting-related accidents over a 10-year period in States selected at random.

COMPARISON OF HUNTING ACCIDENTS
1974-1984

| State | Year | Accidents | | Accidents Per |
		Fatal	Non-Fatal	100,000 Licensees
Utah	1974	5	8	5.80
	1984	0	9	3.69
New Mexico	1974	6	26	20.46
	1984	0	5	3.40
Kansas	1974	3	27	12.83
	1984	0	32	12.86
Maryland	1974	6	31	19.47
	1984	0	21	12.14
Nebraska	1974	2	25	18.08
	1984	1	13	8.06

Training beginning hunters in firearms safety is an area that will continue to require emphasis. As long as hunting accidents occur, the pressure and demand to reduce or eliminate them will continue. In addition, future resource managers will become more dependent on education to increase public awareness of the importance of the hunter in the total wildlife management scheme.

Since hunting is a key element in sound wildlife management, and the future of hunting lies in acceptable behavior by hunters, it is imperative that support for hunter education come from the hunting public, hunting and shooting organizations, the shooting sports industry and especially from wildlife agency administrators. Success will depend on their commitment—a strong, sincere and positive attitude toward the hunter education program and its goal of producing an informed, responsible hunter. Emphasis must be placed on developing well-trained hunters who practice an ethical and moral attitude toward wildlife, the land, other people including fellow hunters, and themselves before, during, and after the hunt.

States that expose hunter education students to proven training techniques will have the most successful programs. The most effective techniques include placing the student in realistic hunting situations where he or she is forced to make critical decisions—with these decisions being weighed carefully and thoughtfully by their peers to determine whether or not they are acceptable to the majority. Students exposed to this type of teaching are more likely to make mature and ethical choices while hunting.

Keeping Current

Continued training of professionals in the field of hunter education is also necessary if they are to keep up with the "state of the art." In addition, the volunteer instructors need more advanced training if they are to cope with the more complex resource issues that are anticipated for the future. To quote the late Fred Evenden, "Success in these directions will assure continuation of wildlife resources and the agency's rights to manage those resources and assure the future existence of the sport of hunting."

The Fish and Wildlife Service's Federal Aid Division, which administers P-R, is presently working with the States, the National Rifle Association, the North American Association of Hunter Safety Coordinators and the International Association of Fish and Wildlife Agencies to standardize State hunter training programs and the hunting accident reporting system.

In addition to funding, P-R provides training for program administrators through professional workshops, comprehensive program evaluations, guidance for the development of target shooting facilities, and many other technical assistance activities. The grant-in-aid program also assists States in research efforts designed to measure effectiveness of programs, determine program needs, and develop new and innovative teaching aids and techniques. Although funding support for social research has not been a popular activity of most wildlife agencies, Federal financial assistance is used to study hunters' behavior and relationship to other outdoor resource users. The results of this research are being used effectively by States to modify the attitude and behavior of hunters through education and involvement.

Aldo Leopold wrote that "the ultimate test of a hunter's ethics or sense of responsibility is when he is hunting alone and no one is there to observe what he does."

Hunting is a privilege. As such, it carries with it a responsibility for the general public's impressions of hunting and the need to eliminate behavior which is unethical, illegal, or offensive to others. Hunter education is designed to create an awareness in each hunter of how his behavior affects others. Responsibility training is also directed toward the resource, the environment, and the landowner. Respect for private and public property and the rights of others is an essential responsibility to the general public including non-hunters, since they share equally in use of the wildlife resource with the hunter. Other responsibilities extend to hunting companions and even to hunting dogs. In short, hunter education that teaches responsibility puts ethics into all aspects of hunting.

When property owners feel they must post a sign like this, many true sportsmen and sportswomen feel a sense of loss and outrage toward *"slob" hunters. Hunter education has put increasing emphasis on ethical conduct afield.*

Canada geese at Fountain Grove Wildlife Area, Missouri, acquired in part with P-R funds.

Wildlife Benefits and Economic Values

by F. Reed Johnson

Several years ago, a survey of sportsmen undertook to measure the willingness of hunters to pay for hunting opportunities on public lands. Hunters were asked: "Suppose you were offered a job in another part of the country where you would not have the hunting opportunities you now have. How much money would the job have to pay in order to get you to move?" One avid sportsman responded that no amount of increased income would induce him to give up hunting and that, in fact, life itself would not be worth living without hunting.

The discovery of such attitudes puts attempts to place values on public uses of wildlife resources in perspective. The chase and the kill, the quiet observation of creatures in their natural habitat, and the simple knowledge that there are still places where wild things run free are not really valued in the same way as a movie ticket or a new car. Nevertheless, we must make choices about wild things in the inevitable competition for limited public funds. Without claiming to have captured all the important values, economists have succeeded in quantifying some of the benefits of public uses of wildlife. These estimates often demonstrate that expenditures on wildlife management and conservation are productive and cost-effective investments relative to the benefits obtained.

It would clearly be impractical to try to identify what part of the national economic benefits of wildlife management are attributable specifically to the 50-year-old Pittman-Robertson program. Instead, this chapter examines a few sites where P-R funding has been important, and makes an attempt to quantify some of the resulting benefits in dollar terms. The examples span both the breadth of the continent and the variety of wildlife-related activities, and are representative of the hundreds of P-R projects that have been carried out over the past 50 years. The examples include wild turkey hunting in Georgia, waterfowl hunting in the Fountain Grove Wildlife Management Area in Missouri, big game hunting in the Crex Meadows Wildlife Area of Wisconsin, and fishing and nonconsumptive activities in the scenic Skagit Habitat Management Area in Washington State.

Economic Benefits of Wildlife-related Recreation

Public agencies must continually weigh the merits of seemingly desirable, but conflicting alternatives. Should old-growth timber be preserved or cut to improve habitat for elk? Should rare species be isolated from visitors or roads built to improve access for visitors to enjoy other species? Will society benefit

Dr. Johnson, Associate Professor of Economics at the U.S. Naval Academy, Annapolis, has concentrated his scholarship on environmental economics. He has worked for the U.S. Interior Department's Office of Policy Analysis; was a consultant to the British Columbia provincial government on valuing natural resources; and has consulted for Resources for the Future, the U.S. Forest Service, and (currently) the Environmental Protection Agency.

more from encouraging hunting activity in an area or from encouraging nonconsumptive activities?

Wildlife management must also compete for resources in a larger context. The immediate financial rewards to a farmer of draining wetlands to expand his cultivatable acreage are powerful incentives. It is important to document the very real economic loss to society as a result of the progressive destruction of valuable habitat. These losses are particularly tragic when the farmer's incentives are a result of government price supports rather than market forces. Developing credible estimates of the economic value of habitat preservation may induce policy makers to search for alternative means of dealing with agricultural and other problems.

The purpose of deriving dollar values for public use benefits is not to attach a price to each gobbler and pintail. Benefit estimates provide instead a basis for judging whether Pittman-Robertson expenditures on land acquisition, wildlife management, and research generate more than enough measurable benefits to justify a particular project. These estimates also indicate what the relative benefits of alternative wildlife investments might be. Such values assist public agencies in allocating scarce natural, financial, and labor resources more efficiently among competing projects.

The P-R program has distributed excise tax receipts of well over $1.5 billion, matched by more than $500 million by the States. These funds have supported land acquisition, scientific wildlife management, and research to restore depleted populations of many desirable wildlife species. These investments provide outdoor recreation for millions of users. Hunters alone now spend as much as $10 billion a year on hunting-related activities. The sales of supplies and equipment by sports shops, the revenues of motels and restaurants, and the income of local residents who supply a variety of goods and services to hunters and other visitors are important measures of the significance of wildlife recreation in our economy.

While relatively easy to measure, these dollar expenditures by sportsmen generally do not measure dollar benefits to the Nation as a whole. A resident of Minnesota who travels to Wisconsin to hunt may buy a bag of groceries in Wisconsin. However, his trip resulted in one less bag of groceries being sold in Minnesota that week. Since Wisconsin's gain is Minnesota's loss, the Nation's net economic gain from the transaction is zero. Nevertheless, the fact that the hunter willingly undertakes the trip despite the cost of trip-related supplies, equipment, and travel indicates that the benefits he enjoys from the wildlife experience are greater than those costs. Access to well-managed wildlife resources thus increases the value of our national resources by the difference between the hunter's willingness to pay and his actual costs.

There is also a clear national interest that is served by programs that stimulate depressed rural economies. The redistribution of economic activity that results from outdoor recreation expenditures is an important element of national economic policy. In many parts of the country, wildlife-related tourism enables families to preserve traditional ways of life, creates jobs, and generates tax revenues that support provision of essential local services.

Because travel and equipment spending is relatively easy to measure and is a relatively familiar consequence of wildlife management programs, this chapter will focus primarily ôn the difference between users' total willingness to pay and their actual expenses: the net economic benefits of wildlife-related recreation. It is important to emphasize that the latter benefits are different from the benefits of stimulating local and regional economic activity. Investments that give rise to positive net economic benefits actually increase the size of the national econom-

Economists are still developing ways to calculate what people like this deer hunter have contributed to the local, State and national *economies over their many years as active sportsmen and women.*

ic pie, while expenditure effects divide the pie more fairly among regions and groups. Net economic benefits are more difficult to measure than hunters' out-of-pocket expenses. However, researchers have made substantial progress in developing methods of estimating such benefits and in collecting data to support credible benefit calculations.

It is also important to realize that the willingness to pay for wildlife management may be motivated by concerns other than direct user values (actual hunting and/or viewing). Option values (value of preserving the opportunity to hunt or view sometime in the future), and existence values (satisfaction from knowing that wildlife and wildlife habitat are being managed) yield additional benefits. Option and existence values are particularly difficult to measure and some controversy has surrounded attempts to do so. Still, we certainly should keep in mind the potential unmeasured benefits of wildlife management as we focus on more easily estimated user values.

Ways of Measuring User Values

In 1949, the National Park Service hired a young economist named Roy Prewett to explore ways of estimating the economic value of parks. He in turn sent form letters to a number of well-known economists. One of the most famous, Harold Hotelling, was among the few who wrote back. Hotelling suggested that information on the distances that park visitors traveled could provide a measure of net benefits. Suppose the visitor who travels the furthest distance to a particular site incurs $100 in costs. If his maximum willingness to pay is $101, the trip is worth the expense. Taking the $100 maximum observed travel cost as an approximation of the maximum willingness to pay for the site, it follows that a visitor who lives closer to the site and incurs only $25 in travel costs enjoys net benefits equal to the difference between $100 and $25, or $75 per trip. A public investment that provides such an opportunity thus creates $75 worth of enjoyment or well-being that did not exist before.

The basic idea is very simple and enjoys the advantage of relating benefit estimates to users' actual decisions. There are of course a number of practical difficulties in actually implementing the travel cost method. Nevertheless, experience with the technique over the last 35 years has made it a standard tool for estimating user benefits.

More recently, economists have also developed survey techniques called the contingent valuation method to ask people directly how much they would be willing to pay for wildlife management under particular circumstances. Contingent valuation has been used extensively to measure user values. It is also the only known method for estimating the benefits of "just knowing something exists," whether or not the person plans to visit or consume the resource directly. However, applications of this approach to option and existence values are regarded as more experimental. We use both travel-cost and contingent-valuation estimates in what follows.

Public Use Values Related to Pittman-Robertson Projects

The net economic benefits of wildlife-related recreation vary considerably depending on the particular site and activity involved. The reason for this is obvious—visitors differ widely according to their interests, income, skill, knowledge, and other factors that influence the benefits they derive from wildlife recreation. The settings in which they seek recreation also vary widely according to scenic characteristics, abundance of desirable species, time of year, accessibility, crowdedness, and other factors.

To approximate the likely range of user values for each of our examples, we will use estimates derived for the same or similar activities in the same part of the country. Values based on both the travel cost and contingent value methods were obtained from estimates provided by the Division of Program Plans, U.S. Fish and Wildlife Service. The 1980 National Survey of Fishing, Hunting, and Wildlife-Associated Recreation (referred to later as simply the 1980 Survey) provided the necessary data. Use statistics were provided by State wildlife management agencies.

One may never backpack, but preserving the option to do it can be valuable, too.

222

Studies comparing the two techniques indicate that contingent value estimates tend to understate net economic benefits. Contingent value estimates derived from the 1980 Survey tend to be roughly half the estimated value using the travel cost method. To simplify the presentation we generally report the midpoint between the two types of estimates. Actual benefits associated with the given activities may therefore be as much as a third larger or smaller than the reported benefits. Total site benefits are sure to be larger than the reported values because in each case we are measuring only part of the total benefits of wildlife management at each site. All dollar values have been converted to constant 1980 dollars to facilitate comparisons.

Wild Turkeys: Georgia

For various reasons, the total wild turkey population in Georgia had declined to about 10,000 birds by the late 1960's. Because Georgia contains a vast amount of potentially suitable wild turkey habitat, a turkey restoration project was initiated in 1972. The population has now risen to about 150,000 birds. The average annual cost of the current restoration program to date has been $80,000 of which about $48,000 each year has been financed by Pittman-Robertson funds.

Hunters bagged 4,648 turkeys in 1980 during 79,885 hunting days. Using average daily expenditures for food, lodging, and fees for all Georgia hunters, it is estimated that turkey hunters spent about $640,000 in 1980. There are no travel cost method estimates available for wild turkey hunting per se, but turkey is classified as big game in the 1980 Survey. Travel cost method estimates for big game hunting vary from $20 per day to $45 per day in various parts of Georgia where wild turkeys have been restored. The contingent value estimate for deer hunting is about $17 per day for Georgia as a whole. Using a value of $25 per day gives estimated net economic benefits of hunting wild turkeys in Georgia in 1980 of about $2 million.

We should note that wild turkey hunting days increased 133 percent between 1980 and 1984, with economic values increasing accordingly. The relationship of estimated benefits to costs of this program appears to be impressive. The net economic benefits of hunting wild turkeys in Georgia in 1984 alone were more than four times the total cost of the restoration program over a 12-year period.

Waterfowl Hunting: Fountain Grove Wildlife Area, Missouri

Fountain Grove Wildlife Management Area was the first waterfowl management area developed by the Missouri Conservation Commission. Pittman-Robertson funds assisted in the purchase of the initial 3,433 acres in 1947 for $2,300,000 (1980 dollars). As a result of extensive clearing, draining, and cultivation of surrounding watersheds, Fountain Grove gradually evolved into a silting basin for increasingly constricted river flows that significantly degraded the wetlands. In view of declining duck populations and environmental considerations, it was decided in 1960 to develop the area primarily as goose habitat. Acquisitions between 1962 and 1976 expanded the management area to 6,200 acres. Annual management costs currently total about $175,000.

There are significant public uses of the area for a variety of outdoor recreation activities. The area also provides habitat for a number of threatened and endangered species. However, the most important activity continues to be waterfowl hunting. Decline of wetland habitat statewide, together with the rising popularity of hunting for Canada geese, has resulted in increasing public demand for hunting opportunities in north central Missouri. Reservation requests for goose hunting at Fountain Grove increased from 4,097 in 1965 to over 13,000 on 1981. Limited facilities constrained the actual reservations issued to 2,300.

Hunters bagged an average of 1.06 migratory birds per visit during 6,867 hunting days in 1980 and spent about $35,000. Estimated net economic benefits of migratory bird hunting at Fountain Grove in 1980 were $240,000, based on a value per day of $35.

The case of migratory birds illustrates one difficulty in isolating the benefits of a single project from national wildlife management efforts generally. Visitors to Fountain Grove and similar sites enjoy the benefits of wildlife management projects in distant locations that have provided habitat and food for migratory populations. Some of the benefits of investments at Fountain Grove really belong to other projects, but some of the costs at Fountain Grove are offset as well by benefits at other sites.

Big Game Hunting: Crex Meadows Wildlife Area, Wisconsin

Crex Meadows is located only 90 minutes from the Twin Cities in Minnesota, from which most of the visitors come. Large-scale commercial drainage and agricultural development in the 1890's changed the ecology of the area from a productive wet prairie to a dry sedge marsh. Nesting and migrant waterfowl use declined. As a result of wildlife management programs, dikes now flood 11,000 acres of marsh. Extensive prescribed burning is conducted annually to improve and maintain prairie habitat. Over 20,000 migrating ducks and geese now use the area. Sandhill cranes and prairie-chickens have been re-established in the area. A total of 245 species of birds have been observed in Crex Meadows, including a number of threatened and endangered species.

Almost 90 percent of the prairie and marshland has been purchased, beginning in 1945. The Pittman-Robertson share of average annual cost of acquisitions, habitat development, maintenance, and general operations has been about $765,000. The State matches these expenditures with an additional 25 percent.

Public use at Crex Meadows in 1980 totaled about 116,000 visits. Twenty percent of annual visits to Crex Meadows are for the purpose of gun and bow hunting of big game, including deer, bear, and predators. These visitors spent about $300,000 in trip-related expenditures. Estimated net economic benefits of big game hunting in 1980 were about $920,000 based on a value per day of $30. This value is about equal to average annual cost, indicating that benefits generated by only 20 percent of the total use are sufficient to offset costs.

Fishing and Nonconsumptive Uses:
Skagit Habitat Management Area, Washington

The Skagit Habitat Management Area is located on the Skagit Bay estuary and consists of over 12,000 acres, the majority of which is estuarine marsh. Six hundred acres of farmland are utilized to provide food for wintering waterfowl and other wildlife. Skagit supports a wide diversity of species, including as many as 200 species of birds. The estuary is a primary wintering area for migratory waterfowl of the Pacific Flyway.

The major recreation uses of the area include hunting, fishing, clam digging, bird watching, hiking, photography, canoeing, and other forms of wildlife-related outdoor recreation. Because of its proximity to Seattle and other major

224

Wildlife photography is another use of P-R assisted Wildlife Management Areas whose economic importance is growing, but difficult to measure.

Robert J. Shallenberger, U.S. Fish and Wildlife Service

population centers, the Skagit has become one of the more important publicly owned wildlife areas in Washington State, with 94,600 use days in 1981.

Pittman-Robertson funds provided $122,000 for original acquisitions in the 1950's as well as supporting a number of development projects over the years. Currently, 75 percent of operation and maintenance costs are funded by P-R money, amounting to about $75,000 per year.

Fishing values have been estimated from the 1980 Survey. Public use for this activity was 9,750 fishing days with related visitor expenditures of $78,000. Estimated net economic benefits of trout fishing are $170,000 based on a value per day of $18. Non-consumptive use of the Skagit was nearly 41,000 in 1980. Unfortunately, daily expenditures for non-consumptive activities are unavailable. If we assume the same average expenditure as for sportsmen in Washington, total expenditures in 1980 would total $408,000. It is also not possible to estimate net economic benefits of non-consumptive uses from the 1980 Survey. However, estimates of net economic benefits have been reported using various methods and data from various regions for picnicking between $8 and $16 per day and for hiking of between $10 and $28 per day. Taking $12 per day as a representative value would yield net economic benefits of $490,000. Estimated net economic benefits of fishing and non-consumptive use on the Skagit thus totaled $660,000 in 1980.

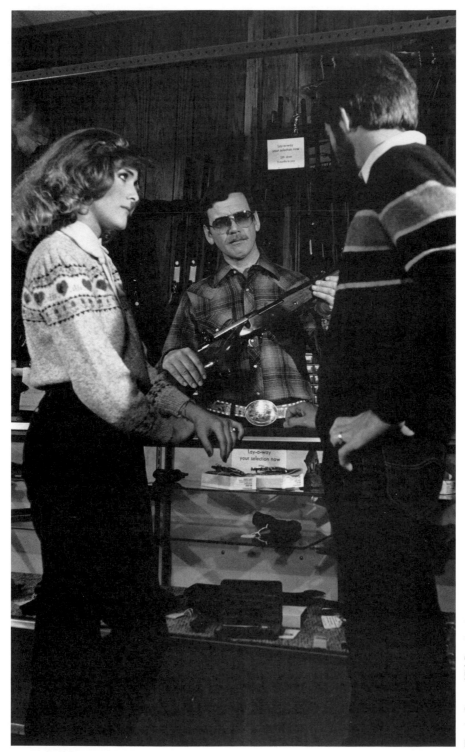

"Hunters alone now spend as much as $10 billion a year on hunting-related activities."

226

Conclusions

In a recent auction for Nevada desert bighorn sheep tags, a Texas hunter bid $67,500 for the opportunity to hunt this rare and elusive animal. The unusually high price is partly due to the fact that only a small number of tags is available to out-of-State residents, combined with the wealth and zeal of that individual. Even so, the average net economic benefits per tag during the 1984 hunting season were estimated at $1,638.

None of the four examples discussed in this chapter have the dramatic economic values of desert bighorn sheep. Our examples were selected to represent typical wildlife management programs rather than to highlight unusually dramatic success stories. Nevertheless, because of the large number of visitors to these sites, the total annual benefits of wildlife-related recreation are quite large relative to costs in each case. Remember also that we have quantified only part of the public use benefits in each area, and have done nothing with option and existence values. Some studies have estimated these non-user values at roughly twice the size of user values. If this is so, then our traditional emphasis on hunting-related expenditures and user values may have led to gross understatements of the actual value of wildlife resources to the Nation.

It is safe to conclude that the net economic benefits of Pittman-Robertson expenditures are generally very large relative to the modest public investments. Furthermore, most of these projects are located in rural areas of the country with relatively depressed local economies, so that expenditures of visitors to these areas also improves the distribution of economic activity in the Nation as a whole.

John Krutilla's 20-year-old classic article, *Conservation Reconsidered,* did much to revive the interest of economists in natural resource problems. He concluded that

> *there is a need to recognize, and make provision for, the widest range of outdoor recreation tastes, just as a well-functioning market would do. We need a policy and a mechanism to ensure that all natural areas peculiarly suited for specializd recreation uses receive consideration for such uses. A policy of this kind would be consistent both with maintaining the greatest biological diversity for scientific research and educational purposes and with providing the widest choice for consumers of outdoor recreation.*

The Pittman-Robertson program is a major component of such a policy. The program has produced tangible and measurable benefits that have made a significant and continuing contribution to the well-being of all Americans.

Observing wildlife is a major objective of family camping trips.

Nongame wildlife like these Hawaiian seabirds, beneficiaries of P-R projects, provide photographers and many other nonhunters with enjoyable outdoor recreation.

Restoring Nongame Wildlife

by John M. Anderson

The year was 1952. Around the kitchen table of the old Winous Point Shooting Club in Ohio, four duck hunters, including a wildlife biologist, had their boots off, their bellies full, and were discussing the present, past and future of wildlife management. The biologist made the comment, "I work for the Division of Wildlife, not the Division of Ducks, Deer and Pheasants. Here on Winous Point, you have savannah sparrows nesting in the meadows, prothonotary warblers in the swamp, bald eagles nesting on Elm Island and Graveyard Island, least bitterns in the cattails. The State over-protects our pheasants, grouse and squirrels, and we advise you as to how you can produce more of them. But we don't do anything for nongame birds. And yet, they're not tame, so they must be wildlife, and should get our attention."

From the technical standpoint, my young friend over-simplified the situation. For in 1951, the State of Ohio, using Pittman-Robertson funds, had purchased the privately-owned Magee Marsh, on Lake Erie. Since then it has been managed as a waterfowl research station, State park, and public hunting area. Although these Federal Aid funds were generated by an excise tax on sporting arms and ammunition, to which the non-hunting public contributed not one dime, the beautiful Magee Marsh soon became a favorite spot for birders, photographers, picnickers, and other non-hunters from near and far. The reason? It provided optimum habitat for nongame species and outdoor recreation.

A colony of black-crowned night herons was an immediate attraction. On the beach in an ancient cottonwood, a bald eagle's nest was visible from a radius of 2 miles; it had been there as long as anyone could remember. Nesting prothonotary and yellow warblers, indigo buntings, tree swallows, Baltimore orioles and house wrens, plus waves of migrants, kept the spring birders all a-twitter.

It soon became obvious that providing public access to superb habitat for these nongame species was a two-edged sword. Some visitors were not content to view the incubating eagles at long-lens distances. And because a closeup of an eagle in flight was more spectacular, pounding on the trunk of the old cottonwood provided a view of a bird most residents of Detroit, Toledo and Cleveland had seldom, if ever, seen. By 1954, the eagle nest was abandoned. It still is.

This sad tale is not intended as a blanket indictment of wildlife photographers and birders. The vast majority of them are intent upon providing top quality habitat at all times for all wildlife. Unfortunately, the relatively few slob hunters have their counterparts among the over-zealous wildlife photographers and birders.

Mr. Anderson has been Director of the National Audubon Society's Wildlife Sanctuary Department since 1966. He is the author of a book, The Changing World of Birds, *has published articles in technical journals, and writes a weekly newspaper column dealing with ecology.*

Breathes there a game manager with soul so dead, who not unto himself has said, "I know enough to manage game; but people are a different story!"

The so-called game manager and nongame manager are members of the same profession: wildlife management. I trust it is unnecessary to remind professional wildlife managers that such is the case. On the other hand, it is hardly safe to assume that either the hunting or the non-hunting public see themselves— and the wildlife that draws them from their beds before daylight—as belonging to the same plant-animal community, subject to the same natural laws of biology and economics.

One of the earliest and greatest American wildlife observers, John Muir, put it this way: "When you try to pick anything out of the universe, you find it hitched to everything else." That being the case, we cannot save game species from the drainage ditch and bulldozer without providing suitable living space for nongame. A marsh that is ideal for mallards and muskrats produces a myriad of critters which the nimrod and trapper will not pursue. By the same token, when the Ohio Division of Wildlife purchased the Magee Marsh with hunters' tax dollars, the number of non-hunters who benefited far exceeded the sportsmen. And so, by 1952, albeit unintentionally, the State had already initiated a nongame program for warblers, grebes, wading birds, silky dogwood, and prairie dock through habitat preservation.

In The Beginning . . .

For some time after the Federal Aid in Wildlife Restoration Act was in effect, State wildlife administrators quite understandably spent most of their Federal and matching State funds on game species. If a landowner's income is derived from timber, corn, or pheasants, and not from roseate spoonbills or showy lady-slippers, the landowner will naturally spend his money on those crops that produce his income.

Furthermore, there were limits to the funding provided by the Pittman-Robertson Act and other limits imposed by various State legislatures, which placed some constraints on the amounts that could be spent directly for nongame wildlife. But my young colleague of 1952 was not alone in his realization that there was a lot of wildlife out there that could benefit from the sale of all those guns and shells without getting shot at. Professional wildlife managers were quick to see that if they couldn't stop subsidized wetland drainage, no restrictions—or even a complete moratorium on duck hunting—were going to save waterfowl. The same can be said for aquatic nongame species.

Pittman-Robertson funds, used largely for preservation and restoration of wetlands in those early days, laid the foundation for waterfowl conservation, nongame and endangered species management, and conservation education.

In 1975, some 36 States spent a total of $176,426,734 for all wildlife management, research and enforcement. Of that total, $3,356,038 were spent on nongame programs, in which Federal Aid funds played an important part. Not a large percentage, but it was a clear sign that times were changing fast. Direct as well as indirect benefits to nongame species, and to non-hunters as well, have continued to grow in both relative and absolute terms ever since. By the mid-1980's, one in every ten projects undertaken with P-R funding was being designed to benefit nongame, and less measurable spinoff benefits to nongame were being realized from several of the other nine. Considering that P-R funds come entirely from aficionados of the shooting sports, it was an impressive statistic. Yet it wasn't, and still isn't, nearly enough to ensure a decent future for nongame wildlife.

Where Are the Votes?

Wildlife managers should realize that they must acquire enough political clout to influence those who decide whether a marsh, old-growth forest, or any other habitat will or will not be destroyed. We seem to have two choices: Acquire political clout or take up golf and wind surfing. So the wildlife manager, regardless of the species he deals with, needs all the help he can get; not only from other wildlife managers, but from those millions of hunters, birders, hikers, and picnickers who spend leisure time and dollars outdoors.

As our human population becomes more and more urbanized, there is less and less chance that Uncle Charlie will teach Johnnie how to trap a muskrat, call a turkey gobbler, or care for a fowling piece. In suburbia, Johnnie is more apt to learn to identify blue-jays and white-breasted nuthatches at the birdfeeder than to learn how far to lead a mallard in the marsh. I am not saying this is as it should be; it's how it is. And wildlife managers will do well to take due note of same, because it has a direct bearing on our efforts to provide habitat and protection for wildlife of all kinds.

He Who Dances...

It is safe to say there is not a wildlife management area, be it State, Federal or privately owned, that has escaped the attention of those who would like to see changes in its use so they could make money on it. As condominiums and golf courses spread from Miami Beach to Chesapeake Bay, economic pressure on wildlife habitat increases steadily. At the Federal level, the competition for our tax dollars is fairly obvious. The entire annual budget for the U.S. Fish and Wildlife Service would hardly run the Department of Defense for one-half a day.

Magee Marsh on Lake Erie was acquired by Ohio with P-R assistance, primarily for water-fowl hunters, but is also heavily used by birders, picnickers, camera fans and other non-hunters. It contains excellent habitat for nongame species.

231

So far, the Federal Aid in Wildlife Restoration Act has withstood every attempt by the Office of Management and Budget to divert its funds. It follows that not much in the way of general funds can be expected to be appropriated for wildlife restoration. Therefore, an excise tax similar to the P-R tax on guns and shells, but levied on the sale of bird feed, bird houses, bird identification books, binoculars, off-road vehicles, backpacking and camping equipment, deserves serious consideration. User fees on Federal lands, as well as State outdoor recreation lands, are another potential source of funds for wildlife management. Other possible sources include motorhomes, Federal timber and firewood sales, skis and equipment, and recreational diving equipment.

The Fish and Wildlife Conservation Act of 1980 (Forsythe-Chafee Act) authorized the "Feds" to provide money to the States for wildlife, especially nongame. The Act also instructed the USFWS to study various sources of revenue. Although Section 11 of the Act authorized an appropriation of $5 million a year for four years, no money was appropriated. Which gives us a clue as to what we are up against.

Nongame wildlifers in search of the long green will do well to study *Potential Funding Sources to Implement the Fish and Wildlife Conservation Act of 1980,* Biological Report 85(5), FWS. While estimates are as yet quite rough, the study does provide a fair working knowledge of potential revenue from a 5 or 10 percent Federal excise tax on bird seed, bird houses, wildlife identification books, and outdoor recreation equipment.

In 1980, annual expenditures for recreational activities relating to nongame wildlife were estimated at more than $1 billion. Direct expenditures estimated at $500 million included bird seed, bird houses, feeders, binoculars, field guides and natural history books. In 1982, estimates of expenditures for all outdoor recreation exceeded $50 billion. From these figures a rough estimate of the potential income from a tax on such sources can be made.

On the current American business scene, there is a relatively new, but healthy, industry. Sales of bird feed bring in ready cash to retail outlets, to National Audubon chapters, and to the sunflower and corn farmers. Furthermore, in Minnesota, for example, stores are sprouting that deal entirely in bird-related merchandise. But is the scarlet tanager, the oven bird, or the wood thrush going to be around if and when the hardwood forests are gone? What happens to the prothonotary warbler when the swamp forest disappears? Upland sandpipers have little to fear from the mighty nimrod, yet their beautiful song is seldom heard in spring except on managed grasslands such as the Audubon Society's wildlife sanctuary at Alkali Lake in North Dakota, or on suitable State and Federal habitat such as Arrowwood National Wildlife Refuge, or Minnesota's Buffalo River State Park.

Can the merchants stop the chainsaws, gangplows and bulldozers without help from the birders? Suffice it to say that an industry based on birds is on pretty shaky ground unless the habitat for birds has a solid base.

For the well-being of all concerned, the birder and bird-oriented businessman must see to it that the nongame and endangered species managers have sufficient funds to maintain their priceless commodities. If P-R funds are stretched to the limit, supplementary sources must be considered.

Historically, nongame and endangered species programs have been hampered by lack of reliable funds. And while the accomplishments in this field through the use of Pittman-Robertson funds have been substantial, the search for income from other sources is never-ending. On a nationwide basis, about 77 percent of the money for State fish and wildlife agencies comes directly from hunters, fishermen, and trappers. This is not because the birders, botanists, and

Serious wildlife watching is an increasingly popular form of outdoor recreation. P-R projects have aided States in acquiring prime areas to help restore nongame wildlife.

other nongame enthusiasts are unwilling to pay their share. In fact, a poll by the Eagleton Institute in New Jersey in 1980 showed that Garden Staters overwhelmingly supported nongame and endangered species work and that 76 percent would contribute funds for it.

If the situation in New Jersey is representative of other States, then we obviously need a mechanism whereby the nongame enthusiasts can put their money to work. In addition to possible excise taxes discussed above, we can profit from a look at other ways and means.

Checkoff Is Chancy

In 1977, the Colorado Division of Wildlife hit upon an ingenious scheme for raising money earmarked for nongame and endangered species. Nowadays it is commonly referred to as the income tax checkoff. By adding a line to the State income tax return form, taxpayers eligible for a refund are encouraged to donate part of that refund to be used specifically for nongame and endangered species. In 1978, Colorado received $338,264 from this source. In 1979, it amounted to $511,405; in the third year, $664,005. It peaked in 1981 at $746,506. Since then it has gradually declined. The initial success of the checkoff in Colorado quickly caught the attention of other States. By 1983 the checkoff was alive and well in 31 States, and raised over $6.5 million. In 1984, this program brought in about $9 million.

By 1985, however, the checkoff had also come to the attention of special interests ranging from animals rights to prevention of child abuse. It can be argued that, unlike wildlife, such causes do not represent a public trust—a natural resource to be passed on, more or less intact—to future generations. We could argue that wildlife is the collective property of all the people and therefore entitled to special consideration at the State and Federal level.

233

That argument is logical and biologically right. But in the real world of people and politics, biological truth is seldom a powerful weapon. In the State Capitol, it is apt to fall on deaf ears because organizations for the prevention of cruelty to baby seals and baby humans, rape, cancer, and heart attack, will have more political appeal than "dickey-birds and bats."

But a dash of realistic cynicism should not become an overdose of pessimism. On the contrary. Several States have done an excellent analysis of how the checkoff system works, its strong points and weak points.

In Minnesota, for example, checkoff revenue of $476,580 in 1981 grew each year to reach about $700,000 in 1984. But between 1981-83, the nongame wildlife program experienced four legislative attempts to end the checkoff or to divert money from it. The good news is that massive citizen response was generated by news stories written by wildlife's allies in the media. Interested legislators also came to the rescue. Which shows that Nongame Supervisor Carroll Henderson, and his staff, had done an outstanding job of getting the citizenry involved right from the start of the program.

According to Henderson, it pays to identify your various interest groups, get them involved so the nongame program becomes "their" program, and keep them informed. Included are bird clubs, women's clubs, wildlife rehabilitators and other State and Federal resource agencies. By no means should you overlook hunters, fishermen, archers, trappers, sportsmen's clubs and even land developers. This may sound like mixing good scotch with ginger ale, but these groups have a common ground; all stand to benefit from the nongame program.

The osprey, or fish hawk, disappeared from large parts of the country several decades ago. It has been restored to many States, often with P-R help.

Charles C. Allin, Rhode Island Department of Environmental Management

Black-tailed prairie dog, like this specimen, has been the object of a P-R project in North Dakota.

235

The Minnesota Trappers Association, the Minnesota Audubon Council, and the Raptor Research & Rehabilitation program at the University joined hands and persuaded the Wildlife Commission to prohibit open-bait trap sets. This reduced the accidental injury to hawks and eagles, and helped the trappers avoid the snapping jaws of the anti-trappers. The Willmar Sportsmen's Club, St. Paul Audubon Society, and Minnesota State Archery Association each donated $600 to help pay for reintroduction of river otters on the Minnesota River. With the cooperation of such diverse interests, funds for nongame wildlife, while not guaranteed, are far more secure.

The Show-Me State Shows Us

In Missouri, money matters took a different turn. In 1976, the people approved a State constitutional amendment to levy on themselves a ⅛ of 1 percent sales tax, to be earmarked for a broad-based program known as "Design for Conservation". They could hardly have done themselves a greater favor.

In its fourth year of operation, the tax contributed about $21 million to the Department of Conservation budget. To show for it, Missouri by 1985 had acquired 110,000 acres, including wildlife areas, State forests, community lakes, stream access points, bat caves, virgin prairies, natural sloughs and marshes, eagle roosts, and spring branches. Many of these are the best remaining examples of pre-settlement community types and are managed as natural areas. According to Jim Wilson, Endangered Species Coordinator, public services have been expanded in every part of the conservation program. With assistance from several P-R projects, he estimates about $2 million annually is spent for nongame, including land acquisition.

Biologists and Bucks

Several States in which Pittman-Robertson funds are inadequate for essential research and management have considered other methods to help finance nongame and endangered species programs.

In Texas, which does not impose an income tax, the Audubon Council proposed a voluntary program based on the sale of decals or stamps, along with royalties from the sale of wildlife art. The proposed legislation, introduced in 1983, was modeled after the successful Texas waterfowl program. Audubonners lobbied for it. Legislators were convinced that lots of people cared about nongame wildlife, and passed the bill. The artists paid entry fees amounting to $250,000 in return for royalties on the sale of their works. The sale of stamps and decals netted about $12,000. The Lone Star Staters claim this is a good start, and are thinking of new ways to rope recalcitrant legislators.

According to Tom Owens, Washington Department of Game, the sale of personalized auto tags raised $500,000 for nongame in 1981.

No matter from whence cometh the money, wildlife managers must appeal to those who hold the purse strings. For such an appeal to be effective, an analysis of the public we are trying to reach is necessary. There is abundant evidence that those outdoorsmen and women who do not hunt or fish are in the majority. And many of them do not know what we mean by "game" and "nongame". Nevertheless, as the study in New Jersey showed, they are more than willing to contribute to management of these species if given a convenient way of doing so.

Unfortunately, some of these non-hunting outdoorsmen and women appear to be ignorant of the contribution of Pittman-Robertson funds. The birder who

*Evening grosbeaks at a bird feeder. Would this
be a feasible source of revenue for nongame
wildlife?*

visits a wildlife management area in spring may resent the presence of hunters in
the area in the fall. Ohio's Magee Marsh Wildlife Area and the Sportsmen's
Migratory Bird Center were built entirely with P-R funds. One visitor who
apparently enjoyed the marsh, nature trails and museum displays signed the
visitor's register and offered the following comment: "Send me any free literature, and TAKE THE SHOTGUN SHELLS OUT OF THE BIRD DISPLAY. THEY
DON'T BELONG THERE!!"

It is to the credit of Manager Karl Bednarik that he patiently explained that
the Magee Marsh had been a famous wildfowling area for 100 years. The antique
duckboats, decoys and guns had been donated by neighboring duck clubs. He
wrote, "The display of avian wildlife is for both hunters and non-hunters in a
facility funded by sportsmen . . . It is apparent that many of our visitors neither
hunt nor fish. Fine. The license-buying sportsmen have never opposed songbird
displays, bird walks led by our naturalist, maintenance of the Bird Trail and other
non-hunting, nature-oriented functions here. Conversely, some birders take
umbrage over the fact that waterfowl hunting is an annual operation here and
that duck hunting artifacts are promininently displayed. I have enclosed the
literature you requested. While there is no charge, I respectfully wish to point
out that all Division of Wildlife publications costs are borne by license-buying
hunters and fishermen.

"I hope you will again visit the Sportsmen's Migratory Bird Center and other
wildlife areas. You certainly are most welcome."

I suspect this anecdote has been, and will be, repeated many times in many States.

In the early years of Federal Aid in Wildlife Restoration, research naturally focused on game, or "economically important" species. For some 60 years, research on endangered species such as whooping cranes, Everglade kites, ivory-billed woodpeckers, California condors, and roseate spoonbills was supported almost entirely by the National Audubon Society. Fortunately, this situation is changing rapidly. That the public is spending millions of dollars annually to see and hear whooping cranes, spotted owls, alligators, and Atlantic puffins has attracted the attention of the tourist industry and other businesses. The attention of the politician naturally follows. Hence, the Endangered Species Act of 1973 and the Fish and Wildlife Conservation Act of 1980 were passed.

Coming of Age

The wildlife management profession appears to be recognizing this state of affairs. In the prestigious *Journal of Wildlife Management,* Volume 49, 1985, 46 or 21.4 percent of the research reports were devoted to nongame and endangered species.

In 1985, 38 of the 50 States were spending Federal Aid funds for research on nongame and endangered species. Bald eagles were being studied in 12 States, golden eagles in 1. Peregrine falcons were receiving attention in 9 States. Kansas, Nebraska, New Mexico and Texas were working on whooping cranes. Ospreys drew attention in Delaware, Maryland, Maine and Virginia. Research on least terns went on in 5 States.

Of the mammals, gray bats were studied in 1985 in Kansas and Missouri, Indiana bats in Missouri, New York and West Virginia, while Arkansas was researching various endemic bat species. New Mexico, New York, Texas, Kansas and Arizona were working on several endangered and small nongame mammals. Manatees were of concern in Florida. Florida and Georgia were checking on panthers. Montana and Wisconsin were studying wolf populations.

As the backlog of necessary information and literature evolves, management techniques and implementation are sure to follow. Translation of research findings from the file cabinet to actual management out there on the land is usually a slow process, involving selling the program to the public and the administration. There are, however, several outstanding success stories. For example, the greater prairie-chicken is listed as a State endangered species in Colorado. On the Tamarack State Wildlife Area, Wilbur Boldt, Federal Aid Coordinator, reports prescribed burning and seeding with native grasses on about 800 acres of grassland. Watering facilities specifically for the prairie-chicken were developed. Work began three years before reintroduction of the birds in 1983, and by 1985 there were verified reports of them booming and nesting. Apparently this is a case of an endangered species becoming a nongame species, and eventually perhaps a game species.

In Wisconsin, Pittman-Robertson funds support not only extensive research and sound management of prairie-chickens; they play the key role in providing nesting platforms for herons, cormorants, and ospreys, research and habitat for raptors, timber wolves, barn owls, sandhill cranes, pine martens, fishers shorebirds, terns, and loggerhead shrikes.

Mississippi uses Pittman-Robertson funds for prescribed burning to help maintain habitat for the rare Bachman's sparrow and red-cockaded woodpecker. Although P-R legally may be used only for birds and mammals, these burns also enhance endangered gopher tortoise habitat, whose burrows also provide shel-

Nesting platforms for cormorants have been built in Wisconsin using P-R funds.

ter for threatened species including the indigo snake, black pine snake, and dusky gopher frog.

Management of nongame and endangered species in New Mexico depends heavily on Pittman-Robertson funds. Beneficiaries include the Mississippi kite, white-tailed ptarmigan, ground dove, gray wolf, black-footed ferret, and desert bighorn sheep. The outstanding *Handbook of Species Endangered in New Mexico* provides management guidelines for endangered birds, mammals, reptiles and invertebrates.

Pittman-Robertson funds have contributed about 35 percent of New York's Endangered Species Program effort, which includes bald eagle and peregrine falcon restoration.

In North Dakota, two black-tailed prairie dog colonies are re-established thanks to Pittman-Robertson.

The 8,000-acre Sauvie Island, about 20 minutes from downtown Portland, Oregon, is a favorite with duck hunters and a prime area for birders every month of the year.

In Rhode Island, P-R funds helped purchase 16,818 acres encompassing a wading bird rookery, preserved nesting sites for least terns, provided nest boxes for bluebirds and barn owls, platforms for ospreys, and an impoundment in Great Swamp for wading birds, marsh hawks and other wetland species.

Pittman-Robertson funds were put to good use in another case, involving least terns and black skimmers near Rockport, Texas. Historically, both species nested along the central Texas Coast, but were almost completely displaced by housing developments. With development come dogs and beach buggies, and the disappearance of birds that require undisturbed stretches of bare beaches.

In 1977-78, according to Bruce Thompson, the Texas Parks and Wildlife Department began working wth interested local residents and members of the National Audubon Society to develop a plan for managing the colony and resolving the conflict. Plans were made for a shell nesting pad on Key Allegro Isle. Parker Brothers of Houston provided 250 cubic yards of fine shell, Houston Oil and Mineral Company provided a barge, towboat, backhoe and coordinating personnel. Vermilion Construction Company provided a crane. A Girl Scout troop from Austin helped the Audubon biologist and Texas Parks and Wildlife personnel in final spreading of the shell.

It took a lot of signs, cables, and cooperation from the Navigation District authorities to finally control the vehicles, waterskiiers, dogs, and juvenile delinquents. But by 1985, over 100 pairs of least terns nested successfully, along with about 80 pairs of black skimmers, and the public is quietly proud of "their" birds.

If space permitted, there are equally encouraging stories around the country that could and should be recorded.

In 1982, the Nongame Wildlife Association became a reality under the umbrella of the International Association of Fish and Wildlife Agencies. We might summarize the situation as follows:

Whereas in the 1940's, nongame management played the role of Poor Little Match Girl, peeking through the window at the rich folks, this formerly shy maiden is coming of age, with enough sex appeal to be invited to cocktail and dinner parties.

What started with hunters' license fees and P-R funds led inevitably to more awareness of nongame wildlife's needs and to independent State action. Many States now have special nongame accounts—modest as yet, but helpful, and likely harbingers of more to come. And now we hear wildlife agencies agreeing with that young Ohio biologist, "We are the Division of Wildlife, not the Division of Ducks, Deer and Pheasants".

Ding Darling, the great conservationist cartoonist, struck this chord in the 1930's, still timely for friends of nongame wildlife.

Hawaiian gallinule, prominent in Polynesian legend, has suffered from heavy loss of wetlands.

The Challenge of Islands

by E. Alison Kay

The biological communities of oceanic islands evolved in isolation from those of the continents and from one another. No two island assemblages of plant and animal life are alike, but all of them share one great problem in common: they have been invaded and often overrun by animals, plants and people from somewhere else.

The forces of change thus set in motion on islands centuries ago have led in our time to many actual and threatened extinctions. Biologists are faced with the special challenges of learning a great deal about island ecologies with limited funds in a short period of time, and of applying the lessons fast enough to help.

Restoring wildlife in an island environment poses many questions: Can both native species and the generally more adaptable imports coexist? If so, where and how? What human activities may need to be curtailed to ensure the survival of native communities? Which strategies of wildlife management will work on a particular island; which strategies won't?

The Pittman-Robertson program began its work in an era of traditional attitudes and limited knowledge. It was responsible for certain imports of game species from around the world into United States island territories,where some found their own niches while others failed. Managed game on some islands still includes free-running "wild" cattle, pigs, sheep and goats which have been hunted at least since the early 1800's. Pittman-Robertson funds also have been used effectively to learn about and to help native non-game species, including some which are endangered. What started out as a fairly straightforward effort to improve hunting opportunities has evolved with time into a far more intricate and difficult problem: the survival of species.

The Fragility of Islands

Charles Darwin recognized both the significance of the biological cargoes of islands and their fragility. The similarities and differences between the Cape Verde Islands of the Atlantic and the Galapagos Islands of the Pacific, and the differences among the islands of those archipelagoes which he noted with such care, led him to his theory of evolution by natural selection. His observation that introduced (non-native) species of plants and animals were often more successful than indigenous ones showed him that adapations were not perfect.

Just how fragile island ecosystems are is perhaps no better told than in the story of Laysan, the largest of the Northwestern Islands of the Hawaiian archipelago. Laysan, about 1.4 square miles in area, was in 1857 a low sand island with beach grass, a half dozen small palm trees, some seals and turtles—and literally covered with sea birds, perhaps as many as 800,000. By 1891, 27 varieties of plants, five kinds of land birds, and several species of insects had been recorded,

---

Dr. Kay, Professor of Zoology at the University of Hawaii, has spent nearly 30 years studying the natural history of Pacific islands. She has taught a course in Hawaiian Islands natural history for nearly 15 of those years, edited a book on the subject, and written books and 45 professional papers on natural history and on marine mollusks, a subject of special interest to her.

in addition to the sea birds, seals and turtles. It was a remarkable biological assemblage: four of the plants and all five land birds were endemic to the island—not found anywhere else.

In 1891, guano digging operations began, and in a dozen years more than 100 tons of guano had been hauled by narrow-gauge rail to ships sailing for Honolulu. By 1903, the guano deposits were depleted and the business was abandoned. Rabbits imported by the manager were, however, left behind and over the years they increased in numbers. In 1913, the rabbits were described as swarming by the thousands and exterminating "first one species of plant then another . . ." In 1923, visitors to Laysan found "on every hand . . . a barren waste of sand," a few scrubby plants, perhaps 100 each of Laysan finches and Laysan ducks, and fewer than 30,000 sea birds.

In less than 35 years, man and his imports had resulted in the destruction of two endemic plant species, nine native plant species (species which had arrived on the island without the aid of man), three endemic land birds, and a number of endemic insects. The populations of the finches, ducks, and seabirds were greatly depleted. Elimination of the remaining 150 rabbits and artificial planting of grasses on the island started the island toward recovery. Today Laysan is re-vegetated, the duck population is about 1,000, there may be as many as 10,000 finches on the island, and the seabird population is estimated at about 500,000. The resilience of the animals and plants which survived is remarkable. But the animal and plant species which disappeared are gone forever from the earth.

The story of Laysan is extreme. Yet all islands, whether they be Guam and the Northern Marianas in the Pacific or Puerto Rico and the Virgin Islands in the Caribbean, are subject to pressures such as those which impinged on Laysan. A more detailed picture of the biological significance of islands and of the effects of man on island ecosystems is to be found in the story of other islands in the Hawaiian archipelago.

Evolution—Hawaiian Style

Because Hawaii is separated from two continents and other islands by thousands of miles of Pacific Ocean, the ancestors of its animals and plants had to be carried by wind and sea to take root among the islands of the Hawaiian archipelago. The first colonists may have been the 275 plant species, 15 birds, 250 insects, and 22 snails which biologists estimate were necessary to found the populations which gave rise to the native biota. That community of life consists of approximately 1,000 species of higher plants, 7,000 to 8,000 insects, 1,000 land mollusks, 100 birds, four or five freshwater fish, one bat and one seal. More than 95 percent of these animals and plants are endemic, found nowhere else in the world.

Most of these original immigrants seem to have come from elsewhere in the Pacific to the south and west of Hawaii. What arrived was only a small part of the pool of animals and plants which occur to the west, and only those organisms which could make the long journey arrived—generally plants with small, readily dispersed seeds, small insects and small snails. Thus among the immigrants there were no bamboos and no hoofed mammals. Once in the islands, isolation—from other land masses, between islands, and on islands with deep valleys, mountain peaks and lava flows—permitted evolution at a relatively rapid rate. The result is a native biota without either mechanical or sensory defenses against predators, and unable to adapt to very rapidly changing habitats. Established in the canopies of rain forests, on the leaves of trees, in lava tubes, on the snowclad slopes of

Laysan, devastated by exploitation and swarms of imported rabbits years ago, again is home to hundreds of thousands of seabirds, including these native albatrosses.

Mauna Kea, in steam fumeroles of the volcanoes, in the water table underlying the basalt, in kipukas (vegetated islands on lava flows), and along the shoreline, the Hawaiian biota is one of the most extraordinary in the world.

Each of the islands is unique, with its own snails, its own insects, its own birds and its own plants. On Oahu, more than 40 species of the jewel-like snail genus *Achatinella* evolved; on Maui and Molokai the tree snails with different colors, patterns and shapes are in different genera (groups of species and subspecies). The plant called silversword is found only on Hawaii and Maui, the greensword on Maui, and yet another genus on Kauai. On Kauai, there are giant land snails and on Nihoa monster crickets. More than 600 distinct species of drosophilid flies occur in Hawaii; studies of their chromosomes, behavior and ecology are showing the way that species may have evolved on all the islands. The Northwestern Islands are far simpler in terms of habitat than are the main islands, but make up for their lack of species numbers with density; more than 10 million seabirds, representing 22 species, nest on less than seven square miles of land.

The Influence of Man

Hawaii's first human settlers arrived by canoe more than a thousand years ago. The immigrant Polynesians settled in an unfamiliar land with plants and animals different from those which they knew in their homeland. They brought with them chickens, pigs, and dogs, and such useful plants such as the coconut, taro, breadfruit, sugar cane, kukui and banana. With the aid of fire and the digging stick, the land was cleared and crops were planted. Vast acres of valley floor were covered with taro, and hillsides were terraced with sweet potato and banana. The archeologists tell us that there is scarcely an area in the lowlands with more than about eight inches of annual rainfall that does not yield evidence of Polynesian agricultural use. Indeed, by the time Captain James Cook arrived in Hawaii in January 1778, the lowland scene had been shaped to support an estimated population of 200,000 Hawaiians—an average of 22 per square mile in the lowland areas on the eight main islands.

The Cook voyage initiated yet another wave of colonization, a wave which continues to roll over the islands. Cook left on Niihau a "Ram goat and two Ewes, a Boar and Sow pig of the English breed, and the seeds of Millons (melons), Pumpkins and onions." Vancouver in 1794 left a "young bull calf nearly full grown, two fine cows, and two very fine bull calves, all in high condition" on Hawaii. The cattle, protected by a king's *kapu* (tabu), multiplied so rapidly that within the next 30 years "immense herds" were described as roaming the slopes of Mauna Kea and Mauna Loa. Horses arrived by ship in 1803. Wild turkeys came from Chile in 1815. Chinese ring-necked pheasants and California valley quail were brought in by 1865. Axis deer were a gift to King Kamehameha V in 1868. The mongoose was brought in to control rats in the sugar cane fields in 1883, and the carnivorous snail, *Euglandina,* was introduced to control the giant African snail, another import, in 1955-56. Mouflon, pronghorn antelope and black-tailed deer were introduced for recreational hunting between 1954 and 1961. Bulbuls, imported tropical birds, may have escaped from cages into the wild about 1965.

The 200 years since Cook's arrival in the Hawaiian Island have been marked by continuing change. Westerners and immigrant labor arrived to plant and work sugar cane plantations and ranches. The new waves of immigrants introduced potentiallly useful plants, and brought with them accidentally a host of injurious weeds and insects. Rice paddies replaced taro patches in the 19th Century, and shopping centers and housing developments have in turn replaced rice paddies in this last half of the 20th Century. Sandalwood forests were destroyed for commercial purposes in the 19th Century; ohia and koa forests have been bulldozed and replaced by eucalyptus and other imported timber trees in the 20th Century. Vast acres of mountain slopes have been stripped bare of their vegetation by feral animals—descended from domestic animals which escaped or were turned loose by their owners.

Today the vegetation and animals of Hawaii's lowlands are human artifact, a landscape transported by plan and by accident. Despite the decimation and extinction of the islands' animals and plants, however, there still survive remnants of the extraordinary products of evolution in the mountains of the higher islands, on the slopes of Mauna Kea and Mauna Loa on Hawaii, on Haleakala, Eeke, and Puu Kukui on Maui, in the mountains of Molokai, and in the Alakai Swamp on Kauai.

The fate of all plants and animals is eventual extinction, but island species appear to be particularly vulnerable. Populations are comparatively small and are restricted in range. Moreover, island animals and plants evolved features which make them vulnerable to introduced predators and to changes in habitat. Flightlessness is one of those features. At least 30 species of flightless birds and perhaps as many insects are known in the native Hawaiian biota. The reproductive features of the Hawaiian goose, nene, and the tree snails—such as relatively large eggs, late maturity, and long incubation period—were adapted to conditions with no predators, but make such animals vulnerable to predators brought in either accidentally or on purpose.

When the Hawaiian Islands were discovered by Cook in 1778, there were 67 endemic species and subspecies of resident Hawaiian land birds in Hawaii; of these, 23 are now thought to be extinct. Thus Hawaii has lost more of its native bird life than any other area in the world. Among the tree snails in the genus *Achatinella* from Oahu 41 species were known, of which at least 22 may be extinct. Botanists report that 255 species, subspecies and varieties of native Hawaiian plants are extinct, 11.6 percent of the total number known.

Extinction cannot be attributed to man alone. The Pleistocene fossils of a giant oyster at the basalt base of a reef core on Oahu, and the Pleistocene skeleton of a fossil goose on Hawaii, attest to the disappearance of species long before man arrived. Prehistoric man, however, sped up the process. Thousands of fossil bird bones have been discovered in the Hawaiian Islands since 1971. They include the remains of at least 39 and probably more species of land birds that did not survive into the historic period. Many of the bones were found at cultural sites, and the indications are that the extinction of these species was due to predation and destruction of lowland habitats by humans before the arrival of Europeans.

Conservation

For all the seemingly wanton destruction of land and biota which has occurred in Hawaii, there was in prehistoric Hawaiian culture a love and deep respect for nature. Seabirds congregating over schools of fish guided fishermen to productive fishing grounds; crows and sharks were household *amakua* (gods); the magnificent cloaks and helmets of the *alii* (chiefs) were made of the red and yellow feathers of birds, said to have been released back into the forest once the feathers had been removed. In legend, chant and dance, the moods and nuances of nature are celebrated time and again.

From the time of their arrival, Westerners too were interested in the natural history of the islands. On the Cook ships alone, more than 300 species of animals and plants were taken back to England to be enshrined in the natural history cabinets of Europe and described and recorded in the great catalogues and

The iiwi, endemic to Hawaii, is well adapted to feed on nectar of plants like this mamane. Unlike some other forest birds, it is enough of a generalist to be widely distributed, and is not listed as endangered or threatened.

Robert J. Shallenberger, U.S. Fish and Wildlife Service

Mouflon, a wild sheep species of Mediterranean origin, were imported to Lanai, Kauai and Hawaii to provide more big game hunting opportunities.

collections of the day. In the Islands, at least one early visitor, the Russian naval officer Kotzebue, expressed a prescient concern for the effects of Europeans on the islands' biota: "The art of using the productions already existing, is a more urgent want than the introduction of new ones," he wrote in 1821. But it was not until the middle of the 19th Century that the essential questions were asked by Hawaii's physician-botanist William Hillebrand: "Where are the forests of sandalwood trees which used to shed a halo of fragrance around the mere name of the Hawaiian Islands?" What is the meaning of "the startling fact that the whole plateau of Waimea, in Hawaii, over twenty miles in length and five in breadth, has been spoliated entirely of its original forest, . . . by the agency of wild cattle; not a tree or shrub is to be seen now from Kawaihae to the opposite sea-shore"?

There emerged in late 19th Century Hawaii two themes which were to dominate conservation policy in the Hawaiian Islands for the next 100 years: to protect the water supply, forests were to be preserved; to protect agriculture and ranches, feral animals were to be hunted. In the last decade of the 19th Century and the first decade of the 20th, public law and government reflected those themes. Queen Lilioukalani in 1892 signed a law prohibiting the killing of certain birds beneficial to agriculture; and a Bureau of Agriculture and Forestry was established and directed to protect forests and to regulate or prevent entry of animals and their diseases which could damage agriculture. In 1908, stimulated by President Theodore Roosevelt's aggressive stance on the wilderness, Governor Frear appointed a Territorial Conservation Commission of Hawaii to investigate the natural resources of the Territory and recommend wise development and use. The first forest reserve was established in 1909 when 66,600 acres were put under government protection and control. In 1909 also the Northwestern Hawaiian Islands (then called the Leeward Islands) were placed in the Federal Government's care as a bird refuge, one of several created by President Theodore Roosevelt. As we have seen, it would be many years before Laysan could recover from past abuse.

Public hunting has had a continuing influence on the conservation of wildlife. Apart from prehistoric Hawaiian bird hunters, the earliest hunters in Hawaii may have been the men who chased wild cattle for hides and tallow across the lava flows of Mauna Loa in the 1830's. When subsistence hunting gave way to recreational hunting is difficult to determine, but there is no question that there were generous supplies both of feral mammals and of game. The Hawaiian duck, koloa; the Hawaiian goose, nene; the plover, kolea; and flocks of migratory ducks all were rich rewards for the hunter. In the late 1880's, bags of over half a hundred plover and a dozen nene were not uncommon. With stocks of game birds rapidly becoming depleted, a hunting license system to control hunting with firearms was instituted in 1907. At the same time, hunting was encouraged in the forest reserves to eradicate feral mammals, and the records show that in the 1930's 30,000 "game" mammals such as feral cattle, goats and sheep were killed each year.

The Federal Aid in Wildlife Restoration Act of 1937 was first utilized in Hawaii in 1945 with a contract for a study of game birds. That contract started a continuing source of funding and interest in the establishment of new species of game birds, game management areas, the development of new hunting areas, habitat improvement, and studies of the carrying capacity of the land for mammals. The research plans, beginning in 1949, started with a research and management plan for game birds, and between 1949 and 1972 at least eight species of game birds had become established. Open hunting seasons are supported for substantial populations of such game birds as the gray, black, and Erkel's francolins as well as "older" imports including pheasants, chukars, and California quail. In introducing game birds, special attention has been given to filling possibly vacant niches in the arid and semiarid vegetative areas of the leeward parts of the islands with such species as the gray francolin.

Habitat improvement for both birds and game mammals has been a special interest. Because severe droughts are a problem in leeward hunting areas, more than one hundred water devices, both cachement units and pipeline units, have been installed on all the islands. These units ameliorate drought problems and increase productivity and survival.

Pittman-Robertson funds have also been used for big game management. Two major themes have guided use of the funds in this area: that of filling empty big game niches and that of management *per se*. The first game mammal introduced specifically to fill a big game niche was the mouflon, a wild sheep of Mediterranean origin, brought in to Lanai, Kauai and Hawaii between 1954 and 1962. The pronghorn antelope and black-tailed deer were introduced later under the same concept. Because of the need to develop more hunting opportunity for more hunters on less land as Hawaii's human population increased, wildlife numbers have been regularly inventoried, methods have been introduced to provide maximum harvests, stocking has been designed to establish self-sustaining populations, and consideration has been given to keeping big game numbers within the capacity of the range to feed the animals.

Hawaii's hunters number about one percent of its total population of nearly 900,000. All State-owned Forest Reserve land is now designated public hunting area, amounting to some 731,000 acres, and additional Hawaiian Home Lands, private land and Federal land bring the total public hunting area in the State to about 1,000,000 acres, some one-fourth of the State's total land area. All legal game species in Hawaii now are exotic in origin—introduced from somewhere else.

Inevitably, questions have been raised about how the management of imported mammals for hunting can be made compatible with efforts to preserve the State's unique heritage of plant and animal life. The question is especially focused on the mountains of the Island of Hawaii, where sheep, cattle, goats and pigs have impacted vast areas of forest. Proposals to eradicate feral mammals are met with strong opposition. The hunters argue that the sheep on Mauna Kea have become a "part of the Hawaiian way of life." Yet the sheep destroy the very forest which is a last home of several of Hawaii's native animals and plants. In the mid-1970's, a lawsuit was brought requesting that the State remove sheep from Mauna Kea. One of the plaintiffs listed by its human advocates was a bird, the palila, an endangered species living in the remnants of the forest which encircles the mountain. The palila prevailed. The courts ruled that feral sheep were destroying palila critical habitat (necessary for its survival) and ordered the State to remove sheep and goats and report on their progress each two years. But while feral sheep were systematically removed beginning in 1979, it was not until 1983 that action was taken to control mouflon by extending the hunting season and allowing both ewes and rams to be hunted.

Endangered Species

The Endangered Species Act now identifies for Hawaii more endangered and threatened species of animals and plants than for any other area in the United States. Among the current uses of Pittman-Robertson funds is research to determine how large, imported mammals and endangered species can co-exist in the same habitat without jeopardizing the existence of endangered species. To answer the question there is need for vast amounts of data: inventories, censuses, studies of habitat and requirements of birds, and the like. A major problem in the preparation of recovery plans, distribution maps and population status reports is the limited and insufficient data on status and distribution.

Feral sheep feed on the slopes of Mauna Kea, where even low-lying trees are subject to imported animals' grazing—to the detriment of native species.

The Hawaiian crow, alala, is close to extinction. Captive breeding may be its only hope for survival.

The Pittman-Robertson Wildlife Restoration Act has been more significant than any other public law in providing a mechanism to answer questions about the status of endangered birds. Annual forest bird censuses on some of the islands provide data on the status of the birds, albeit the results are often discouraging. In 1983-1984, on Oahu non-native birds were found to be far more numerous overall than native species in the census and on one transect alone, of 2,800 birds counted, only 7 percent were native Hawaiian birds.

The majority of Hawaii's endangered birds now live on the mountains of Kauai, Hawaii, Maui and Molokai, islands with high-elevation native forest where the birds are isolated from disease-carrying mosquitoes and there is less predator pressure than in the lowlands. The forest birds, like other wilderness animals, are dependent on the maintenance of unique habitat, and it is now evident that if they are to survive and thrive, there must continue to be extensive wild areas. National parks on Hawaii and on Maui, State parks and reserves, and the dedication of several large tracts of land by such private and public-spirited groups as The Nature Conservancy are means for providing something of what is needed.

One of the most remarkable and challenging of biological programs in the world today is that which attempts to promote the actual recovery of endangered species. In Hawaii, the Pittman-Robertson Act is playing a significant role in this effort.

Hawaii's State bird is the Hawaiian goose, nene, *Nesochen sandvicensis,* descended from the true geese but distinguished by its relatively long legs, reduced webbing on the feet, and its habitat on hardened lava flows where standing or running water is almost nonexistent. Unlike most other geese, nene do not migrate. Nobody knows how many nene were living in Hawaii before the islands were settled but there may have been many thousands: 25,000 or more are estimated for the latter part of the 18th Century. From the "vast flocks" reported on Hawaii in 1823, the population declined to a relative handful in 100 years; by 1951 there were only 33 wild nene in existence, half of them in captivity. Legal hunting was banned in 1911, but predation by pigs, feral dogs and cats and mongooses continued. Beginning in 1927, extensive efforts were made to raise nene in captivity and to release them into the wild. Funds for the project have come from the former Territorial government, State government, private sources, the United States Fish and Wildlife Service, and Pittman-Robertson excise tax receipts. A coordinated nene restoration program has been under way since 1949.

Nene now, as in former times, are found at elevations between 5,800 and 8,000 feet on Mauna Loa and Hualalai and at considerably lower elevations in Hawaii Volcanoes National Park. They have also been transplanted to Haleakala on Maui. Through cooperative agreements with landowners, three special nene sanctuary areas totaling some 45,000 acres have been established, and these together with a 38,000-acre State-owned sanctuary encompass the major breeding grounds and much of the habitat which supports the nene on Hawaii. More than $2 million of Pittman-Robertson funds have been utilized for ecological studies of nene, and in 1983-1984 these funds were also used for captive rearing. The 38-year nene restoration program has been impressive and the nene is once again present in its former habitat. However, except for hunting, all of the factors which caused the nene to approach the brink of extinction remain—disturbance by exotic animals including man, and the potential of catastrophic avian disease—and it is clear that the population will not persist without continuing release of captive-bred nene, management, and research.

The project to restore the Hawaiian crow, the alala, is a far more daunting challenge than that of the nene, for the alala population today may now be less than 20 birds in the wild. The alala, a descendant of the American crow but a forest bird rather than one of farmland, is found only on the Island of Hawaii where it lives principally in koa-ohia forests at heights of from 2,860 feet to 5,700 feet on the mountains of Hualalai and Mauna Loa. The alala is known historically chiefly from the Kona area, but it may once have utilized a wide variety of native forest types. It was apparently common in all of its historic range in low numbers, but in recent years there has been a precipitous decline: in the 1974 breeding season 26 were counted; in the 1983 breeding season one crow was seen.

Alala have been under captive management at the State Endangered Species Facility on Hawaii at Pohakuloa since 1976. The captive population has grown with some variations from three in 1976 to a 1985 level of nine. The present facility at Pohakuloa is not suitable for the bird, however, because breeding is disrupted by noise from military operations in the area. The State, with funding from the Pittman-Robertson Act, was moving toward establishing another captive site on Haleakala on Maui at the time this chapter was being written, and it was a race against time.

Of Waterfowl and the Future

Legend tells us that the alaeula, the gallinule, was one of the great benefactors of the Hawaiian people, for in the early days when fire was unknown to them, the bird took pity on the Hawaiians and, flying to the home of the gods, returned to earth with a burning stick. On the flight, the white forehead of the gallinule was scorched by the flames, and so it received the name alae, meaning "red."

In turn, the Hawaiians were the great benefactors not only of the alae, but of its brethren waterfowl, the alae keokeo, the coot; the aeo, the stilt; and the koloa, the Hawaiian duck. The thousands of acres of taro patches planted by the Hawaiians supplemented nature's marshes in the islands, and supported not only the native waterfowl, but great flocks of migratory ducks which once wintered in the islands. With the influx of haole (foreign) culture, those artificial wetlands did not survive. In 1900, there were 19,000 acres of taro and rice paddies; in 1967, only 510 acres remained. In addition, the natural marshes were drained. The giant marsh at Mana on Kauai was drained for sugar cane cultivation in the 19th Century and that at Waikiki on Oahu for hotels and condominiums in the first decades of the 20th Century.

The future survival of gallinule, coot, stilt and koloa, like that of the forest birds, depends on the availability of suitable habitat. In this, the future may be brighter for the waterfowl than for the forest birds, for while natural wetlands are being destroyed, other wetlands are being developed in golf courses, resorts and parks. Nevertheless, there remain the problems of managing predators which cannot be controlled by administrative action, and the inherent problems of the animals themselves, born with evolutionary adaptations which Darwin so early recognized as being far from perfect.

Nene, the Hawaiian goose, is the endangered State bird. Protected against hunting since 1911, nene have been the focus for a long restoration effort, but remain vulnerable to land use changes and the impacts of exotic animals.

Robert J. Shallenberger, U.S. Fish and Wildlife Service

Southeastern Cooperative Wildlife Disease Study, based in Georgia, is another example of professional standards at work.

P-R and Professionalism

by E. Charles Meslow and Ruth Wilson-Jacobs

The Pittman-Robertson program has made major contributions to the development of professional wildlife research and management. Picture the situation in the 1930's when the program began. A small, scattered group of biologists was attempting to tackle enormous sets of wildlife problems and questions. Funds for management and research projects were limited, answers to the same questions were needed in multiple locations, and verbal and written communication channels were poor. Passage of the Pittman-Robertson Act helped correct these problems and hastened development of professional wildlife management and research in three major ways. The Act set professional standards for personnel and projects funded by the Pittman-Robertson program; it provided a dependable source of funds for management and research; and it encouraged and assisted with the transfer of information among developing wildlife professionals.

These are the facts, but the human element went beyond them in the building of a new profession. It is difficult in the 1980's to describe the spirit of adventure and discovery, tempered by scientific objectivity, which fired the imaginations of State wildlife researchers and managers four or five decades ago. Those who have survived into our era remember the early days vividly as a time of low pay, hard work and uncertainty, with many false starts and disappointments mixed in among the successes; more importantly, they remember the undercurrent of excitement that made it all more than worthwhile. Each project was a new probe into an unfamiliar area, aimed at helping a species they—and the public—felt deeply about saving.

Out of many faltering, sputtering starts came an accelerating flow of facts and a new capability to manage with predictable results. This was what nourished and strengthened professionalism as, inch by inch, it displaced the political patronage system from State wildlife agencies. The new breed of professionals grew in confidence and skill as they saw one species after another being rescued from the almost certain oblivion that had threatened them prior to 1937.

Today, the wildlife profession continues to mature and to state its conclusions with ever-increasing scientific detachment, but the self-renewing legacy of that earlier period still motivates its members. The frontiers of wildlife science have been pushed back, but they still exist to stir the spirit of personal involvement and excitement among today's professionals.

Professional Standards

Standards set by P-R have served a vital role in the development of a pool of qualified professionals to conduct research, management, and administrative

---

Dr. Meslow is a Professor of Wildlife Ecology and Leader of the Cooperative Wildlife Research Unit at Oregon State University. Active in The Wildlife Society, he served as its President during 1984-86. Ms. Wilson-Jacobs holds degrees in wildlife biology from Iowa State and Oregon State Universities, and works part time for the Oregon Co-op Unit as a writer and editor.

duties in wildlife and related natural resource fields. People appointed to jobs in State wildlife agencies early in the 20th Century too often were political allies, friends, relatives, out-of-door hobbyists, or others without appropriate training. The P-R program helped overcome this problem by adopting the requirement that persons employed by States to work on Pittman-Robertson projects first had to be approved by Federal program administrators. Early requirements for approval were simple: employees had to be selected for work based on their experience and they had to be qualified to carry out their duties in a competent manner. Later, this translated into a requirement for a bachelor's degree in a natural resource major or equivalent training and experience.

These employment standards yielded multiple benefits. Qualified biologists, such as those emerging from the Cooperative Wildlife Research Units and other developing university programs, rapidly found employment with State wildlife agencies. Improved job opportunities after graduation encouraged more people to obtain both undergraduate and graduate degrees in wildlife biology and related natural resource majors. Increased interest in receiving training in these subjects accelerated the development of degree programs at colleges and universities. More training opportunities encouraged more people to pursue higher education centering on wildlife management. A large pool of qualified natural resource biologists emerged and the array of natural resource disciplines expanded. Trained biologists, many of whom initially worked on Pittman-Robertson projects, moved into management, research, and administrative positions with State and Federal wildlife agencies and occasionally into political office. Some found employment with other agencies or in the private sector, but remained available to advise wildlife staff. Development and application of wildlife research and management could finally proceed under the guidance of a trained group of professionals. This group has expanded over the years to include experts in such disciplines as hydrology, agronomy, realty, law, finance, hunter education and other special fields, just as requirements of modern wildlife management have grown more sophisticated.

The Pittman-Robertson program has recognized since the mid-1970's that States have their own acceptable employee qualifications, and the Federal approval requirement has been dropped. The program continues to assist in professional training by funding employee workshops to improve project accomplishments. This training takes advantage of information and experts from other disciplines. For example, during 1983 and 1984, over 30 P-R workshops were held on topics such as use of computers for wildlife research, endangered species management, design of wildlife radio-tracking studies, hunter education

Professionalism means commitment to the wildlife resource . . .

academies, and project planning and administration. During these times when new information emerges continuously, it is vital for a profession to stay up to date by keeping its members aware of new developments. P-R workshops fulfill a part of this need.

Project Standards

The program has also helped establish high professional standards for wildlife research and management by providing State wildlife agencies with standards for conducting Pittman-Robertson projects. The standards, which are established at a national level, have been revised periodically throughout the program's history with changes in techniques and definitions of professional, scientific conduct. Furthermore, the standards have been applied equally to projects in all States. In effect, the program has crossed State lines and tended to raise the level of research and management to a high common denominator of professional conduct over time. This has improved both the conduct of professional activities and the public's image of the wildlife profession. Professionals in other disciplines and laymen are better able to comprehend what constitutes wildlife management and research because so many activities have taken place under a single set of guidelines. These accomplishments have occurred without losing the important sense of leadership by State wildlife agencies.

Current standards for Pittman-Robertson projects are basic to professional activity in almost any scientific field. Project approval is based on the need for the work proposed, the objectives, the expected results and benefits, and the approach in relation to a State's wildlife management goals. Standards for reporting project results closely parallel the requirements set forth by any scientific publication. Scientific disciplines now emphasize the collection and statistical analysis of numerical information rather than descriptive reporting of observations. Accordingly, Pittman-Robertson reports contain more numbers than they did before, and statistically significant results are required when positive findings are reported. Final reports must be presented in the format of a scientific paper following the style of *The Journal of Wildlife Management,* published by the professional society for wildlife biologists, The Wildlife Society. These reports are less readable to a layman than earlier ones, but are more credible and defensible in scientific, legal, and political circles.

Other national standards have been indirectly, but beneficially, imposed on Pittman-Robertson projects in the form of Federal laws, Executive orders, and

... plus energetic objectivity in finding and evaluating facts ...

Federal regulations that must be honored by any agency using Federal funds. States cannot discriminate on the basis of race, color, national origin, sex, physical disability, or age when spending Pittman-Robertson funds. Requirements must also be met that have been established by numerous Federal acts—the Coastal Zone Management Act, Endangered Species Act, National Environmental Policy Act, to name a few. Executive orders and Federal regulations for wetland and floodplain protection, and others intended to discourage introductions of exotic species must also be followed. These standards were established at a national level in the interests of society as a whole. Their application to Pittman-Robertson activities at a State level strengthens their effectiveness, lends additional protection to natural and human resources, and contributes credibility to the wildlife profession.

Dependable Funds

The Pittman-Robertson program has a long history of providing dependable funds for wildlife management. Dependable funds allow States to set and reach long-term goals, monitor and adjust continuing activities, and apply scientific information when managing wildlife populations and habitats. This differs dramatically from conditions in the early 1930's, when many management projects began and ended spontaneously as funds were gained and lost or gained and rapidly spent. Planned, long-term management is much more beneficial to wildlife than short-term actions and creates credibility for wildlife managers in the eyes of the public. Managers are not only able to act as professionals; they are perceived as professionals because they publicly exhibit competent performance.

Crex Meadows Wildlife Area in northern Wisconsin is one of many examples of long-term management areas purchased and developed in a professional manner with Pittman-Robertson funds. The area has been managed since 1945 to restore non-productive pine lands and sedge meadows to productive prairie, wetland, and upland habitats. The two-fold management goal at Crex Meadows is specifically stated in a written management plan, first to provide a State-owned area for the production of wildlife with emphasis on migratory game birds, prairie grouse, and endangered and threatened species and, secondly, to provide public hunting, trapping, wildlife education and observation, and other compatible recreational opportunities. Methods of reaching the goal are stated in numerical terms: to produce 4,500 ducks on 6,000 acres of flooded

. . . regardless of personal discomfort, hardship, or danger . . .

marsh each year, to produce 1,000 goslings each year from a spring population of 2,000 geese, to provide 2,000 participant-days of fall camping, and so on. New developments, maintenance of existing developments, detailed cost estimates, and a schedule for meeting the goal and objectives are also specified in the plan. The dependable source of funds provided by the Pittman-Robertson program is vital to professional, orderly management of this and other State wildlife areas.

Wildlife research, too, has benefited; dependable P-R funds offer continuity to projects and the completion of objectives that require multiple years of information. Knowledge of a wildlife population that is sufficient for competent management decisions often develops slowly over many years of continuous, intensive study. Disjointed sets of data collected over broken intervals of time are not as informative, and may even lead to incorrect interpretations. This is particularly true if a wildlife population responds differently to changing environmental factors.

Virtually every State now has highly effective research projects funded through Pittman-Robertson to help develop effective wildlife management programs. The projects are usually conducted by State wildlife biologists or under contract with universities or private consultants, depending on preferences of State wildlife agencies. Contracts with universities offer especially productive, cost-efficient means of conducting research. State agencies have always had the option of involving universities in their research projects, but the presence of dependable funds through Pittman-Robertson has allowed them to use the option more often than before. Usually a graduate student completes a project as part of the requirements for an advanced degree in wildlife biology or related major. Project scrutiny from professors on the student's committee, other university faculty, and fellow students assures that the research is of high quality and conducted with detailed understanding of the questions being addressed. Cooperative Wildlife Research Units at universities are often involved in the research because of their unique ties with Federal and State agencies.

Some State wildlife departments and State universities have maximized the benefits of working together by developing interdependent arrangements for conducting research with Pittman-Robertson funds. A department of fisheries and wildlife or similar department at a university essentially serves as the major research branch for some States' wildlife agencies. The agencies identify research priorities and then turn to university faculty and students for assistance with the research. A State can gain financial as well as professional benefits from such an arrangement. Pittman-Robertson funds to a State often are only a small portion of project funding; research grants to the university from other sources provide the rest.

Cooperative Projects

Wildlife professionals are now able to work efficiently with other disciplines and agencies because of the presence of dependable funds through Pittman-Robertson. Cooperation leads to efficiency and economy in wildlife management and research just as it does in other professional endeavors. This cooperation is often more complex and long-term that the agency-university interaction already mentioned.

The Southeastern Cooperative Wildlife Disease Study, housed at the University of Georgia, exemplifies a highly successful cooperative program that has developed under the Pittman-Robertson umbrella. The program was founded in 1957 as the first diagnostic and research service specifically for investigating wildlife diseases. Pittman-Robertson funds were then the foundation of the program and they continue to be significant today. The program involves 13 Southeastern States, with additional help since 1963 from the U.S. Fish and Wildlife Service, and since 1978 from the Animal and Plant Health Inspection Service of the U.S. Department of Agriculture. The State-Federal cooperative structure is the most cost-efficient means of providing high quality wildlife disease expertise to agencies responsible for wildlife and domestic livestock. The program has examined thousands of sick and dying animals involving more than 60 different species over the past 30 years. Its research accomplishments are recognized nationally and internationally, and educational activities have become an important and highly valued aspect of its operation. This is just one example of many professional, cooperative programs funded by the P-R program.

Information Reporting and Transfer

Pittman-Robertson has benefited wildlife professionals by establishing guidelines and providing systems for effective reporting of information on wildlife issues. This role was critically important early in P-R history when communication channels were poorly developed and information needs were especially great among wildlife biologists. In the beginning, P-R required quarterly progress reports on every project and a completion report at the end. It soon became evident that the distribution of these reports from State to State was not getting research findings to everyone who could use them. Some valuable reports were becoming difficult or impossible to locate. So, in the 1960's, with encouragement from the International Association of Game, Fish and Conservation Commissioners, a library repository system was inaugurated for all reports and publications from the Federal Aid program. It became a prime source of fish and wildlife information, not only for State researchers and managers, but also for Federal and private workers.

A further need emerged in the 1970's—how to be sure that a project being planned in one State took into account projects on related subjects underway in other States. There was little chance that a new project could be structured to avoid unnecessary duplication of effort or to maximize use of information from other studies until on-going projects were completed and a final report written. This problem has been corrected by making available an up-to-date catalog of all research and survey work in progress to State P-R project personnel, Wildlife Research Units, and other agencies. In addition, this current Federal Aid Research file and the Fish and Wildlife Reference Service file are maintained as computer data bases. Either can be searched almost instantaneously through a computer terminal to identify projects fitting any criteria such as State, species, habitat, type of work, etc. Thus, the seemingly uncoordinated work of early P-R scientists has evolved into a coherent system of wildlife information.

Formal publication of results of Pittman-Robertson projects has never been required, but has always been strongly encouraged because it is the most efficient means of sharing information. The encouragement has been successful. At times up to one-fourth of the articles in the *Journal of Wildlife Management* have acknowledged support from the Pittman-Robertson program. An index to Federal Aid publications published as early as 1968 listed approximately 4,000 scientific and technical works supported by Pittman-Robertson funds during the first 30 years of the program. Figures like these represent notable contributions to our knowledge of wildlife and commendable success in sharing this knowledge with others.

It is fitting to conclude this chapter by taking note of public acceptance of wildlife research and management as professional disciplines. Unfortunately, it

260

is possible to be knowledgeable, competent, and specialized in a field, but not considered professional until the public grants that recognition. Hunting, changing habitats to attract or repel wildlife, and many other activities directly or indirectly related to wildlife management and research in the public's eyes have historical roots in our society. Wildlife professionals have fought an uphill struggle to distinguish their activities from pursuits of the layman. Even today, people may question why men and women are specifically trained and employed to manage or study wildlife. The Pittman-Robertson program, through roles described in this chapter, has assisted with answers to that question.

Today, wildlife research and management present public images of integrated scientific disciplines with established principles and methods. Wildlife biologists are not simply people who enjoy observing or hunting wildlife. They are respected scientists trained in community ecology, population biology, statistics, computer modeling, and similar complex subjects. The store of biological knowledge is now so vast that many biologists specialize for research and management purposes. Successes like Crex Meadows Wildlife Area in Wisconsin and the Southeastern Cooperative Disease Study positively present the wildlife profession to the public. Continued professional growth, combined with greater acceptance and respect from the public, can only improve the ability of our wildlife professionals to understand and properly manage our wildlife resources.

Crex Meadows, Wisconsin, is an intensively managed State wildlife area where every acre and every work-hour are expected to produce measurable, professional-level results. Note the man-made ponds and the enclosure for geese.

Wisconsin Department of Natural Resources

A Mixed Bag

Many bird and mammal species have benefited from the Pittman-Robertson program, some in ways that the Act's sponsors could not have foreseen. They include species large and small, game and nongame, and even endangered or threatened.

Fur-bearing mammals like the beaver and sea otter were so over-exploited by earlier generations that they had disappeared from most of their once extensive ranges. Now they have recovered to a spectacular degree, protected legally and relocated into areas their predecessors roamed.

The bobcat, long considered a "varmint" by rural people, may owe its future welfare to P-R activities begun in the 1970's. Ironically, some of its difficulties seem to have worsened because of worldwide environmental awareness; but that same awareness has sparked the first serious bobcat research and restoration, financed extensively with P-R funds. It is a striking example of how this flexible program can respond to changing times.

Not even P-R's most ardent supporters claim it as a cure for all of wildlife's problems. The many human uses of the earth we share with wild creatures affect their ranges and numbers more than any one program can compensate for. Examples include the sharp rise and subsequent leveling off of bobwhite quail and ring-necked pheasant populations, an indirect result of changing agricultural economics and technology. Even though financial realities have precluded miracles to restore these popular game birds, P-R has unlocked secrets to guide further research and management, offering hope for their future abundance.

Prospects seem bright for gray and fox squirrels; P-R research indicates that these adaptable mammals can survive massive habitat changes and hunting pressures as long as people leave them access to enough trees bearing acorns, nuts and fruits.

Restoration of the giant Canada goose, widely believed to be extinct until the 1960's, is an unqualified success story which can be credited largely to P-R. This species, like the tree squirrels, has adapted well to man and his works. Mule deer, the West's most numerous large mammal species, also have responded well to P-R research and management, but their future numbers and distribution will depend greatly on more such work as pressures intensify on their living space. And the success of the chukar partridge, an import which found its own niche in overgrazed rangelands amid some of America's harshest climates and landscapes, indicates that not all "exotic" species are bad news to native ones.

This mixed bag of species stories therefore contains many messages about wildlife, its status in the 1980's, and its prospects for the future. If the signals tend to seem unclear, offering few certainties, it is because wildlife management involves many variable factors, defying easy cook-book conclusions and glib generalities. Pittman-Robertson funding has enabled State wildlife agencies to sort out the key factors from the masses of conflicting evidence and half-truths born of earlier ignorance.

Illustration by Bob Hines

263

Mule Deer

by Richard J. Mackie

> *". . . a curious kind of Deer of a Dark gray colour—more so than common, hair long and fine, the ears large and long, a Small recepticle under the eyes like the Elk, the taile about the length of the common Deer, round (like a cow) a tuft of black hair about the end, this Species of Deer jumps like a goat or Sheep."*

Thus, on September 17, 1804, William Clark first described the strange "black-tailed deer" seen on September 7 and later shot by hunters of the Lewis and Clark expedition along the Missouri River above the mouth of the Niobrara River. Though the explorers first called it the black tail deer, Meriwether Lewis later (May 10, 1805) wrote: "The ear and tail of this anamal when compared to those of the common deer, so well comported with those of the mule when compared with the horse, that we have by way of distinction adapted the appellation of the mule deer, which I think much more appropriate." The appropriateness of this distinction was confirmed years later, when the species was formally named *hemionus,* meaning half ass (or mule).

When Lewis and Clark reached the lower Columbia River, they found another form of "black-tailed deer" of which Lewis wrote: "The Black-tailed fallow deer are peculiar to this coast and are a distinct species of deer partaking equally of the mule deer and the common deer." We now recognize this form as the black-tailed subspecies of mule deer *(Odocoileus hemionus).* Today, the mule and black-tailed deer are collectively the most widely distributed and abundant of all species of large mammal native to western North America. In terms of recreation and economics, they are also the most important.

In addition to their distinctive ears, which are large and mule-like, and tail, which is narrow, white to black above, and black-tipped, mule deer can be distinguished by their size—the adults commonly weighing between 125 and 250 pounds and standing 30 to 40 inches high at the shoulder—their typical dark gray coat with conspicuous white to yellowish rump patch, and their movement in either a stilted, stiff-legged walk or a unique four-footed bound with the tail held either below the horizontal or not wagging. Adult males may also be distinguished by their antlers which commonly branch equally above the base to form four major tines or points on each side.

Blacktails are smaller, darker, with smaller rump patch, and have broader tails that tend to be black to brown above as well as black-tipped. Both are distinguished from white-tailed deer by overall appearance, the form and color of the tail, the shape and position of metatarsal glands on the hind legs, the form of the antlers of males, and various behavioral characteristics including the gait or manner of movement when disturbed.

Characteristically animals of dry, brushy range and open forest land, and rugged terrain, mule deer occur throughout western North America from about

Dr. Mackie has been involved in Pittman-Robertson-financed mule deer studies for more than 25 years. He has worked as a research biologist and research coordinator for the Montana Department of Fish and Game; has been Professor of Wildlife Management at Montana State University since 1970; and currently is also the coordinator of statewide deer research studies for the Montana Fish, Wildlife and Parks Department.

the 100th Meridian in the Great Plains to the Pacific coast, and from central Mexico to to northern Alberta and British Columbia. Blacktails are found only in a narrow strip of woodlands, chaparral, and temperate coniferous forest along the Pacific coast from central California to Alaska.

One historian estimated that as many as 10 million mule deer and 3 million blacktails may have existed in pre-settlement days. Others have suggested combined numbers of 5 million or less as more realistic, considering historical records and habitat conditions of that era. Early explorers and settlers found deer scarce in many parts of the West. In the Great Basin, for example, mule deer may have become abundant only during the past 50 to 75 years. Most authorities believe that western rangelands were dominated extensively by bunchgrasses and other vegetation of low value as habitat for deer.

Immediately following settlement, mule deer populations declined drastically due to unrestricted hunting and settlers' heavy reliance on wild animals for food, and to disturbance and preemption of deer habitats for agriculture. By the late 1800's and early 1900's, mule deer were generally scarce.

This trend was soon reversed, however, as other events of settlement and the post-settlement era proved beneficial to deer. Widespread livestock grazing, logging, and burning led to more diverse range and forest vegetation and an abundance of palatable and nutritious deer food plants. Predatory animals were vigorously controlled, while possibly competitive animals such as elk, bighorn sheep, pronghorn antelope, and bison had become scarce or disappeared. Also, hunting was restricted, and game law enforcement became more effective.

By the 1920's, mule deer were extremely abundant in parts of the Southwest. By the mid-to-late 1930's, the increases were spreading north and west to approach a level of unprecendented distribution and abundance over most of

Two "muley" does on western Kansas high plains. Including their black tailed subspecies, mule deer are the "most widely distributed and *abundant large mammal native to western North America."*

Gene Brehm

266

Erwin and Peggy Bauer/Outdoor Life Magazine

Mule deer are identified by their gait, rump markings, typically gray coat, the male's distinctive antler forms, and probably most of *all by both sexes' large, mule-shaped ears. The swollen neck indicates this buck is rutting.*

the West. Although reliable population estimates have never been made, it seems likely that there were at least 7.5 million mule and black-tailed deer West-wide by the early 1960's. Since then, populations have declined in many areas, including the stronghold of mule deer—the mountain-foothill habitats of the Rocky Mountains and other ranges extending from the Southwest northward into Canada. In other areas, populations have fluctuated or gradually increased. Overall, total numbers probably exceed 5.5 million today.

The growing abundance of mule deer through the 1920's and 1930's increased their importance in the West, but also brought new problems. Experiences with dense populations in areas such as the Kaibab Plateau in Arizona demonstrated that great abundance of deer could not be sustained. Overly-large populations soon depleted deer forage and led to lowered fawn production, starvation, and conflicts with agriculture and forestry. It became evident that the management practices of the early 1900's, which emphasized protection and other efforts to increase deer numbers, no longer were best. Similarly, attempts to cope with overpopulation by measures such as winter feeding proved ineffective or questionable. New directions and management measures were necessary.

Perhaps nowhere in wildlife management was passage of the Federal Aid in Wildlife Restoration Act more timely than in management of mule deer. Almost exactly when needed, the Act provided funding to employ technically trained biologists to study deer and deer populations, to develop new techniques for management, and to establish and transmit the need for sound, scientifically-based management to sportsmen, the general public, and legislators who controlled management policies. Because of this, the accomplishments in mule deer management under Pittman-Robertson were almost synonymous with those of mule deer management overall for several decades.

Among the first, and perhaps most significant, of those accomplishments was the accrual of information about mule deer. In the mid-1930's, very little was known about these animals. The efforts of State game agencies were limited largely to law enforcement, predator control, refuges, and, in some places, transplanting. By the late 1930's and early 1940's, however, State administrators, seeking more effective methods to cope with flourishing deer populations, began to spend their new Federal Aid money on research.

Early efforts included general inventories of mule deer populations and habitats, and studies to learn more about the biology of deer and their needs, the effectiveness of winter feeding, and the relations between deer and livestock and foresty. The findings confirmed that deer ranges were extensively overpopulated, that important forage plants on winter ranges were being damaged by overuse, and that crop damage, starvation, and low fawn production were all problems of overpopulation. Further, the studies showed that the answer to these problems was increased deer harvests to control and balance deer populations with their habitat.

This knowledge provided the spark for new deer management programs in all Western States during the 1940's and early 1950's. Organized to manage deer on the basis of scientific facts and principles, these programs included more

This doe, captured unharmed in a "clover" trap amid typical mule deer countryside, will be weighed, examined, radio-collared and released.

Robert J. Fischer

intensive research to establish basic facts about the animals' habitat needs and relationships, and to provide new methods and criteria for management. Deer management units were established; standardized methods were employed to more precisely measure trends in deer populations, habitat conditions, and harvest—and thus, to better identify what managers needed to know. They also helped to improve public understanding of the problems involved in managing mule deer, and of the need for better management. Initially, management focused on setting up hunting regulations that would balance deer populations with their habitat and obtain maximum sport hunting use of surplus animals. Limited bucks-only hunting seasons were replaced by more extensive hunting involving both sexes of deer in the 1950's and 1960's. Between 1950, when estimates were first made in all States, and 1961, the total annual kill of mule and black-tailed deer more than doubled—from about 400,000 to nearly 1,000,000.

The new hunting opportunity further increased the recreational and economic importance of mule deer. At the same time, there were new problems. By the late 1960's and early 1970's, mule deer populations had stabilized or were declining over much of the West, while human populations and demand for hunting were increasing. Also, important mule deer habitat was being lost or deteriorating as a result of man's activities on western rangelands. In this setting, studies began to question the general application of some deer management concepts and techniques, and to point to the need for more refined management.

By the mid-1970's, the early goal of merely balancing mule deer populations with range forage supplies was being replaced by more flexible, broader-based programs. Hunting regulations became tools to serve a variety of human demands as well as deer and habitat management needs. Computer models of deer populations were developed and employed in some States to better predict population trends and calculate allowable harvests; while new techniques like radio telemetry enabled researchers to reexamine prevailing ideas and methods, and to further evaluate the role and importance of all factors in regulating deer populations. At the same time, the growing concern about losses of once extensive and productive deer habitats stimulated new and greater efforts to protect important habitats, restore more favorable vegetation, and reduce potential conflicts with other land uses including livestock grazing, logging and timber management, agriculture, and energy and other human developments.

Today, mule deer management is well established, broadly based, and a top priority activity of wildlife agencies in the West. Much credit for this has to go to the Federal Aid program, under which deer management evolved from little more than an idea to fact. Before the P-R era, deer-related activities were assigned to a mere handful of State and U.S. Forest Service people; now there are respectable staffs devoted to deer studies and management in all States, and in additional Federal agencies and public and private organizations. The knowledge of mule deer that has accrued under Federal Aid studies was especially important. The book, *Mule and Black-tailed Deer of North America,* published in 1981 by the Wildlife Management Institute, provides an excellent review of current knowledge. Of more than 800 literature references in the book, over 500 appear to represent studies that were supported at least in part by Federal Aid funds.

Federal Aid continues to provide much basic support for deer management and research projects, but the overall effort has become much broader-based than in earlier years. Because mule deer, like nearly all resident wildlife, are by law the property of individual States, management of deer populations developed primarily as a function of State governments and their wildlife depart-

Gene Brehm

Mule deer are being pressured in some areas by increasing numbers of elk, and in others by expanding white-tailed deer populations.

Managers are forced to make difficult choices about priorities among species.

ments. The States control little mule deer habitat, however. Much is privately owned, but at least as much or even more is on the national forest and other Federal rangelands that comprise nearly half the total land in the Western States. Because of this, Federal agencies, especially the Forest Service and Bureau of Land Management, which between them administer resource use on more than three-fourths of those lands, have come to play a key role in habitat management for mule deer.

The Forest Service was one of the first government agencies to recognize the need to manage the fast-growing mule deer herds of the 1920's and 1930's. Since then, it has developed extensive programs in research on mule deer-habitat relationships and in management to maintain or enhance habitat for deer on the national forests. More recently, the Bureau of Land Management has become increasingly active in assessing habitat resources and conditions, supporting research, and developing habitat management programs for deer and other wildlife on public rangelands. Both agencies have cooperated extensively with State wildlife departments to more effectively consider and meet the needs of deer in management of timber, range, livestock grazing, and other resource and land use management. Although the National Park Service and the Fish and Wildlife Service administer less mule deer habitat, both agencies have conducted and supported research on deer and have cooperated with State agencies in mule deer management upon and adjoining their lands.

In mule deer management, like other endeavors of man, it is difficult to predict exactly what the future may bring. There is reason for optimism—in the current status of mule deer populations and the adaptability of these animals, in the broad-based and well-funded management programs that are now well established in State and Federal agencies, in the public support given to management, and in extensive research now being conducted to provide new knowledge and further improve deer management. There is also cause for concern, especially about the rapidly expanding human populations and more intensive and complete use of range and forest lands. These continue to threaten mule deer habitats and populations throughout the West and make the task of deer managers increasingly difficult.

For example, increased human habitation of rural areas, subdivisions and other developments on winter ranges, and conversion of rangeland to cultivated farmland are seriously eroding the amount of habitat available to mule deer over much of their range. Energy exploration and development have increased to threaten other areas. More intensive and complete use of rangelands for livestock production poses a major threat to the quality of those lands as deer habitat. The same is true of logging, road building, and more intensive timber management on many forest lands. In some places, increasing populations of other wild mammals in mule deer habitats, and the management priority given to those species, threaten additional competition or less emphasis on deer. Elk populations have increased to overlap extensively with mule deer as a result of management favoring elk. As white-tailed deer spread and became more abundant through the northern Rocky Mountains and Great Plains and southwestern deserts, they have replaced mule deer in some habitats.

As pressures on mule deer habitats and populations increase, management will be forced to become more intensive and refined. Difficult decisions may have to be made about priorities for mule deer as compared with other species and land uses. It may also be necessary to adjust management priorities for individual deer populations and habitats. Those of highest potential and greatest importance may have to be rigidly protected and closely managed, perhaps by excluding other species and land uses, if reasonably abundant mule deer populations and recreational opportunities are to be maintained.

Few species are more popular with hunters than mule deer.

Return of the Giants

by Forrest B. Lee

The restoration of the giant Canada goose *(Branta canadensis maxima)* to the Great Plains and adjacent areas of the United States and Canada is a success story that has few equals in the history of wildlife management. Many shared in the effort—Federal, State and provincial agencies, universities, private organizations and individuals. The Pittman-Robertson program is an integral part of this story, for it supported and continues to support the work of many of the States involved in bringing back a magnificent bird.

This great goose is somewhat of a legend in the writings of sportsmen who hunted it a century or more ago. One was W. B. Mershon, who hunted geese near Dawson, North Dakota, in the 1880's. In his *Recollections of My fifty Years Hunting and Fishing,* published in 1923, Mershon wrote that while the big geese had the general markings of other races of Canada geese, they were lighter colored, and their bodies were shaped differently, being long and oval. They frequently weighed 14 or 15 pounds. (Typical male Canada geese, *B. c. interior,* in the same region average only about 9 pounds, and females 7 to 8 pounds.) On the feeding grounds they were often in what appeared to be family groups which were aloof and did not mix with the other races of Canadas. They usually flew low and would come silently to the feeding area without much circling about.

The pioneers who settled in the Plains regions found the giant Canada goose nesting commonly over most of the region (see map). By the turn of the century, it had disappeared from much of this former breeding range, which includes parts of 3 Canadian provinces and all or parts of 18 States. Excessive hunting and habitat destruction are among the factors believed to have caused this drastic decline. By the 1920's, the giant Canada goose was thought by many to be gone forever. The renowned waterfowl authority, Dr. Jean T. Delacour, stated in his monumental work, *The Waterfowl of the World,* published in 1954, "The giant Canada goose appears to be extinct."

Then in 1962, Dr. Harold C. Hanson, a leading authority on Canada geese, demonstrated that some giant Canada geese were alive and well. The fascinating story of Dr. Hanson's discovery at Silver Lake in the City of Rochester, Minnesota, is best told in his own words, quoted from the preface of his book, *The Giant Canada Goose,* published in 1965. He had observed the Rochester geese on several occasions and noted that they differed from other races of Canada geese he was studying.

The opportunity to solve this wildlife riddle was fortunately afforded me in mid-January 1962, when I was invited by Forrest B. Lee of the Minnesota Department of Conservation to band, weigh, and measure a trapped sample of the Rochester flock ... On that memorable day, the temperature held around zero, and a strong wind blew, but this only added zest to the enterprise in which Forrest B.

Mr. Lee took part in giant Canada goose restoration as a wildlife biologist at both State and Federal levels, first for the Minnesota Department of Conservation and then for the Northern Prairie Research Station in North Dakota. He also has been active for many years in the recovery program for the endangered Aleutian Canada goose, and has continued to serve on the official Recovery Team for that species since retiring from the Fish and Wildlife Service in 1983.

Approximate breeding range of the giant Canada goose prior to settlement. (From Harold Hanson's book, **The Giant Canada Goose,** *1965.)*

Lee, Robert Jessen, Thomas Hansen, and George Meyers of the Minnesota Department of Conservation, and Harvey K. Nelson, Arthur S. Hawkins, and William J. Ellerbrock of the U. S. Fish and Wildlife Service, participated. The work proceeded smoothly except for one hitch—we were obviously using faulty scales. The only question was, "how faulty?" Therefore, we dispensed with further weighing until we could check the scales with some bulk food items of known weight. Arthur Hawkins responded to this fiscal challenge and purchased 5 pounds of sugar and 10 pounds of flour, but not before first weighing these items on the scale at the store. Upon our return to the banding site, a quick test of the scales revealed that the "impossible weights" we had been getting were correct. Now we knew beyond question that we were dealing with a very large race. But what race? The giant Canada goose had been repeatedly written into extinction and could not be a possibility. Only after returning home and checking Delacour's monograph, did I realize that the Rochester flock had to be **Branta canadensis maxima!**

274

After that exciting day at Rochester, Dr. Hanson plunged into comprehensive research of the giant Canada goose. He examined museum specimens and historical documents, and interviewed or corresponded with many persons who provided pertinent information. His investigations revealed that there were many more giant Canada geese in existence than those he had studied at Rochester, Minnesota. He examined numerous captive and free-flying goose flocks over the Plains areas of Canada and the United States, weighing and measuring many of the birds and inquiring about their history. To his surprise, and that of his peers, he found giant Canada goose flocks at many places, including private and public game farms, wildlife refuges and game management areas. A remnant breeding population also existed in the Interlakes region of Manitoba. One of the results of his efforts was the publication in 1965 of his landmark 225-page book about the race. This book, and the publicity that was given the rediscovery, sparked widespread interest in the bird and an awareness of the potentials for restoring it to former habitats.

Among the most interesting findings was an explanation of how the giants had survived. Early settlers sometimes gathered eggs from nests in the wild and hatched them under broody chicken hens. The young were reared and used for food or to start captive farm and decoy flocks. Flightless young were sometimes captured in the wild and reared for the same purposes. After the use of live decoys for hunting was outlawed in 1937, some captive flocks continued to be kept by game breeders and farmers. These practices inadvertently saved some of the original wild stock which was later used in restoration programs. Private

Giant Canada geese were not extinct at all, just scattered and generally mistaken for Canada geese of other races.

game breeders and aviculturists played a prominent role in the restoration of giant Canada geese, not only by supplying breeding stock but also in providing essential know-how for rearing them in captivity.

Some restoration of Canada geese was already in progress as early as the 1930's, when new national wildlife refuges and state waterfowl management areas were established in the Northern Plains region. But the number of breeding Canada geese in the original range of the giant goose was very small. For example, a summary prepared by C. F. Yocom listed 2,741 breeding pairs for Alberta, Saskatchewan, Manitoba, Montana, North Dakota, South Dakota, Wyoming and Colorado as of 1951. As was learned later, most of these really were giant Canada geese. By 1962, the year of Dr. Hanson's rediscovery of the giants, State and Federal areas were hatching and releasing from 4,000 to 4,500 Canada geese each year in the Northern Plains region—setting the stage for a major effort to restore the giant goose. In 1980, C. H. Schroeder and this writer estimated that the breeding population in these three provinces and five States had increased to about 15,000 pairs by the late 1970's.

Following the publication of Dr. Hanson's book, emphasis focused on using giant Canada breeding stock. This strong general interest in restoration prompted recognition of a need for information to improve propagation, release, transplant and other management techniques to make these programs more successful. The publication, *Home Grown Honkers,* became available in 1970 and provided much useful information.

Although the giant goose was believed to be extinct when the Pittman-Robertson Federal Aid in Wildlife Restoration Act became law in 1937, P-R proved to be a great boon for the giant Canada goose restoration program. All 18 States believed to have been included in the original breeding range of the giant Canada goose (see map) have engaged in restoration programs, 17 of them using

Silver Lake in Rochester, Minnesota, where giant Canada geese were "rediscovered." Like other Canada geese, the giants will remain in cold climates all year round if there are food and open (unfrozen) waters.

Pittman-Robertson funding. Most programs were at least partially successful and some have been on a large scale. For example, in the South Dakota State-Federal program, 7,952 giant Canada geese were released at 237 sites in 15 counties from 1967 through 1983. In North Dakota, 6,113 giant Canada geese were released at 83 sites from 1972 through 1981. At least 10 States *outside* the original breeding range engaged in Federal Aid projects involving resident Canada goose flocks, mostly giants.

Starting in 1971, the Tennessee Valley Authority, in cooperation with five State wildlife agencies and two Federal agencies, conducted a vigorous giant Canada goose restoration program in the Tennessee Valley region. By 1985, giant Canada geese were nesting on at least 33 national wildlife refuges in the 18 States within the original breeding range.

The large scale restoration program in the Dakotas stimulated three workshops held in North Dakota in 1971, 1974 and 1982. They drew participants from several Federal, State and provincial wildlife agencies, from universities, private organizations, and individuals.

At first, private game breeders had the only available breeding stock for starting new flocks of giant Canadas. Eggs, goslings, yearlings and paired birds of the strain identified as *maxima* were in great demand as wildlife agencies and private organizations sought to start free-flying flocks. So successful were these ventures that large scale operations soon became commonplace, thanks largely to funds provided through the Pittman-Robertson program.

In later years, after the number of free-flying giant Canada geese had increased substantially as a result of successful restoration efforts, there was some shift in emphasis from releasing captive-reared birds to transplanting. The transplant method involves capturing flightless molting adults and goslings, and moving them to suitable habitats not occupied by breeding Canada geese. Once free-

Monogamous like many other waterfowl, both giant goose parents share in rearing their young. The position of their necks is a defense posture toward the photographer.

Alan Staffan, Ohio Department of Natural Resources

flying flocks were successfully established and the flock size had reached optimum level, some young could be removed for transplanting without harming the flock.

Each autumn, the adult geese in a transplanted group lead the young in migration to a traditional wintering area. The following spring, the adults return to their usual nesting area where they had been captured, while the young tend to "home" back to the transplant area where they experienced their first flight. This homing behavior is an important basic principle which makes it possible to establish new flocks by releasing captive-reared, or transplanting wild-reared geese. Young females or older females that have not flown tend to "home" back to nest at the release or transplant sites where they had their first flight experience. Some flocks, especially in the southern Great Plains, are non-migratory and for them "homing" is irrelevant.

Universities and colleges in the United States and Canada played an important part in the restoration of the giant goose. At least 8 State universities in the 18 States within the original range have supported goose restoration programs with graduate studies.

An outstanding characteristic of the giant goose is its ability to adapt to a wide variety of habitats and other environmental conditions. It may breed on large reservoirs, natural marshes, streams, stock ponds, or even ponds in reclaimed strip-mined lands. It is very tolerant of human activity and will nest in metropolitan and suburban areas as well as in remote wilderness situations. It is partial to isolated nest sites like islands and muskrat houses which cannot be reached by raccoons or other predatory animals which destroy goose nests. The giant's great adaptability—which seems to exceed even that of other Canada geese—makes it possible for people to help it, since it readily accepts artificial nesting sites provided especially for its use. Artificial nesting structures have been an integral part of many restoration programs, and literally thousands have been put out by government agencies, ranchers, farmers, sportsmen and others. Both nesting success and nesting density can be improved by providing artificial structures, islands or other safe nesting places. In recent years, the use of large round hay or straw bales placed in marshes for goose nesting has come into prominence.

This goose has made a comeback due to the combined efforts and teamwork of many agencies, organizations and individuals. The work continues in varying degrees in parts of the vast region but for practical purposes, the restoration job has been done. There has been extensive "pioneering" out from successful restoration sites so much that in some North Central States—notably North Dakota, South Dakota, Minnesota, Wisconsin, and Michigan—giant Canada geese are now found nesting in suitable habitats almost anywhere in the State. Farther west, waterfowl managers have defined two populations—the Hi-line and Great Plains—which are made up largely of giant Canada geese originating from successful restoration efforts. "Hi-line" geese breed in the High Plains region of Alberta, Saskatchewan, Montana, Wyoming and Colorado. "Great Plains" geese breed in Saskatchewan, Manitoba, North Dakota, South Dakota, Nebraska, Kansas and Oklahoma.

We can only speculate on how many giant Canada geese now live in the "approximate breeding range prior to settlement," but the number is substantial, possibly more than 150,000 birds. In fact, restoration efforts have been so successful in some areas that "urban Canada goose problems" are becoming significant and population controls are being imposed. It is appropriate to quote Dr. Hanson again: "The giant Canada goose, newly emerged from obscurity, is again a part of our living heritage."

Sophisticated nesting structures like this are commonly used in captive propagation programs; free-flying giant geese will readily nest on a muskrat house or bale of hay or straw, as long as it is elevated.

279

Beaver Restoration

by Edward P. Hill

Sherlee called his brindle half pit-bull from the shallow pool because it was getting too dark to see. Only one of the two beaver that had been shot was recovered. That made three, a poor showing for such a long hard day. The men were cold and wet, and their spirits were low. That was typical of the last two weeks of 1888.

Sherlee and his two companions had hunted beaver for the last 15 years for the Hudson's Bay Company along the upper and lower Gulf coastal plains of Alabama and Mississippi, but they and hundreds of other beaver hunters had not made expenses the last two winters. When they first started breaking dams and running beaver out of their lodges and bank dens with dogs, their party often took 14 to 25 pelts a day. They soon learned that colonies may have one or two beaver the second year, but none to go back for the third year. By 1890, there was no place within four days' ride from their home where they could hunt beaver.

This pattern of exploitation had been under way across the breadth of North America since the early 1700's; only the techniques differed from place to place. Indian tribes who had earlier used the beaver only for food and clothing, killed them during the spring thaw and traded the pelts for the white men's wares. French, English, and Americans hunted and trapped beaver along the major rivers and drainages across the Great Plains and Rocky Mountains. These pelts made their way through the trading posts, down the rivers to the fur markets such as Astoria (in Oregon), St. Louis, and Montreal, and to the fur centers in Europe where they were fashioned into wearing apparel. Some pelts were made into coats, but most went into hatter's felt. This use created a continuing demand for beaver.

Hudson's Bay Company trapping brigades entered California in 1828, and by 1850 their efforts had become unprofitable. Mountain men, trappers, and Indians had decimated the beaver in Utah between 1824 and 1844. By the early 1900's, active beaver colonies remained only in the most remote and isolated areas of North America. The estimated 60 million beaver that existed in North America before the arrival of the white man had been reduced to an estimated 100,000 by 1900.

That the beaver had disappeared from one drainage after another was mentioned often by mountain men and trappers during their annual rendezvous. However, their way of life was to press on rather than to pause and look back. Although many longed for earlier times when beaver had been plentiful, most were not prepared to restore what they had helped destroy.

To the average American, the beaver had become something one read about, a historical source of exchange and wealth that opened routes for settlers moving into the wild and vast land. With its absence over vast areas of its former

---

Dr. Hill is Assistant Leader of the Mississippi Cooperative Fish and Wildlife Research Unit and Professor of Wildlife and Fisheries at Mississippi State University. During his 25-year research career he has published or co-authored with students some 55 papers with particular emphasis during the past 15 years on fur-bearing animals.

This live-trapped beaver will be transplanted.

range, the beaver became inappropriately yet romantically thought of as a wilderness species. More correctly, it had simply been wiped out of areas where humans lived.

Little was accomplished to re-establish beaver populations before 1920. Only after the formation of State conservation agencies in the early 1900's and the subsequent adoption of regulated harvest systems were conditions right for the long recovery of the continental beaver population. In many States, the beaver was given total protection, and when adequate numbers developed, only limited harvests were allowed.

The first efforts to restore the beaver to its former range had begun with small releases of live-trapped animals in New York in 1904 and 1920, in California in 1924, and in Missouri in 1928. By 1940, 64 beaver had been moved to West Virginia from Michigan and Wisconsin. The real progress was made once Federal Aid in Wildlife Restoration funds were made available through the Pittman-Robertson Act. The restoration of valuable beaver to rural America, still suffering from the Depression, was timely and politically popular. Beaver had been too long and far removed from local landscapes. There was great public support, and in some States, demand for conservation agencies to restore local beaver populations as an income commodity. Pelts had increased again in value to more than $30 each, a lot of money then. Finally, professional conservationists recognized that beaver dams would help prevent soil erosion and benefit other wildlife by establishing wetlands within large expanses of other habitats.

Beaver were live-trapped in suitcase-type traps for release in unoccupied habitat in several States. Beaver from Alabama, Pennsylvania, and Mississippi were moved to Arkansas. Other trap-and-release programs were implemented in the late 1940's and 1950's in Maine, Idaho, California, Wisconsin, Mississippi,

Washington, Iowa, Pennsylvania, Massachusetss, Wyoming, Alabama, Louisiana, and Colorado. In some cases, innovative techniques were used to move beaver into remote localities. Beaver pairs were parachuted into parts of Idaho and Colorado in wooden boxes that opened on contact with the ground. Progeny from these releases spread up and down streamcourses and into adjacent watersheds. In some Canadian provinces, similar but less intensive efforts, combined with their harvest and trapline management systems, provided for a similar recovery.

By the mid-1950's, beaver populations had made dramatic recoveries and were again present on most of the major drainages. Restocking programs and restricted harvest were the important factors in the recovery of beaver in North America, but reduced populations of predators such as wolves, mountain lions, and bears, and the abundant food supply (aspen, willow, etc.) that had recovered during the beaver's long absence, enhanced the rate at which the recovery occurred. When food conditions are good, sexual maturity and breeding in beaver occurs earlier, and the average litter size is slightly larger.

As beaver populations increased, damage complaints began to come into State conservation departments. By the mid-1950's, several States opened trapping seasons to allow limited harvests. Among the categories of complaints were flooding of timber and agricultural crops, blocking of culverts and water control structures, and damage to fish pond dams and irrigation ditches. In some areas of the Midwest, streams slowed by beaver impoundments became too warm for trout production. The benefits of beaver, however, included their creation of wetland habitats for waterfowl and a multitude of other wildlife species, the formation of many small ponds high on watersheds that serve as catchment areas that hold eroding soil, and the warming of waters that had been too cold for sport fish production and growth. Re-establishment of beaver in watersheds of

Beaver make multiple use of trees that grow close to water, employing them for food and to build shelter.

Ken Taylor, North Carolina Wildlife Resources Commission

S.V. Gebbards, Idaho Department of Fish and Game

This fine beaver dam creates new habitat for aquatic life, and helps stabilize the flow of a mountain stream.

some Western States restored year-round flow in streams that had been intermittent for as long as local residents could remember. In both the Rocky and Appalachian Mountains, beaver and their dams have enhanced water quality in some streams by slowing siltation and reducing acidity from coal mine runoff.

By the mid-1970's, beaver, their numbers possibly approaching 15 million, were again on almost all the major watersheds where they existed in pre-Colonial days. Pelt prices fell below $10 and much of the harvest pressure from trapping disappeared. Damage complaints increased, particularly as more people began to move back to rural areas. The beaver became increasingly known for its pest and nuisance attributes. Toxicants had not been developed or licensed for use on beaver, and were believed less effective than traps. Although shooting was legal in many States, trapping with the No. 330 conibear continues to be recommended as the most effective method of beaver control. Snares and leg hold traps are also effective, but generally require greater trapper skill. In relatively flat agricultural and timbered areas, beaver can be expected to cause economic losses unless populations are controlled.

Before we become too "caught up" in controlling beaver, we should look very carefully and cautiously at how and where this animal fits into our present and future well-being. Too little is known about plant succession, tree growth, soil building, groundwater recharge, precipitation patterns, and the positive ecological benefits associated with beaver and their ponds. The potential long-term benefits of beaver colonies for improving conditions critical to man's long-term interests are subtle, yet may be dramatic. The dams of 100,000 beaver located high on a major watershed may prevent flooding more efficiently than a large downstream impoundment. Work should be undertaken to more fully understand the importance of the total ecological contribution that this magnificent rodent now brings to the North American landscape.

Beneath the water, this beaver has begun stacking logs for a new structure.

The Bobcat

By John A. Litvaitis

Few animals inspire an image of wilderness as well as the bobcat. Secretive and silent, it exemplifies a mysterious side of nature. Often the only evidence that reveals the presence of a bobcat is its distinctive track in the snow of winter or mud of spring.

A bobcat resembles a large domestic cat with a short tail. Its coat varies from yellowish brown to gray with numerous black or brown spots and streaks; the underparts are white with black spots. The size of adult bobcats varies considerably. In the Northeast, an adult male weighs about 30 pounds, but in the desert Southwest, perhaps only 12 pounds. Females are usually 30 to 40 percent smaller than males. Bobcats are opportunists and feed upon a variety of prey, with rabbits and rodents the major foods throughout their range. Even deer are preyed upon occasionally by bobcats in northern areas, while southern bobcats depend heavily on small rodents. Unlike foxes and coyotes, bobcats rarely consume fruits.

There are no reliable estimates of the bobcat population of North America. Historically, their range included all 48 contiguous States, the southern tier of Canada, and central Mexico. But during the past 100 years, bobcats were eliminated from large portions of the densely populated Mid-Atlantic States, and from intensively farmed areas of the Midwest. This probably happened because of drastic habitat alteration and efforts to eliminate bobcats and other carnivores that were considered pests—killers of livestock and game animals. Most States allowed year-round trapping and shooting of bobcats and many issued bounties to keep their numbers low.

Until the mid-1970's, bobcat pelts were of little commercial value. The average price paid for a bobcat pelt during the first half of this century was usually less then $10. During the 1970-71 trapping and hunting season, only about 14,000 bobcats were taken in the United States and Canada and pelts sold for an average of $10.60. However, by the 1982-83 season, about 77,000 bobcats were harvested and the average price paid per pelt had increased to $103. This dramatic increase in value and harvest was largely a result of worldwide efforts to protect endangered species of cats. An international agreement strictly regulated the trade of pelts that were traditionally used for garments (primarily leopards and cheetahs). Yet the demand for pelts of spotted cats remained high and fur dealers shifted to bobcat pelts to satisfy that demand, resulting in intense trapping and hunting pressures on bobcats.

As the demand for bobcat pelts increased, the Convention on International Trade in Endangered Species of Flora and Fauna (CITES) and several national conservation and preservation organizations became concerned over the future of the species. As a member nation of CITES, the United States was required to determine the status of bobcats and whether trade in bobcats pelts was detrimental to the species. State wildlife agencies were requested to provide data on

Dr. Litvaitis, Assistant Professor of Wildlife Ecology at the University of New Hampshire, has studied carnivorous animals in Maine, New Hampshire, and Oklahoma. He recently completed a four-year study of bobcats in Maine.

Remington painting by Tom Beecham courtesy of Calendar Promotions, Inc., Washington, Iowa.

Secretive whenever possible, bobcats are seldom far from cover.

bobcat population trends, size of harvest, habitat availability, and mechanisms to control harvest. However, many States lacked quantitative information on bobcats. Few had conducted any field research on bobcats because previous harvest demands had been limited and any management efforts toward bobcats had been to reduce or control their populations. Understandably, some State wildlife agencies were less than happy about the new requirements for bobcat information.

In 1982, Congress extended the life of the Endangered Species Act and included an amendment that indicated no detrimental effects of harvesting bobcats could be found—but under its terms, bobcat populations and harvests would still be monitored. State wildlife agencies now had a mandate to monitor and manage bobcat populations. The result was a number of State research and management projects on bobcats, most using Pittman-Robertson funds. Such circumstances illustrate the ability of the P-R program to respond to unforeseen problems and the fast-changing conditions of wildlife management. Without the availability of Pittman-Robertson funds to support research efforts, many States would have been hard pressed to obtain information on their bobcat populations.

Wildlife biologists met at national and regional bobcat workshops to discuss research priorities, common management problems, and possible solutions. Several research priorities were identified as necessary for proper bobcat management, including improved methods to monitor bobcat numbers, studies of the effects of hunting and trapping on bobcat populations, and the identification of environmental factors that influence bobcat abundance.

To evaluate the effects of hunting and trapping, biologists first have to estimate bobcat density and population trends. Direct counts of bobcats are not possible because of their secretive nature and low densities. Traditional ground or aerial surveys used to monitor populations of large animals such as deer, elk, or moose are not effective. Therefore, the States explored several imaginative, new methods to estimate bobcat population size.

Many States studied bobcat home range by mapping the movements of animals fitted with radio collars. Information on home range size and the amount of overlap with adjacent ranges was used to estimate bobcat densities within study areas. Researchers observed substantial variations; for example, home ranges of bobcats studied in California averaged about 1 square mile, but home ranges of Minnesota bobcats were up to 60 square miles. Home range size varied with prey density, bobcat density, and bobcat body size. Thus, limited information on home range size could not always be applied over large areas.

Other researchers investigated the use of track counts or scent station surveys, which use a scent to attract bobcats. The number of stations visited (based on tracks) is used as a relative index to population size. In Florida, biologists also marked bobcats with a safe radioisotope that was detectable in their feces. Bobcat feces then were collected within the study area and a comparison of the number of "marked" and "unmarked" feces was used to estimate the bobcat population. In Arizona, bobcat density was estimated in a small area using trained hounds to flush individual bobcats. Other wildlife agencies examined the potential of using captures per licensed trapper to evaluate any change in bobcat populations.

However, the results of all these studies indicated that no single method can provide a sensitive index or estimate of bobcat density. Biologists will need to continue to evaluate methods to monitor population change. In the meantime, two or more techniques should be used by each State agency to monitor bobcat populations, and these methods can provide a check on one another.

Biologists managing bobcat populations also need more information on factors influencing harvest levels, and more data about the effects of harvesting on bobcat population changes. Some of the initial reports conflicted, suggesting regional variation. In Oklahoma, trapper- and hunter-harvest rates were suspected of causing a decline in that bobcat population. High rates of harvesting also were suspected by biologists in Idaho to be disrupting bobcat social organization by frequently removing resident animals and preventing the establishment of a stable social order. However, researchers in Maine observed that intensive harvest levels apparently did not disrupt bobcat social organization when young, transient bobcats were present to reoccupy vacated ranges. Transient bobcats apparently spread out from regions that were difficult for trappers and hunters to enter because of few roads. These results indicated that closing some areas to trapping and hunting may provide intensively exploited bobcat populations with a refuge from which individuals can disperse and repopulate nearby areas. In Virginia, trapper license sales and bobcat pelt prices showed no relationship with bobcat harvest levels. However, the number of bobcats trapped did show a positive relationship to fox and raccoon pelt prices, suggesting that as trappers increase their efforts to capture foxes and raccoons, more bobcats are caught in the traps set for those furbearers. In Washington, hunter- and trapper-killed bobcats differed; hunters harvested more male bobcats and their average age was less than those taken by trappers. In States where bobcat hunting is a popular sport, hunters and trappers harvest about the same number of animals. Overall, however, trappers account for about 75 percent of the annual bobcat harvest taken nationally.

Several studies have focused on environmental factors that may influence bobcat abundance. In New Hampshire and New York, researchers have studied the food and energy needs of captive bobcats as the first step in estimating the prey requirements of free-ranging bobcats. Researchers in New England observed that during winter when small prey (mice, rabbits, hares) are less available, juvenile and female bobcats become especially vulnerable to starvation. Adult males, being about a third larger than adult females, are able to prey upon larger animals such as deer during winter. In Texas, biologists observed that bobcats quickly responded to a decline in the abundance of major prey species by switching to other foods. Biologists in Idaho also are examining the relationships between bobcats and cougars and coyotes to understand what effects a change in density of one species of carnivore may have upon the abundance of the others.

In recent years, public attitudes toward predators have changed. Bobcats and other carnivores now are recognized by many people as important components of an ecosystem. In addition, woodland habitats have regenerated in portions of the bobcat's original range that had been cleared for agriculture by early settlers. In the Mid-Atlantic States, farming has declined during the past 50 years and second-growth forests now dominate some areas. As a result of these factors, the New Jersey Division of Fish, Game, and Wildlife in 1978 launched a restoration program to re-establish bobcats. The restoration of wildlife populations was the primary objective of the Pittman-Robertson Act when it was drafted 50 years ago. Original sponsors might have balked at helping bobcats, but they wrote the Act broadly enough to accommodate changing conditions and attitudes, and so New Jersey's restoration project was supported with P-R funds. Through a cooperative agreement with the Maine Department of Inland Fisheries and Wildlife, biologists were able to obtain and release 24 bobcats into secluded woodlands of northern New Jersey from 1978 to 1982. Track surveys and sightings reported by sportsmen indicate that these bobcats are establishing themselves and reproducing in the release sites. Although bobcats may never become abundant in New Jersey's limited habitat, biologists are confident that their efforts to return bobcats to this portion of their native range have been successful.

The efforts of wildlife biologists in New Jersey and throughout the United States have made a difference in assuring the continued success of the bobcat. Much has been learned about this fascinating feline. Yet additional information is still needed, especially on methods to determine population size. In some areas, the harvest still may be too intense for local populations and should be reduced. Accurate information on bobcat population sizes and trends will enable biologists to gain support in controlling harvest pressures. State agencies also should be encouraged to restore bobcat populations that have been extirpated if habitat is available. With continued research and management, the bobcat can become a true success story. As it now stands, the outcome could go either way.

Like other feline species, the bobcat is an excellent tree climber.

The Sea Otter

by Donald B. Siniff

The sea otter *(Enhydra lutris),* the largest member of the mink family, once occupied the near-shore waters of the northern Pacific Ocean from Mexico to Japan. For over two centuries, its relations with man have made it the subject of controversies. Prized for its luxurious fur, it was hunted to near extinction. Today, increasing otter numbers bring joy to nature lovers, but present problems for shellfish industries.

Sea otters are among the smallest marine mammals; adults usually weigh between 45 and 90 pounds. Unlike most other marine mammals, they do not possess a blubber layer; instead they rely upon their extremely dense fur for insulation from the cold water in which they live. To prevent hypothermia, sea otters have a very high metabolic rate and, hence, require about twice as much energy as other mammals of the same size. They must consume large numbers of prey daily in order to maintain this metabolic rate; as a result, they often reduce populations of shellfish and directly compete with man for these resources.

Sea otters are creatures of the near-shore community, where they feed on abalone, clams, crabs, and other species found there. Because otters usually forage in shallow water (less than 100 feet deep), they are fairly easy to observe, and their feeding behavior has been well studied. The otter frequently has been seen to float on its back and pound hardshell mollusks against a stone or another mollusk which it holds on its chest. Pounding is also used underwater to remove species such as abalone from the rocks to which they are attached. Evidence exists that the otter first breaks an abalone's shell and removes the viscera; this kills the abalone so that it releases its hold on the rock and thus is easy to bring to the surface.

Along the Alaskan coast, most sea otter pups are born in April, May, and June. In California and the Aleutian Islands, this spring peak is less pronounced and births occur throughout the year. Pups generally are born in the water, but sometimes on land. Litter size is typically one; twin fetuses have been reported, and the birth of twins actually observed, but there are no records of sea otters successfully rearing two pups. Females generally don't reproduce until they are three years old, and then produce only about one pup per year; thus, their potential for increase is relatively low.

Population Reduction and Subsequent Recovery

Around 1740, Russians began to hunt sea otters in the Aleutian Islands, while European settlers hunted them along the California coast. The fascinating saga of exploitation lasted about 170 years, during which the otters were exterminated from much of their range. In 1911, when an international treaty finally gave them protection, 13 remnant populations were left, scattered from Mexico

Dr. Siniff, a Professor in the Department of Ecology and Behavioral Biology at the University of Minnesota, has been studying marine mammals since 1968 and focusing particularly on sea otters and Antarctic seals. He has written more than 50 scientific papers and served on several marine mammal committees and commissions.

to the Kuril Islands north of Japan. Some of these populations have grown large under protection, while others have become extinct. Full recovery over their entire range has been limited by the otters' slow dispersal between isolated populations.

Human efforts to speed up the recovery process have included a program in which groups of sea otters were moved to areas that were once part of the species' range. The first translocations were attempted in the late 1950's with otters from Amchitka Island on the Aleutian chain. These initial efforts were plagued with difficulties simply because information on handling and transporting otters was not available. Researchers soon found that sea otters held in dry cages could not keep their fur clean. When they were returned to the water, their soiled fur became wet; they quickly chilled and usually died. Another mortality factor involved overheating; high air temperatures during transport caused heat stress and eventually death. It became evident that if the otters were given water they suffered less stress and less likelihood of overheating. Eventually a method for making water readily available during transportation was worked out, and survival improved dramatically. In 1965, sea otters were transported from Prince William Sound to southeast Alaska in their first successful translocation.

Between 1965 and 1972, the Alaska Department of Fish and Game in cooperation with State, Federal, and Canadian provincial agencies released sea otters in eight locations from southeastern Alaska to southern Oregon. Most all of the releases in Alaska were successful as well as the ones in Canada and off the coast of Washington. Only the release in southern Oregon appears to have failed. In 1956, before the technique for movement was fully developed, seven sea otters

Living in cold Pacific waters, sea otters need plenty of high-energy food. They feed heavily on shellfish, competing with a long-established industry.

Robert D. Jones, Jr., U.S. Fish and Wildlife Service

Sea otters resting in a rocky cove.

were liberated in the Pribilof Islands and this population also appears to have failed. The successful populations seem to be expanding into new areas and it is likely that sea otters will eventually recolonize most of their previous range.

The success of the translocation program owes much to Pittman-Robertson (P-R) funding. Safe methods of transporting sea otters were developed entirely with P-R funds, which enabled the State of Alaska to develop an active sea otter program beginning in 1962. In addition, Pittman-Robertson contributed to all of the successful translocations between 1965 and 1972. In those early days, P-R funds were crucial for such work because other programs and sources of funding were not yet in existence. Karl B. Schneider, who took prominent part in the Alaska Department of Fish and Game's pioneering work during that period, has written that "P-R provided the seeds which resulted in re-establishment of sea otters in a 2,000-mile stretch of vacant former habitat. It is quite possible (I think likely) that without P-R the transplants would never have occurred."

Current Status

Today, most authorities consider sea otters in North America to consist of two separate groups, or populations, one in coastal areas of Alaska and Canada and the other along the coast of California. The California population numbers around 1,500 animals and extends from about the Santa Rosa River on the south to just beyond Santa Cruz on the north. This population is thought to have expanded from about 50 otters that remained after 1911 in an area just south of Monterey. It is regarded by some scientists as a separate subspecies and, in 1976, was classified as "threatened" under the Endangered Species Act. The other group is scattered from Washington to the far islands of the Aleutian chain. Those in Alaska and Canada have expanded from remnant populations or from animals transplanted from Amchitka Island and Prince William Sound.

Currently, there are an estimated 150,000 sea otters in Alaska, and in many areas their populations seem to be expanding. Clearly, the Alaskan populations are now large enough to allow a harvest for fur pelts. However, current legislation, particularly the Marine Mammal Protection Act of 1972, and public pressure against the killing of marine mammals make it unlikely that any commercial hunt will occur in the near future. Nevertheless, there is considerable pressure in Alaska for harvest by Indian, Eskimo, and Aleut peoples as part of a subsistence "take" allowed under the Marine Mammal Protection Act. At present, items made from marine mammals cannot legally be sold unless they are classified as native arts or crafts.

The economic importance of sea otters also may be measured by the monetary loss to commercial and recreational shellfisheries that compete with otters for resources. Some scientists suggest that large scale depletions of shellfish stocks cannot be unequivocally blamed on sea otters because commercial and recreational shellfishing may also have reduced these stocks. However, several other scientists provide convincing evidence that sea otters do reduce shellfish stocks so that commercial shellfish harvest by man is no longer an option. The competition between sea otters and shellfish industries for near-shore resources undoubtedly will continue as otter populations expand into new areas.

In California, sea otter numbers seem to have changed little in about the last 10 years. This population's inability to expand is believed to be related to certain human activities along the coast. For example, a gillnet fishery operating in shallow water along the coast has been implicated as a major cause of sea otter deaths. As such mortality factors are removed, it is likely that the sea otter population in California will expand once more. In addition, there is a translocation effort to establish another population of California sea otters by moving animals to an area outside the current population's range. Several possible transfer sites have been suggested, with the current U.S. Fish and Wildlife Service plan favoring San Nicolas Island, in the Channel Islands of Southern California. As this was written (1986), translocation operations were planned to begin in 1987.

Given the likelihood that sea otter numbers will grow in future years, management needs to focus on resolving the conflict between human and sea otter uses of shellfish. The conflict may be resolved through a policy called Zonal Management, which has been suggested by the Marine Mammal Commission and the U.S. Fish and Wildlife Service. Under such a plan, some parts of the coast would be deemed sea otter areas while other parts would be designated non-otter areas. If necessary, otters would be removed from or kept from expanding into non-otter areas. Unfortunately, the legalities of adopting such a management strategy, at least in California, seem formidable at the moment; the Endangered Species Act and, perhaps, the Marine Mammal Protection Act may have to be modified before such management plans could be executed.

Already in Alaska, there is adverse reaction to the sea otter's expansion. Kodiak Island and Prince William Sound are now the focal points of such opposition primarily because of dungeness and king crab fisheries. However, as sea otter populations continue to grow, animosity undoubtedly will spread to other locations. Growing animosity, in turn, may lead to substantial increases in illegal killing of otters. Solutions to these resource conflicts must be found soon in order to prevent the development and spread of such scenarios. Zonal management is probably the best compromise that can be implemented.

Sea otters were nearly wiped out by the early Russian fur trade. Despite legal protection under a 1911 treaty, the appealing little mammals were unable to restore populations in most areas until Alaska began transplants with P-R support.

Bobwhite Quail

by Bill T. Crawford

Few upland game hunters and landowners will argue about the traditional title of "King" for the bobwhite quail. The right to wear the crown is undisputed whenever this cherished American game bird is up for discussion. For the farmer, hearing the familiar musical whistling of ah-bob-white-ah-bob-white can be enough to make his day of hard work not only tolerable, but more satisfying. For the hunter, as one writer puts it, "the quail is poetry in a special package." Being in a spot to hear quail whistling from the roost, and then walking up behind your lead dog's point, followed by the heart-stopping explosion of birds becoming airborne—the scenario that hundreds of quail hunters have experienced annually since settlement days—is a difficult combination to improve on.

But the future enjoyment of this esteemed sport is sorely threatened. The trend in quail populations is downward at an ever-increasing pace. Quail numbers have declined severely since the early 1950's as their habitats have been drastically changed. Some occasional population increases have been experienced due to excellent weather conditions, but the long-term habitat problems associated with commercial agriculture and forestry prevail across the bobwhite's range.

The downward trend is very well documented. The commonly heard complaint "By golly, quail hunting just ain't what it used to be" has a ring of solid truth. In an age when success stories abound concerning forest-loving species such as deer, wild turkey, and ruffed grouse, it is a sad note that our expectations for the bobwhite hold so little promise.

In the late 1920's and 1930's, Stoddard, Leopold and Errington conducted landmark studies on quail biology. The management and research activity increased in the late 1930's and 1940's by expanding staffs of State biologists working under the newly implemented Pittman-Robertson Federal Aid in Wildlife Restoration program. A large part of the published literature on quail biology and management came from this source of support. The facts on the quail's needs appear to be well developed except for some problems dealing with the new era of agricultural intensity. Actually, it seems like a modern miracle that quail are able to survive at all under today's farming methods. All authorities agree on the primary causes for population decreases.

The bobwhite is known to be a product of diverse habitat. It is associated largely with rough pastures, small grain and hay fields, thickets, woodlots and fence row borders with brushy vegetation. Quail were ever-present on the American pre-settlement landscape. With immigration and settlement, pioneer farming developed on a grand scale. Quail response was phenomenal; populations soared in the Eastern and Midwestern United States. Before this primitive farming created edge habitat around new cropland and pasture borders, quail

Mr. Crawford headed the Wildlife Research Section—Wildlife Division of the Missouri Department of Conservation for 35 years prior to his recent retirement, specializing in small game and habitat-soil wildlife relationships, and authoring numerous publications. He served The Wildlife Society as President, Vice-President and Sectional Representative.

Remington painting by Tom Beecham courtesy of Calendar Promotions, Inc., Washington, Iowa.

299

generally had been limited to the natural edges and drainage patterns where prairie and woods met.

As the family farm became the dominant agricultural pattern for the Eastern, Southeastern and Midwestern United States, bobwhite quail habitat was solidly in place. Under the land use system of the day, a covey of quail could find most of its needs for shelter, food, nesting, and movement in a 20- to 40-acre tract. This pioneering, horse-drawn agriculture, so common everywhere, favored the bobwhite and resulted in an enormous increase in population throughout its range. It was a heyday for the bobwhite, and it also became a heyday for the great sport of quail hunting. High populations of birds with much open accessible range encouraged people to take up the sport. Along with that situation, pointing dog interest and ownership developed, and so did intense field trial activities. With better road systems, travel equipment, and improved firearms, quail hunting became a winner. Contributing further to the bird's popularity were its excellent holding, fast flushing, and target qualities. And it didn't hurt it one bit to be classed high on the list of great table fare.

By the approach of the 1930's, however, it became evident that with more settlement and intensive farming, habitat would become more limited and poorer in quality. Brushy woods were being converted into bare, overgrazed pastures. Weedy rail-fence rows and borders were replaced by naked wire, and hedge rows were uprooted from prairie farmsteads. But even into the late 1930's there remained a core of good habitat which supported excellent quail populations throughout the bird's range.

For a 10-year period after World War II, quail fairly well held their own. The family farm was still a reality. Special "set-aside" government programs allowed farmers to benefit from letting fields go fallow. This in turn worked to the

Bobwhites thrived on horse-powered farms like this one in Kansas with its interspersed woody cover and cropland.

advantage of small game—notably bobwhite. Farming was still partially a subsistence operation where the horse and mule remained important. There were few large modern tractors, combines and rolling balers. Pastures were heavy with clovers and lespedezas. The system of managed pastures had not yet made its appearance. Some farmers still shocked corn, and many still picked and shucked by hand and never thought of fall plowing.

By the early 1950's, changing cropping and land use systems began to move like a plague across the quail landscape. They basically resulted in a number of stressful habitat conditions: (1) larger field sizes with subsequent elimination of cross fences and cover lanes; (2) clean farming with strong dependence on mowing and pesticidal chemicals; (3) fall plowing, which eliminated food and cover during critical winter periods; (4) loss of rotations of legumes and small grains, and the introduction of new pasture grasses, notably of the Bermuda-fescue types; (5) intensive single-crop culture systems, eliminating the vegetative diversity needed by quail; (6) elimination of the plains type osage-orange fence rows and associated travel lanes; (7) loss of fallow ground; and (8) elimination of natural waterways and associated wild vegetation.

In the Southeast, still another factor began to weigh against the bobwhite as the forest products industry expanded. Small farms and old-growth pine forests, many of which had provided prime quail habitat, gave way to large, short-rotation pine plantations. During the first two or three years in the life of these new stands, quail tended to do well, but then a steady downward trend set in and continued.

Taken together, these practices became overpowering forces in the decline of farmland quail. The shift to the monoculture system brought almost total use of tractor-power as the replacement for horse-drawn equipment. This in itself forced a great change in farm vegetation; growing oats, timothy and associated grains for horse feed was no longer necessary. Soon the bulldozers, heavy tillage and earth-moving equipment eliminated much of the quail range. Fields were reshaped, drainage ditches dug, rough pastures converted, and odd areas of timber, brush and creek borders were eliminated. This was particularly true in the regions of fertile soils where the potential was high for wildlife.

In the new farming system, habitat remains only in small islands or pockets. With pressures such as hunting, predation and other disturbances on these same areas, the population becomes reduced. Reproductive problems follow because of lack of nearby cover from which other birds can come. Anything that affects these isolated islands of cover reduces the ability of quail to recover. Coupled with farming changes has been the widespread sprawl of cities, housing, highways, large multi-purpose lakes, and commercial developments covering the landscape with something that won't support quail.

Since settlement days, the bobwhite has in most cases been considered a by-product of the farm system. If the present system does not allow for the quail by-product or if the by-product carries no economic incentive, quail production falls through the crack.

To describe the problems and wring our hands is not constructive. The question is what we can do to improve quail populations.

For years cries have been heard for stocking to supplement low quail populations. Stocking sounds like an easy, quick-fix remedy, but like most quick fixes, it doesn't work. Many State Pittman-Robertson research projects have been conducted on restocking efforts. All have been negative. Repeatedly, hand-reared quail have shown very short lifespans on release and end up as expensive food for natural predators. Too often, people demanding quail stocking fail to note that their lands or hunting grounds have lost their carrying

Male bobwhite (white markings) and two
females in good protective cover.

capacity for wild quail. To place birds in such a harsh environment and expect results is folly. Another alternative—that of trapping wild quail to put into pockets of good habitat—is prohibitively expensive and not very practical.

We must attack the real problem, the steady reduction of quail habitat through current land use programs. We must raise the question as to how and to what extent we can really retard the deterioration and loss of quail habitat. One very expensive approach to solving the problem is providing payments to landowners to create quail habitat. Money for such a program would have to come from a new source or from some other conservation activity, which is unlikely at this period of time in public funding.

There are some available sources of help for interested landowners and sportsmen, often at little direct cost. Set-aside cropping programs have existed for several years and many farming practices within these programs benefit quail. Some Federal and State conservation agencies have trained personnel who will draw up free wildlife management plans for a farm, specific for quail—if requested. Along with this service, these programs frequently provide free food and cover seeds and low-cost trees and shrubs. Demonstration farms are available in some counties. These are working, no-subsidy operations that show landowners how to produce both wildlife and a living. Demonstration practices include no-till cropping, use of native grains, timber and fuelwood production, erosion control and contour strip cropping.

It is conceivable that the currently recognized serious nature of soil erosion could result in a blessing for quail. Current Federal farm programs are seeing a marriage of conservation and agriculture. The new soil erosion farm legislation with "sodbuster" and "swampbuster" provisions will take away Federal fund eligibility from farmers who convert present grazing lands or wetlands to crops. This concept could allow millions of acres throughout the bobwhite range to

302

again support quail food and cover. The challenge to landowners to provide the right vegetative mix is an opportunity for quail management. It could help turn around the monoculture trend and provide a new diversity of more suitable habitat.

One major problem for quail production on private lands has been the lack of economic incentive. Current trends hint at this problem through leasing of hunting rights. Leases are common between deer and turkey hunters and landowners. This idea is starting to catch on with quail hunters, spreading particularly in the South. Quail hunting is worth dollars to people—both hunters and landowners. In most States, 90 percent or more of the land is in private ownership, and this is where the quail habitat restoration has to be done. If landowners cannot see a personal or business incentive to manage for quail, there will be no wide-scale habitat program.

If we want to maintain or increase quail numbers, there is no alternative to re-establishing natural habitat. The widespread loss of premier habitat has become a national quail disaster. The problems of research and management of quail need to be strongly addressed and improved upon, particularly because the changing landscape constantly poses new unsolved dilemmas.

The 50-year Pittman-Robertson program has been a tremendous help in documenting the problems of quail and developing management techniques and plans. The program's opportunities to help solve the severe challenges of quail are still ahead. State and national strategies must be developed that can be applied on a local basis. Will we take advantage of the talents and the wildlife science provided through these P-R funds to bring a turnabout in the bobwhite story? Citizens, hunters, outdoorsmen, landowners—the knowledge and skills are available. Now it's your turn at bat.

Bobwhites can survive considerable snow and cold as long as habitat is adequate. Unfortunately, much quail habitat has been lost in recent decades.

Oklahoma Department of Wildlife Conservation

The Ring-Necked Pheasant

By Robert B. Dahlgren

One of the few imported game birds that have done well in the United States, the ring-necked pheasant has become endeared to hunters across the country. They consider it to be their own. Asian in origin, the pheasant has been carried by man in centuries past to Europe and from England to the eastern seaboard. Stocking attempts in the 1700's in the Northeast failed, but of many attempts in the late 1800's, some were successful.

The big break-through into North America began in Oregon. Ringnecks from Shanghai, China, were stocked there in 1881. They prospered, and were later transported across the Northern States where their genes were mixed with the English black-necked pheasant in the East. Nowhere were they more compatible with the climate and the farming patterns than in the Midwest. Wherever they were introduced, it seems to be a pattern that their populations peaked from 20 to 40 years after introduction, and then declined. Aside from the Oregon-Washington populations, which declined after the first decade of the 20th Century, most midwestern and eastern populations peaked in the 1930's and 1940's, then declined with a loss of prime habitat. In Iowa, however, active transplant programs under P-R allowed pheasant populations to adapt to the southern part of the State while populations in more intensively cultivated northern portions declined steeply. Missouri and Pennsylvania are other States where active P-R transplant programs in the past several decades have helped populations to develop.

Only about a dozen States, chiefly in the warm and humid Southeast, have no pheasants. Irrigation has made possible the spread of the pheasant into the seemingly harsh and dry climates of the Intermountain West and the Southwest. Almost everywhere the pheasant has succeeded, the plow already had created a gap to which most native bird species were unable to adapt.

Even in the 1970's and 1980's, healthy populations of pheasants existed where habitat and weather combined to favor reproduction. Nowhere are these pockets so large and expansive as in the Midwest. The ringneck in the heartland breadbasket of our country has had a profound influence on the local hunters and the local economy. Typically, in the Midwest, opening day of pheasant season has been a special day. This was especially true in the 1930's and 1940's when regional ringneck populations were at their best. Shops closed so dads and sons could go hunting. No need to go to the barbershop to get a haircut. Likely you'd find a sign on the door that read, "Closed—gone hunting."

Ringnecks adapted to early Asian farming practices. Their prime habitat requirements are early stages of plant succession created by the farmer. They

---

Dr. Dahlgren is Leader of the Iowa Cooperative Fish and Wildlife Research Unit and Professor in the Department of Animal Ecology at Iowa State University. He previously worked 16 years for the South Dakota Department of Game, Fish and Parks, chiefly on pheasant research; for two years he headed the agency's research program. Best known of his many published works on pheasants is a series of newspaper articles, published as a booklet by South Dakota in 1967.

have done their best in situations where from about half to three-fourths of the land is in cultivation. Enough undisturbed or idle farmland is needed so they can hatch their eggs. They're prolific re-nesters, and such crops as spring-sown grains serve as excellent nesting cover if early nests are lost. The diverse crops grown on many farms in the Midwest in the 1930's and 1940's suited their needs very well. Small grains, native or tame haylands, a little corn or sorghum, some pasture for the cattle, a few shelterbelts and uncultivated odd areas here and there, weedy fencerows, headlands at the end of the field for machinery to turn, a few sloughs or marshes—and you had pheasant heaven. If the winter was severe, pheasants could fly out from the thick cattails in the marsh or from the shelterbelts to feed in the cattle or horse tracks in the cornfield or feed from the spillage around the cattlebunks. That doesn't describe the modern midwestern farm of today, however. Things have changed!

Today, many of the fencerows are gone, the headlands are gone, many of the old tree claims, odd areas, farmsteads, shelterbelts, pastures, and marshes are gone and farmed-over. Few cattle forage in the large corn and soybean fields in the bleak winter landscape. It doesn't seem to matter, for the waste grain was plowed under in the fall, anyway. We are in an era of intensive farming with sophisticated farm machinery that mandates large fields. Chemical technology and advances in plant breeding have favored monocultures of corn or soybeans on most of our agricultural lands. Herbicides have modified plant composition,

Cock pheasant can find protective cover in this good habitat despite his gaudy plumage.

Gene Brehm, Kansas Fish and Game

Adapted from a map prepared by Robert B. Dahlgren, Carl G. Trautman and Victor S. Janson, 1971.

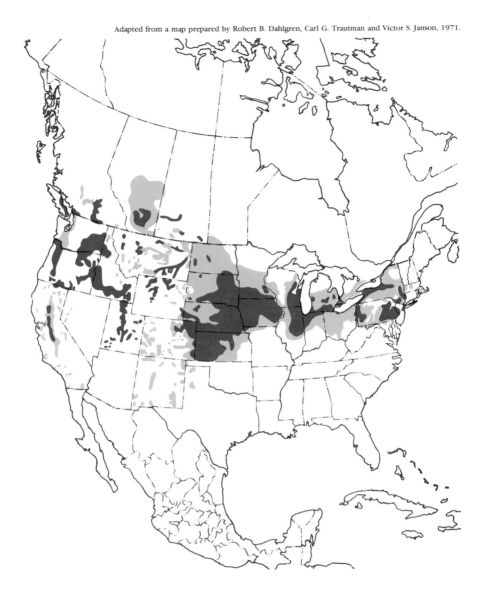

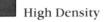 High Density

Low Density

Distribution of ring-necked pheasants, with darker shaded areas indicating highest population densities as of 1971. Distribution patterns remain almost the same, although densities have varied somewhat since then.

307

Burning off weeds in early spring, as shown at left roadside, destroys nesting and escape cover for pheasants and other birds. Natural weedy growth like that on the right roadside can be highly productive.

even in the roadsides which are the mainstay of many modern, meager pheasant populations.

Our farm was a good example of change. My father purchased the farm from Grandfather, who had homesteaded it in southwestern Minnesota in the late 1800's. My hunting territory as a boy included the crop fields, a slough filled with smartweed in the summer and water in the fall where I shot my first migrating mallard ducks, a creek bend filled with native grasses and brush that we nick-named the "jungle," a steep-sloping creek bank planted to jack pines with willows along the creek, a "tree claim" consisting mostly of giant cottonwoods, a shelterbelt planted to Chinese elm in the 1930's that was full of weeds, and a sidehill field that was alternated with hay and oats. The creek flowed all year long when my Dad was a boy, and he speared northern pike in the deep pools. When I first learned to fish, I caught only minnows that came up in the spring, and were stranded in pools when water slowed to a trickle in the summer. Now there is only one flow of water during the year, a great erosive gush in the spring that dries up by June to leave the gravel riffles exposed.

The first pheasant I shot was in the 1940's in the shelterbelt; that's bull-dozed and farmed now. The slough was tiled and the jack pines died when that area was fenced for a hog lot so that my college education could be financed. The last of the trees were cut down on the tree claim. The last pheasant I shot there was in the jungle. After my father died, and the farm was sold, the jungle disap-peared under the bulldozer that leveled even the steepest creek banks. My mother told me stories of the prairie-chickens that came in waves during their migrations, I tell my grandchildren about how I outwitted the pheasants, and now the farm consists of silent fields of corn and soybeans.

Pheasants didn't go anywhere, i.e., they didn't migrate. Essentially they were unable to find a place that was undisturbed during the nesting season.

Proof that nesting cover was important to the success of the pheasant came in the Conservation Reserve (Soil Bank) program. Just before 1956 in South Dakota, when the Soil Bank program began, pheasants numbered 4 to 6 million. By 1961, the population had more than doubled to about 11 million. Further proof that nesting-cover removal was the cause of pheasant population decline came with the expiration of Soil Bank contracts. Declines in Soil Bank land closely matched downward changes in pheasant population levels. With all the changes in our methods of farming and in the landscape, we needn't wonder where all the pheasants went.

Pittman-Robertson projects entered the game late as far as pheasants were concerned. Nevertheless, the P-R program is inextricably entwined with the later history of pheasant populations. The gains that have been made in range extension through trapping and transplant programs are almost exclusively due to P-R. These programs, and experimental stocking of new strains and crosses of subspecies, may hold some hope for the future.

Some of the greatest gains made by P-R are due to the biologists employed in the program who have personally dedicated their careers to educating the public. When pheasant numbers became only a shadow of their former prominence, the sportsmen and interested citizens naturally wondered why. There were lots of opinions among the public and often these opinions incorrectly focused on a single reason, such as pesticides, disease, or predators. Biologists knew that the real reason was a complex interplay of many factors. Without the

This pheasant hen, lured by corn, has walked into a trap. She will be fitted with a miniature radio transmitter to help biologists learn more about how pheasants are affected by experimental cultivation practices.

Pheasants flushing from winter cover in a farm shelterbelt. These birds can survive harsh winter weather if cover — and high energy foods like corn — are available.

ability to create a favorable environment for itself, the pheasant was entirely subject to the weather and what habitat man would provide. To unweave this complicated web, to understand it, and to communicate the ecological principles to a resistant and opinionated public was a monumental task. The change in the American people over the past 20 years in their understanding of such principles as diversity, pollution, and animal and plant changes in response to environmental changes has created a new vocabulary now familiar to the public, and a new awareness and concern for the environment around us. Many dedicated State employees, hired with P-R funding, donated countless hours to explaining pheasant ecology to citizen groups and sportsmen's organizations.

Two other groups deserve mention. One comprises the State employees who made cover plantings to furnish nesting cover and winter cover for the pheasant and the land managers who maintained quality cover with just the right bit of diversity in the landscape. The other group are those game managers and administrators who have made good progress in sound and sensible season-setting regulations based upon data gathered under P-R. As long as we're shooting cocks only, seasons with a generous length that cover an entire State or a broad part thereof are both easily interpreted and safe for the wildlife resource.

Biologists did their work well in the early P-R program, and learned much about the pheasant. Some have retired and some have passed on. They were replaced by pheasant biologists in the 1950's and 1960's with whom I've had the pleasure of working. Some of these now have responsibilities as highly placed educators and administrators. Their work also was done well, and a simplified, knowledge-based pheasant program has resulted. Pheasant numbers are fewer now, but the biologists in the present pheasant program under P-R are well-trained, enthusiastic, and capable of appealing successfully to the modern environmental conscience. Further, they have allies in many conservation groups.

The future for the pheasant is not entirely bright, but it is clear. We cannot hope to go back to the good old days, because too many irreversible changes have taken place. We may plant safe nesting cover, but the fencerows, the headlands, the marshes, and the diversity that complement it are gone. There is a more pressing need for soil conservation now, however, than ever before. When we address that need in a meaningful way, it will mean that some land area will need to be dedicated to permanent cover. The pheasant and other species such as the bobwhite will be benefited. The 1985 Farm Bill enacted by Congress has for the first time "sodbuster," "swampbuster," and conservation reserve provisions that are a response to the conservation community's concern about the environment and soil erosion. If administered properly, the conservation-reserve provisions that could idle 40 to 45 million acres could now be a shot in the arm for pheasants, as the Soil Bank provisions once were. Many feel that the present agricultural system, sustained as it is by cheap power, foreign fuels, long transportation hauls, and chemical supports, is subject to failure and is not a sustainable system. If modern agriculture should trend toward control of soil erosion, regional diversity of crops, or lessened inputs, pheasants would benefit. It may be that crosses of subspecies of the pheasant may be produced that will be more suited to conditions imposed by present-day agriculture. Whatever happens, the knowledge gained and applied in the last 50 years of pheasant work under P-R will be put to work to serve this fine game bird even further.

Newly hatched pheasant chicks. Reproductive success is possible only if there is grassy/weedy cover for nesting.

Kent Olson, South Dakota Department of Game, Fish and Parks

The Chukar Partridge

By Glen C. Christensen

There is scarcely a major game bird species on earth that has not been trapped and caged and shipped to some far-off point on the globe with the hope that upon release it would become established and supplement the native fauna. The United States has a long history of exotic game bird introductions, most of which failed. However, several species did succeed in finding their niche, and the chukar partridge was one of them.

This sassy little stranger is one of the seven species of red-legged partridges found widely throughout Europe, northern Africa, and Asia. The bird that has succeeded in the Western States is the Indian subspecies *(Alectoris chukar chukar),* a native of the rugged, mountainous areas of northern India and Pakistan.

The chukar is a quail-like bird but larger. The sexes look alike, but the male is slightly heavier, weighing up to one and a half pounds, while the female seldom exceeds one pound. It is an easy bird to distinguish in the field with its red legs and bill, black-barred flanks, and the white throat set off by a black line running through the eye and down the sides of the neck.

Chukars were first introduced into the United States in 1893 when 5 pairs were imported from Karachi. In the years that followed, large numbers of chukars were released by State game departments, sportsmen's clubs and interested individuals in 42 mainland States and 6 Canadian provinces, in Hawaii, and in New Zealand.

Since little was known about the habitat requirements of the chukar prior to 1950, the early introductions were hit-or-miss efforts. Nevertheless, an interest was created in this Asian import, particularly in the States of California, Nevada and Washington, where nucleus populations began to thrive. This gave State wildlife biologists the opportunity to take a closer look at the chukar, its life history and habitat needs. Important data was collected and disseminated to other biologists by agency publications and reports and through annual workshops and published reports by the Western States Chukar Committee and later the Western States Exotic Game Bird Committee. Significantly, during this time, most of the Western States took advantage of Federal Aid funds which had recently become available through the Pittman-Robertson Act. These early P-R projects not only helped finance many chukar partridge introductions and redistribution efforts, but also helped make it possible for subsequent research, survey and inventory, and development programs.

Between the time of the first release in 1893 and a 1968 poll, at least 806,000 chukars had been released in North America and Hawaii. Most came from game farm stock; however, several Western States (most notably Nevada and California) initiated trapping projects in areas where the chukar had be-

Mr. Christensen began working with the chukar partridge in 1951, soon after he joined the Nevada Department of Wildlife as an upland game biologist. From 1959 to 1961 he conducted ecological evaluations of chukars and other game birds in remote areas of India, Pakistan, and Afghanistan, studying their suitability for introduction into the Western U.S. Later he was Chief of the Game Division of Nevada's wildlife agency for nine years before retiring in 1980.

Remington painting by Tom Beecbam courtesy of Calendar Promotions, Inc., Washington, Iowa.

come established. These wild birds were released in suitable, but unoccupied, habitats in many western locations. More than half of these releases were made after 1954 and the sites were "selected" on the basis of newly available research data as well as judgments formed by biologists who had visited areas where chukars were proving successful. This scientific approach resulted in fewer and fewer releases in States which obviously lacked the necessary habitat. Biologists concentrated their efforts on the western ranges which met the research standards. By 1970, the fruits of these efforts were realized, and the chukar partridge occupied 100,000 square miles of habitat in North America and the Hawaiian Islands.

Why has this cocky little import adapted so well to western North America? Let's take a look at the bird's native land.

Chukar habitat in India and Pakistan lies chiefly within massive mountain chains such as the Himalayas, Hindu Kush and Karakorums, some of the most rugged terrain anywhere. Numerous valleys, many with beautiful streams and rivers, weave a pattern through the mountains and, where conditions are suitable, the land is cultivated. The climate is arid to semi-arid with rather short, hot summers and cold winters. Precipitation occurs primarily in the winter and spring and varies from 3 to 13 inches annually. The vegetation is primarily short brush with a grass-forb understory and sometimes a scattered overstory of small conifers. The chukar partridge inhabits the broken terrain from the valley floor (usually 4,000 to 6,000 feet high, but as low as sea level in Sind and Baluchistan) to mountain slopes and peaks as high as 16,000 feet.

Many parts of western North America are an almost perfect match for the chukar's native Asian environment in climate, vegetation and topography, particularly the Intermountain Plateaus of the Western United States. California, Nevada, Oregon, Washington, Idaho, Utah, Colorado and Wyoming harbor the greatest chukar populations. However, isolated colonies exist as far south as northern Baja California in Mexico, and north into south-central British Columbia, Canada. The chukar is now established on six Hawaiian Islands—Oahu, Kauai, Maui, Lanai, Molokai and Hawaii.

It seems the history of land use in the Western United States opened the way for the successful introduction of the chukar partridge. Sagebrush and grass dominate most of the areas now occupied by the chukar. Typically, these western ranges were heavily overgrazed in the late 1800's and early 1900's, allowing for the invasion of annual Mediterranean grasses which replaced many of the native perennials.

Several species of brome grass became common, most importantly cheatgrass, which has been very influential in creating excellent chukar habitat (by perpetuating itself through fires) and in serving as a primary chukar food supply on a year-around basis. Thus intensive land use in the West, followed by the introduction of the exotic grass and forb species, may well have set the stage for the introduction of the exotic chukar, who is well adapted to a set of similar land use patterns in the Old World.

Native game birds which share parts of their habitat with the chukar are the mourning dove, California, Gambel's and mountain quail, and the sage grouse. In many areas, the only meeting ground for these species is at springs, mountain meadows and near rivers and creeks, suggesting that the chukar competes little, if at all, with native species.

Within recent times, large expanses of sage grouse habitat have been lost through range deterioration (overgrazing, drought and fire). This has been particularly noticeable in Nevada, and as the sage grouse faded out, the chukar moved in and occupied what could have been a serious void.

314

*These chukars were among the first of their
species to be released in northeastern Nevada
after being trapped elsewhere in the State in an
early 1960's P-R financed project.*

The chukar partridge, a colorful little rimrock dweller, has added a new
dimension to the western wildlife scene. It is monogamous, and by mid-March
the pairing commences. Length of daylight, temperatures, and food conditions
play a part in determining when pairing will occur.

During the pairing process, calling by both sexes is very commonplace.
One of the most common calls, and the one from which the bird derives its
name, is a throaty "chucking" which can be heard for long distances.

The nest is merely a depression scratched in the ground and lined with dry
grasses, stems and feathers. However, nests are so well concealed among the
brush and rocks on the mountain slopes that they are very difficult to locate.

Egg laying commences in March or April (depending on latitude and elevation) with the hatch occurring in May and June. If a nest is destroyed, the hen
will usually renest, and therefore it is not uncommon to observe downy young in
late August. The limited data available about active nests suggests that the number of eggs laid may vary from 10 to 21. The chukar's reproductive potential is
finely tuned to its environment, and during years when climate and food
supplies are favorable it is a very prolific bird, averaging over 13 chicks per
brood with individual broods containing as many as 20 chicks. Brood integrity is
often lost as the season progresses, resulting in the gathering of communal
broods of 50 to over 100 chicks of various sizes accompanied by several adults.
During drought years, the average brood size will drop drastically and there will
be little or no population growth. Consequently, a "boom and bust" population
pattern emerges which can generally be predicted by the biologist who corre-
lates annual data concerning precipitation, temperatures, the availability of key
food plants, and brood sizes.

315

Chukars are well adapted to seemingly inhospitable country, with its rough rock surfaces and hardy vegetation.

The daily movements of chukars revolve around feeding, watering, escape from predators, and roosting. The birds may travel up to one mile, usually to find water, during the spring, summer and early fall. In the winter, heavy snow will prompt the birds to move to lower elevations where feed is available. When the birds pair, there is a general movement throughout their range.

Chukars feed on a wide range of plant species and relish green grass leaves, seeds of grasses and forbs, and the nuts of the pinyon pine. Insects do not make up a large part of the diet, but grasshoppers are quickly devoured when available. Although unusual, it is possible to find a "partridge in an apple tree" if the two happen to meet at an isolated grove. In the arid West, food supplies can vary dramatically from year to year, and during extended droughts the chukar eats dry grass stems and rootstocks if seeds and greens are not available.

On the other hand, the chukar itself has provided a new item to the menu of the bobcat, coyote, great horned owl, golden eagle and a number of species of hawks. It is not an easy prey, though, since it blends in with its rocky environment and, if flushed, will dive speedily downhill, over the rimrocks, to the canyon below.

With the "introductions" phase of the chukar program completed and the parameters of the range which they occupy established, what more could be done to enhance the populations of this splendid little bird? Wildlife biologists were quick to recognize that one of the major limitations was the lack of water. Water developments were undertaken in several States to satisfy this need, often hand-in-hand with chukar releases. The gallinaceous guzzler, used so successfully for desert quail, now serves the chukar partridge equally well. Its use has made many square miles of additional habitat available to the chukar, and water development projects for this purpose are still active in most States.

Here is a bird that is in tune with the current use of western rangelands. It lives, for the most part, on public lands managed by Federal agencies. Consequently, this beautiful little bird can be enjoyed by a wide range of people, from the ardent nature lover to the most diligent hunter, without the usual landowner-public conflicts. During "boom" population years, it can provide unexcelled sport (and cuisine) to the western hunter who has successfully adapted his hunting techniques, dogs, stamina and attitude towards pursuit of this nifty little newcomer. Even during "bust" years, the hardy hunter can still search out that little pocket of survivors in hopes of securing a limited bag, knowing that if he does, there will still be sufficient brood stock left in the many inaccessible areas of its range to provide for bountiful reproduction when the cheatgrass gets green again.

Man-made guzzler devices have helped chu-kars and many other bird species.

Fox Squirrels like small woodlots near fields.

Bob Hines

Gray and Fox Squirrels

by Vagn Flyger

Gray squirrels and fox squirrels rank high among North America's favorite game animals and also among the Nation's most visible wild mammals. In spite of their abundance in the eastern half of the United States, it is only in recent years that much has been learned about their habits and needs—largely through Pittman-Robertson research.

These acrobatic, frisky rodents are remarkably adapted to living in trees. Each toe is tipped with a needle-sharp claw for holding firmly to tree trunks and small branches, while their characteristic bushy tails help maintain balance or serve as parachutes in case of falls. These tails also are signal flags, and any frightened or excited squirrel that waves its semaphore alerts every other squirrel within sight. Their senses of vision, hearing and smell are remarkably acute.

Gray squirrel fur is actually a mixture of brown, black and white whose proportions vary seasonally. In Northern States, black squirrels are sometimes common; they actually represent a color phase of the gray squirrel. Young of both colors are often found in the same litter just as a human parent can have both blond and brunet children. Fox squirrels have the greatest variety of coat colors of any American mammal, ranging from black to light silver-gray or reddish-brown, yellow-orange, gray with black heads and feet, and other combinations. A fox squirrel has black soles on its feet and the tail is not edged with white. Fox squirrel adults weigh about two pounds and occasionally three pounds; grays average slightly more than a pound. Weights of both species will vary with season and geographic locality. Both squirrels are basically eastern and midwestern species, and both have been released in parts of the West, where they have become well established.

Although fox and gray squirrels often exist together in the same woodland, they have different habitat preferences. Both species like mixtures of mature hardwood trees, especially oaks, hickories, walnuts, and beech. Gray squirrels prefer moderate to large tracts of woodland; fox squirrels like small woodlots—especially where woodlands meet prairie, grassland or crop fields—and thrive in woods where fires or browsing by cattle keep shrubs or other plants low and sparse. Both species are often abundant in cities and towns.

During the past two or three centuries, the fortunes of the two squirrel species have changed with the landscape. Dense eastern forests of North America were ideal gray squirrel habitat. Grays were so abundant that they became a menace to the crops of pioneer farmers. Squirrels were such a problem that some Colonies accepted squirrel scalps for payment of taxes. Colonists became such crack marksmen from shooting squirrels that they devastated the ranks of British soldiers during the American Revolution.

Dr. Flyger is a Professor of Wildlife Biology at the University of Maryland. He has been studying gray and fox squirrels for some 38 years with particular emphasis on their behavior, movements, and population dynamics; he has published copiously on squirrels and on white-tailed deer, beluga whales, polar bears and Weddell seals, his other chief subjects of interest.

Illustration by Bob Hines

319

As forests were cleared for farming and for towns and cities, gray squirrel habitat declined until today there is only a fraction of the numbers that plagued colonial farmers. During the 19th century, immense hordes of gray squirrels occasionally swarmed across the land, even swimming across rivers and narrow lakes. Many thousands drowned and washed up on shore. Ernest Thompson Seton estimated that a half billion gray squirrels took part in one migration.

In parts of the Midwest where only small woodlots remain, gray squirrels have been replaced by fox squirrels and the range of the fox squirrel has expanded into Western States—Colorado, Nebraska and the Dakotas, wherever a few trees grow. Unfortunately, fox squirrels did not replace the grays in the Eastern States. Instead, fox squirrels themselves declined and often disappeared because of habitat destruction caused by short-rotation forest practices and fire suppression. An example is the big silver-colored Delmarva fox squirrel, which today is found only in portions of four counties of Maryland's Eastern Shore, whereas it once ranged as far north as New York City. The Delmarva squirrel is now classified as endangered, and current projects in Maryland, Delaware and Virginia involve re-establishing it in parts of its former range.

But eastern fox squirrels are doing well in—of all places—the artillery impact area of the Army's Aberdeen Proving Ground, north of Baltimore. This park-like open wood has an understory of blueberries and grass no more than a foot high. Bursting artillery shells cause frequent fires, which prevent growth of high shrubs and provide the open habitat that fox squirrels prefer.

Happily, gray squirrels have made a comeback since the turn of the century because forests have reclaimed many abandoned farmlands of the East. However, they have still not reached the abundance of colonial times, possibly because a favorite food (the American chestnut) is gone. Small gray squirrel migrations have again begun to occur, notably in the southern Appalachians in 1968 and in eastern Massachusetts in 1978.

Nuts and acorns provide squirrels with most of their calories but not all of the other necessary nutrients, such as vitamins and minerals, so they vary their diet with tree buds and flowers, fruits, berries, insects, young birds and birds' eggs. Fungi of many types are important, including mushrooms poisonous to man, tree cankers, dead wood or bark containing strands of fungi and the truffle-like fruiting bodies of underground fungi. Squirrels also will raid farms and gardens to eat corn, apples, other fruits and flower buds. They are selective when it comes to acorns, preferring those from white oaks over those of the more bitter black oak group. Other foods are osage-orange fruits, wild gourds, soybeans, buckeyes, and cockleburs. But gray squirrels, ever the opportunists, have been reported entering vending machines to get crackers, and searching automobile radiators in parking lots for tidbits such as dragonflies, butterflies and grasshoppers. Fox and gray squirrels have similar food habits but fox squirrels tend to eat more corn and other cereal grains because they will forage farther away from the forest edge.

Beginning in August, tree squirrels seem to be under contract with Mother Nature to bury all the acorns and nuts that they find. Their keen noses find these buried nuts later. So sensitive is their sense of smell that they can dig unerringly straight through several inches of snow to find a buried nut.

Gray squirrels are homebodies and seldom wander far except when relocating. In a densely populated wood this writer (on a P-R research project) found that home ranges averaged only 1.4 acres. Subsequent studies by others have found gray squirrel home ranges in less densely occupied habitat to be 2 to 4 acres, while fox squirrels may range over 10 to 40 acres. Gray squirrels spend more time in trees than do their bigger, more easy-going cousins. Grays do not move far from the safety of trees but the bolder fox squirrels may travel as far as half a mile into open land and away from woodlands.

Late August, September and early October are the months when squirrels are busy storing nuts and acorns for winter. This is also the time when the young, born during February and March, move out from their birthplaces to establish homes of their own where they will spend the rest of their lives. A few adults also may make such moves. This emigration is called the fall shuffle; emigrating squirrels settle wherever they find abundant food that can be stored for winter. Occasionally, when squirrels are unusually abundant but acorns are scarce, a fall shuffle can become a migration. Many squirrels will be moving about, but being unable to find a winter food supply, they keep moving and searching. The mortality rate during such migrations is high and the number of squirrels killed on roads becomes striking enough to attract television and newspaper reporters. Only gray squirrels make these spectacular migrations, which occur almost always in September.

The love life of tree squirrels generally begins about Christmas and continues through January. After 40 days, females give birth to one to six young (usually three) in February or early March. A second mating season occurs in June and July, with young born in August and September, but this happens only when food supplies are good; successful reproduction depends on adequate nourishment.

Squirrel populations do not seem to be much affected by predators. Occasionally but not often, they are caught by hawks, raccoons, foxes, bobcats or coyotes and only rarely by owls. Sometimes snakes enter dens and swallow any young that they find.

Occasionally a major die-off of squirrels results from a combination of severe weather, food shortage, and external parasites, especially mange mites. When cold, wet snow, or rain and wind keep squirrels confined to their snug dens, they do not eat enough to stay healthy. Prolonged, close contact with other squirrels permits the spread of mange mites, which burrow under the skin,

Hunters bag tens of millions of squirrels annually, but appear to make little impact on next year's numbers. Food supply and winter weather are the principal factors governing squirrel abundance or scarcity.

Irene Vandermolen/©Leonard Rue Enterprises

causing some individual squirrels to lose as much as three-fourths or more of their fur. To relieve the intense itching, the squirrels scratch themselves, and their sharp claws often cause open sores which may become infected. Combined with lack of food and harsh weather, the infections and loss of insulating fur can can kill up to 80 or 90 percent of all the squirrels in a wooded area over a two-month period.

Reliable statistics on squirrel hunting are difficult to come by, but a recent estimate indicated that in 1980, nearly 4 million hunters shot about 44 million squirrels in the United States. This sounds like a dreadful toll, but studies in West Virginia and Great Britain demonstrated that even the heaviest harvest did not measurably affect the abundance of squirrels the following year. Contrary evidence was found in Ohio where fox squirrels were sometimes eliminated from small woodlots by over-hunting, and several years could elapse before they became re-established in the more isolated woodlots. According to one study, approximately 40 percent of the squirrels in a woodlot could be harvested by hunters without affecting next year's squirrel population.

If hunting and predators do not influence squirrel abundance, why are there more squirrels some years than others? Disease epidemics have been suggested as a cause but there has been no evidence of this. Mange, weather and food shortage combination have already been mentioned, but these often are overcome rather quickly by reproductive success, made possible by abundant food. Bumper crops of acorns and nuts are often followed by good squirrel years, indicating that many new squirrels have been born. Failures of food crops are often followed by poor squirrel years, reflecting higher mortality or fewer births or both.

Much of our knowledge concerning these two squirrel species has been the result of research supported by Pittman-Robertson funds. One of the earliest of such studies, conducted by Durward Allen, appeared as a book titled *Michigan*

Fox squirrels "have the greatest variety of coat colors of any American mammal," says the author.

Terry Shankle, North Carolina Wildlife Resources Commission

Gray squirrels are seldom seen far from trees,
and generally prefer dense tree stands.

Fox Squirrel Management (1943) now considered a classic in the field of wildlife management. It is impossible to give credit here to all of the many people who have studied squirrels with Pittman-Robertson funds. Their work has provided many insights into the lives of squirrels and continues to provide information helpful toward maintaining and managing these two interesting and important species.

Squirrels can care for themselves if provided with adequate habitat. Their numbers fluctuate from year to year due to natural causes but this should be no cause for alarm. They can be encouraged by protecting forests and managing woodlots, by encouraging such food-producing trees as oaks, hickories, walnuts and beeches. Fox squirrels can be encouraged by leaving rows of corn standing next to forests and sometimes by carefully controlled burning of woodland understory. Squirrels readily use nest boxes for raising their young, but making, erecting and cleaning such boxes every year is expensive and rarely practical except for small woodlots or suburban backyards.

Pittman-Robertson research has taught us that tree squirrel populations can be managed over a long period of many years by managing forests and woodlots. No matter how hard they are hunted, good squirrel populations can be sustained with good habitat.

323

Wildlife Tomorrow

by Daniel A. Poole and Richard E. McCabe

Probing the future, particularly the distant future, is not an exact science. What it boils down to, really, is guesswork fashioned from experience, intuition, wishful thinking and a number of variables so complex and unreliable that they make Murphy's Law seem like one of the Eternal Verities.

Also, most visionaries, including those in the wildlife business, tend to be chronic pessimists. Such pessimism apparently comes with the territory. At least until now. We look upon wildlife's future with a sense of optimism for these reasons: in the U.S., unlike in many other countries, wildlife is owned *per se* by the public; about one-third of the country is public land, which assures a continuance of habitat; the tremendous interest of our fellow Americans in perpetuating wildlife; and the organizational responsibility, availability of funding and scientific capability in this country to manage wildlife in the best interest of the public *and* the wildlife itself. Our optimism, guarded though it is, is supported by historical perspective.

What faced the first European settlers of this country was, in the words of Plymouth Colony leader William Bradford, ". . . a hideous and desolate wilderness full of wild beasts and wild men." Well, we certainly put an end to that. After nearly four centuries of diligent effort, we've now got wilderness skinnied down to a few scattered parcels of land, mostly in the West, and they are not the least bit hideous. The only honest-to-goodness wild men we tolerate anymore are professional wrestlers, and their only threat is to good taste. And as for those wild beasts, well, we've got them cornered *and* surrounded.

It is truly ironic that We the People are inclined to lament what was put asunder in the name of civilization, growth and prosperity. Nowadays, we think back on the resources exploited by this country's pioneers and settlers, and shake our heads sadly, knowingly and self-righteously. But we fail to realize the so-called "Exploitation Era" of the 1800's was the time that kindled this Nation's greatness. It fashioned the spirit of free enterprise and self-determination. It availed unbounded opportunities for personal and societal well-being. And it ultimately fostered an awareness of the need for conservation.

In many ways, the exploitation of land, water and wild living resources during the century past was really quite trifling—in volume and intensity—compared with the hi-tech onslaught of today—still in the name of civilization, growth and prosperity, with national defense thrown in for good measure. Yesteryear's exploitation was a gouging of the environment's top and most visible layer of resource wealth. Today's exploitation is deeper and more insidious—as much a matter of undermining the future productivity of the resource base as it is a matter of abusing the resources themselves.

Mr. Poole has been with the Wildlife Management Institute in Washington, D.C., since 1952 and has served as its President since 1970. He has directed organizational/operational studies of wildlife agencies in 16 States, and of fish and wildlife programs of the U.S. Forest Service and Bureau of Land Management. Mr. McCabe, Director of Publications for the Institute since 1977, has written more than 90 articles on wildlife and natural resource matters and has edited and designed five award-winning wildlife texts currently in print.

325

So far, this assessment of the *future* of wildlife smacks vaguely of the rhetoric of the Nation's heavy environmentalism period in the late 1960's and early 1970's. That was when we became a society of high-eco-minded Henny Penny's vowing to dedicate ourselves to reasonably painless forms of self-discipline so as to put Spaceship Earth back in its proper orbit. But it is not. It simply voices the opinion that we, our Nation, its land and water and wild living resources, are moving to another era. And barring nuclear holocaust or plague, it probably won't be bad. But, inescapably, because of human population growth, the next era will feature less of some habitat and less of the types of wildlife—desirable *and* undesirable—dependent on such habitat.

Those who deplore that outlook and tend to pine for "the good ol' days" may be forgetting that this country did not have wildlife until about 100 years ago. It couldn't afford to. Oh sure, there were the "wild beasts" that William Bradford described, plus other teeming "creatures." But those weren't what we know today as "wildlife"; they were the Pilgrims' groceries, fabrics and currency—or else threats to personal safety, domestic animals and crops. In either case, the European newcomers also arrived with a long-standing Judeo-Christian mandate to assert dominion over all living things. It was to get a good test in the New World.

As time progressed and the civilizing Colonies depended less on native fauna for food, apparel and commerce, and were increasingly less fearful of wildness, the beasts became "critters" and then "game." It wasn't until Americans were firmly entrenched from sea to shining sea, until the majority no longer depended even seasonally on wild animals for food, and until the Nation's natural resources cornucopia showed bottom that people began to see these untamed creatures as another living entity, *then* as wild life, *then* as wildlife.

About Those Good Ol' Days . . .

We must also remind the good-ol'-days advocates that those times weren't so good and aren't so old; they were relative. For the duck hunter today, for example, the good ol' days were the mid-1960's, preceding the advent of the point system. For the duck hunter of the mid-1960's, the good ol' days were in the early 1940's when the season in most flyways was longer and it was not uncommon to reach the allowable daily limit of 15 ducks. For the hunter of the early 1940's, the good ol' days were the late 1920's, when 25 ducks a day seemed a pernicious limit. For the hunter of the late 1920's, the good ol' days were a decade or so before, when a person could hunt during the entire fall migration and shoot what his boat would hold. And for the waterfowler of that time, the good ol' days were anytime before 1900, when there were no hunting seasons and his bag was restricted only by his ammunition supply or what he could hit.

It follows, then, that at a time when some popular species of waterfowl reportedly are at an all-time low, right now may be the good ol' days of the near future. Not necessarily. During the present century, waterfowl have reached other all-time lows on several occasions, usually following extended drought in the major nesting grounds of Canada and the United States. And after each hand-wringing crisis, the ducks recovered, or nearly so, to selectively remembered good-ol'-days levels.

Knowing that waterfowl, like other wildlife, recovered from previous depressions is a cause for hope. But it certainly is not cause for complacency. We know, by the fact of their existence, that the Nation's wildlife species are a pretty hardy lot. Over millions of years, they have survived countless ecological changes and catastrophic natural events by adapting, evolving, or moving. Those that couldn't adapt often enough or evolve fast enough or move far enough simply became extinct. The resilience of waterfowl and most other modern wildlife to environmental changes and natural events, such as drought, seems to give merit to the hip adage that "what goes around, comes around." Except that we, mankind, keep changing the rotation. In the rest of the animal kingdom, life is predicated on the basic urge to survive. For man, at least 10 million years removed from his closest evolutionary relative, the basic urge is to survive in style.

The Conservation Era

Following last century's Exploitation Era, however, we decided to be somewhat reasonable. Laws were passed to protect certain wild species from overharvest, select areas were set aside as refuges, agencies were formed to monitor and manage our wildlife "legacy," and ecology ultimately became a science rather than merely a buzzword among eccentric nature enthusiasts. These were noble actions, and they helped to halt some of the worst kinds of direct abuse of wildlife. Some of the actions were taken more to mitigate guilt than damage; some were concessions to the broad and vague public good; some were to appease or accommodate special-interest factions; some were unadulterated pork barrel. Only a few, including the Federal Aid in Wildlife Restoration Act, were taken primarily as an ecological responsibility.

But until the 1960's and 1970's, the public was too preoccupied with its resourcefulness to recognize its course toward impending resourcelessness. Awareness came because the environment, like a filter clogged with impurities, began to show a back-up. Air and water had taken on unnatural colors, textures and smells, and the landscape gave the appearance of a poorly planned landfill. Only then did the words and wisdom of such visionaries as Thoreau, Marsh, Muir, Theodore Roosevelt, Leopold and Rachel Carson finally register in the American conscience. After a period of shock, then indignation, then finger-pointing, it became painfully evident that rehabilitation would take time and self-restraint. And since self-restraint tends to run counter to "the American way," conservation would have to be legislated and enforced and, hopefully, in time, ingrained.

The self-restraint concerns the human impact on habitat—the space, food, water and shelter required in some combination by each animal population. Wild animals occupy the habitat they need; humans occupy the habitat they desire.

Keeping in mind that the native animals had developed an ecological balance and rhythm in America for at least 11,000 years, let's review a bit of what has happened to habitat in the 400 years or so since our forefathers started keeping house and asserting dominion in this country. Such a review will help clarify why we are moving toward a new era.

Change Is a Constant

To begin with, it has been estimated that pristine America contained 950 million acres of virgin forest. Today, there are about 720 million acres of forestland, 66 percent of which is termed "commercial" forest. Also at the time adventurers and explorers broached the continent's interior, there were 250 million acres of tallgrass ("true") prairie. Less than 2 percent remains today. And in 1492, the land area that we know today as the United States then supported approximately 215 million acres of wetlands. There now are less than 100 million. Eighty-six percent of the loss was for agricultural purposes. And we continue to usurp wetlands at a rate of 458,000 acres per year, despite the fact that we now recognize wetlands as one of our most biologically productive and ecologically valuable natural resources. And even though the Nation's farmland is producing millions of tons of surplus grain each year.

And who are *we*? In 1790, after nearly 200 years of hand-to-mouth struggling and finally becoming an independent Nation, we numbered just under 4 million, on a land base then of 865,000 square miles. That equated to 4.5 of us per square mile. Then we got serious, very serious, about Manifest Destiny. In *each decade* for the next century, our population ballooned by no less than 25 percent, to 63 million. Simultaneously, we bought, bartered and bullied 2 million more square miles of national domain, so that in 1890, we averaged 21.2 of us per square mile. That last decade of the 19th Century supposedly marked the end of the much-reviled Exploitation Era. Since then, we have grown about 375 percent (to nearly 240 million people), for a population density average of approximately 67 people per square mile on a land base that has increased about 20 percent, to 3.5 million square miles. (The 20 percent "increase" in our land area since the turn of the century was almost entirely due to the U.S. Census Bureau's inclusion of Alaska and Hawaii in its statistical tallies after the two former U.S. territories formally achieved statehood in the 1950's.)

At present, we are adding to our population at a rate of 1 percent a year, or nearly 7,000 per day. It takes slightly more than a year and a half for current growth to exceed the human population level of 1790—300 years after North America was "discovered" and almost 200 years after colonization began.

People and Farms

Back in 1790, rural Americans accounted for 95 percent of the country's population. By 1890, that percentage had dropped to 65. In 1937, the year that the Federal Aid in Wildlife Restoration Act was enacted, less than 45 percent of the American public lived in rural settings. Today, only 26 percent of us live outside urban environments. And despite a brief back-to-the-soil movement in the 1970's, the current trend clearly and once again is back-to-the-pavement. In the past 50 years, while the total U.S. population rose 80 percent, rural America did not contribute at all to the increase. Since 1937, the number of people living on farms has decreased by 25 million.

Also, back in 1937, there were more than 6.5 million farms in the United States. Today, there are about 2.4 million—a decline of 64 percent. Near our peak of agricultural productivity, in 1960, approximately 1.84 million square miles were being farmed. Now, 25 years later, that amount has shrunk by almost a quarter-million square miles.

Where has the farmland gone? At present, the Nation is losing farming operations at a rate of 250 per day. Bad advice, bad markets, bad judgment, bad debts and bad weather have combined to force the liquidation of many family farms. It appears that most of the land changing hands remains as farmland, absorbed into other small but solvent operations, or is bought up by the growing number of large corporate farms, including those with foreign ownership. However, some goes unclaimed or is purchased by land speculators and is reverting to forest and field. Some is bought by the legions of second-home and recreation-property owners, and some is the target of exurban and suburban development. And nearly 34,000 square miles have gone to urban residential and commercial sprawl that has doubled the geographic extent of metropolitan America since 1960.

Even in what we now think of as the good old days of waterfowl hunting, people were looking back on an earlier period as the REAL good old days.

In addition, we pave 11,200 miles of new streets, roads and highways in this country each year, adding that sum to a total roadway system (including rights of way) that already covers an area equivalent in size to the States of Rhode Island, New Hampshire, Vermont, Massachusetts and Connecticut combined. Nearly 85 percent of improved public roads are in rural areas.

There now are more than 90 million housing units in the United States, 32 million of which have been added since 1960.

What the statistics reveal is that our rapidly growing human population is being fed, housed and transported at the expense of a shrinking agricultural land base. And not only do U.S. farms provide food and fiber for our needs, but they have been increasingly relied on to do the same for foreign populations growing even faster than ours. So, despite significant losses of farms and farmland in recent decades, the agricultural effort has been stepped up. This is accomplished by more-intensive farming—producing more crops on less land. Fencerows, shelterbelts, wetlands, woodlots, grass fields, rested fields, etc., have been sacrificed to maximize cropland and pastures. Intensive farming also has included increased irrigation, use of fertilizers and pesticides, and drawdown of groundwater tables, and tended to emphasize monotypical (one-crop) production. Each aspect of intensive farming dramatically alters one or more habitat elements, for wildlife, for man.

The reason for focusing on urban versus rural trends of human population is that the shift of people away from the land and its resources is not just a physical movement. It also is a cultural movement—our society losing contact with its organic origin and foundation. And it reflects a changing public attitude, in which opportunity and enrichment are sought increasingly in the highly artificial cities. We are becoming more dependent on one another, and less personally and directly dependent on the land, which we often tend to view not as a

329

fragile complex of resources, our only real heritage, but too often merely as a dispenser of services and amenities. By now, thanks to our brief and environmentally violent history, we ought to know better.

The Good Life?

And perhaps we do. But knowing and caring enough to stem the tide of our overwhelming presence are two very different matters. We want, on one hand, to retrieve and retain the natural resources, including wildlife, of a more pristine time, of some vaguely recalled good ol' days. But on the other hand, we are loath to sacrifice, really sacrifice, any of the one characteristic of animal habitat that is unique to humans, to wit, comfort. A Louis Harris poll in the 1970's revealed that 65 percent of Americans felt they were highly wasteful, and 90 percent felt they would have to find ways to reduce wasteful consumption. And 75 percent *wished* they sought greater pleasure in experiences rather than in possessions. But competition for comfort, or at least the trappings of comfort, seems to be the American instinct. This instinct, like the "exploitation" of the 1800's, is not inherently bad or wrong. It is the motivation to *have* more and better. And when in tandem with *doing* more and better, the instinct is potentially healthy and productive. But only when such competition permits resource utilization at a sustainable level is it in the best interest of society now and in the future.

Very unlike the exploiters of the past century, we know that non-renewable natural resources are finite and that renewable resources, including wildlife, have tolerance levels. We also know the consequences of our own untempered competitive instinct. But despite such reflective wisdom, and because of our burgeoning growth, we simply are overwhelming the environment and ignoring the consequences. This point was made clearly by a World Bank economist who recently noted that a child born in the U.S. will consume in its lifetime 20 to 40 times as much resources as will a child born in a poor country.

Of Water, Wood, and Energy

More specifically, to support our rapidly growing and urbanizing population, we now use more than 450 billion gallons of water daily, as opposed to 270 billion gallons in 1960—a per capita increase of about 25 percent. We now irrigate with on-farm pumped water eight times the amount of cropland so irrigated 10 years ago. In the past 35 years, groundwater withdrawals have nearly tripled, creating serious shortages in parts of the arid West. In the Lower Colorado River Basin—encompassing nearly all of Arizona and portions of New Mexico, California, Utah and Nevada—daily water consumption exceeds the renewable supply by 500 million gallons.

We presently use more than 285,000 tons of pesticides annually on our field, vegetable and fruit crops. We now consume 15.6 billion cubic feet of forest products each year, in contrast to 11.35 billion cubic feet in 1960—a per capita increase of almost 10 percent. Our use of fisheries products has increased by 15 percent in the past 20 years. Overall, our per capita consumption of major food commodities has risen almost 9 percent since 1960.

We now have more than 162 million motor vehicles registered in this country, compared with less than 74 million in 1960. And we had about 6,900 airports a quarter-century ago and have since made room for 8,300 more.

Of the nation's 47 major dams and reservoirs, 27 were completed after 1960. Overall, U.S. energy production increased 67 percent from 1960 to 1980, while energy consumption rose 58 percent.

Besides paving, irrigating, mining, filling, cropping, grazing, cutting and building on the landscape—and thereby altering wildlife habitat, its carrying capacity, and species composition and diversity—human activity produces other significant environmental disturbances. Among the most serious are air and surface water and groundwater pollution. And even though reductions have been made in some kinds of pollution since 1970, we still emit each year more than 140 million metric tons of polluting chemicals, gases and particles into the atmosphere. We annually discharge from *reported* sources 20 million gallons of pollution in U.S. waterways. And the amount of water pollution from unknown and unreported sources likely exceeds by several times that total.

We presently generate about 156 million tons of garbage per year, nearly double the amount in 1960—and a per capita increase since that time of 42 percent. In addition, more than 254 million tons of hazardous waste are produced annually in the U.S. And although there are approximately 5,000 hazardous waste-treatment facilities in the country, 14,000 hazardous waste-disposal sites have been identified. The exact nature of all toxic pollutants is not certain, but it is well-known that many are very widespread and persistent in the environment. When laws regarding their disposal are not complied with and not enforced by regulatory agencies, the risk of toxins infiltrating the natural and human food-chains is increased manyfold. In 1983, 39 States reported hazardous waste contamination of some groundwater, and 19 States reported such contamination of some surface water.

Another by-product of human activity that alters habitat directly and indirectly is soil erosion. Overuse and misue of agricultural lands, and land excavation for construction projects in the U.S., account for the erosion of 4 billion tons of topsoil per year, a 35 percent increase from 50 years ago when much less was known about soil conservation. At the current erosion rate of 7.3 tons per acre, *all* topsoil on American croplands could be gone in 100 years.

What the foregoing tendencies and trends show is that sociologists, not biologists, *may* be the best predictors of what the future bodes for wildlife in America. This might come as a surprise to the sociologists, but biologists have known for a long time now that wildlife and wildlife management are inextricably linked to the human condition. But, by the same token, most biologists aren't willing yet to turn over predicting the future of wildlife, because, through the morass of doomsday statistics, there are several bright rays of hope.

Federal Lands

The first is the land in public ownership. Federally "owned" public land constitutes more than a quarter of the country's total area. By far the most of those 700 or so million acres held in trust for the public are managed under the principle of multiple use, such that wildlife is supposed to be accorded equal consideration with other products, services and opportunities of the land. Thanks to a succession of progressive laws—including the Fish and Wildlife Act of 1956, the Sikes Act of 1960, the Multiple-Use and Sustained-Yield Act (1960), the Wilderness Act of 1964, the Forest and Rangeland Renewable Resources Planning Act of 1974, the Federal Land Policy and Management Act of 1976, the National Forest Management Act of 1976, and the Public Rangeland Improvement Act of 1978—most Federal public lands represent a vast, diverse and reasonably secure reservoir of wildlife habitat.

These laws evolved in response to various misuses and abuses of public lands and the resulting public outcry. The *spirit* of those laws still is being strained in some cases, such as mitigation of wildlife habitat loss associated with

Ding Darling's 1947 soil erosion cartoon could have been drawn in the mid-1980's, when Congress was considering the problem in writing a new farm bill.

certain Federal water-development projects, and the *letter* of those laws still is being grossly abused in some cases, such as livestock overgrazing on many western public domain rangelands. But there is continual effort to prevent such myopic practices by refining the existing laws or generating new legislation to protect the vast and significant, long-term public interest in those lands. The landmark National Environmental Policy Act of 1969 requires environmental assessments and environmental impact statements, which provide a mechanism for public involvement and scrutiny of plans to alter the landscape; citizens still dissatisfied can use those environmental impact statements to seek redress in the courts.

Important in such progressive legislation is not just the fact of security, but the acknowledgment or outright declaration of wildlife resources as national assets.

State, Local, Private

In addition to the Federal public lands, there are State and local public lands totaling more than 155 million acres, or 7 percent of the total U.S. land area. Nearly half is in parks, forests and other open-space lands that are some kind of wildlife habitat, including much that is managed specifically for wildlife or wildlife-related activities.

Finally, there are the private lands, which comprise 60 percent of the United States' land surface. All but about 6 percent of these lands are rural, including cropland, pasture, rangeland and forest. Although most of these rural lands are not managed for wildlife, they do represent habitat for a significant portion of the Nation's wild animals.

In sum, even though much of America's landscape has been altered dramatically in the course of the Nation's history, very little—*less than 3 percent*—has been made entirely unsuitable as habitat for at least some kinds of wildlife.

Wildlife Professionals

A second ray of hope is the wildlife management profession. Fifty years ago, wildlife management was the pragmatic business of propagating and protecting game species. Today, it is a science that emphasizes the dynamic balance of wildlife populations, wildlife habitat and other competitors for habitat, including man. And the focus is on nongame as well as game. Fifty years ago, very few States were involved in wildlife management beyond the simple expedients of occasional stocking and enforcing weak game laws. Today, each State has such an agency to administer its wildlife conservation and recreation programs in concert with public demand and the best interest of the wildlife. Fifty years ago, the wildlife management practitioners were peripherally trained zoologists, ornithologists and foresters, and a small cadre of "woods cops." Today, there are at least 10,000 wildlife professionals who were formally educated at least to completion of a Bachelor's degree level in wildlife science or a closely related discipline. Also, a recent survey (1984) indicated enrollment of more than 7,500 students in wildlife curricula of 95 colleges and universities in North America. Nearly 20 percent of these students were enrolled in graduate (Master's or Doctoral) degree programs. And besides the biologists in place and the new generation of biologists preparing to take on the complex, full-time job of providing stewardship of wildlife resources, there surely are more than 20,000 non-biologists employed as support staff—technical, informational, clerical, etc.—who provide yeoman service to the biologists, to wildlife and to the public. Wildlife management, therefore, is no passing social or academic fancy. It is a national mission, and it is in the hands of a growing legion of highly trained, skilled and motivated professionals and dedicated support staff.

Scientific Research

In 1937, the wildlife literature was small, fragmentary and imprecise. There was, then, only one textbook on wildlife management, Aldo Leopold's *Game Management* (1933). Today hundreds of popular and technical articles, papers, reports and books are written on wildlife topics annually. The amount of useful information on wildlife, wildlife habitat and management of both, continually generated in journals, professional meeting symposia, government reports and a variety of other forums, is staggering.

Wildlife research was virtually nil in 1937 and, except for crude "censusing," was disparaged by administrators of fledgling wildlife agencies. Now, such research is recognized as the backbone of scientific management by the agencies. In addition to dozens of private and public research centers that focus on wildlife matters, there are the renowned Cooperative Wildlife Research Units in 29 States located at land-grant universities. The Units are a research program sponsored cooperatively by the U.S. Fish and Wildlife Service, the universities, the wildlife agencies of the States in which the universities are located, and the Wildlife Management Institute. Initiated first in Iowa more than 50 years ago, the program has made invaluable contributions to the art, science and theory of wildlife management, not only through research, but also by virtue of its graduate-level training of biologists.

Thus, the wildlife management profession has the expertise, ability and enthusiasm to manage properly all of America's wildlife resources. If given public support, adequate funding and opportunity to keep refining management, the profession is quite capable of maintaining wildlife's numbers, diversity, and myriad public and biological values.

Active Public Involvement

A third ray of hope is the convincing demonstrations by the public of its regard for wildlife. One such demonstration has been the increased demand for wildlife-associated recreation. A U.S. Fish and Wildlife Service report (1982) of citizen activities in 1980 shows that 59 percent of all people six years of age and

The golfer-goose confrontation may be comical, but serious conflicts do arise.

334

older in the U.S. *actively* took part that year in at least one wildlife-associated activity. Nearly 20 million hunted, 54 million fished and 95 million enjoyed nonconsumptive wildlife-related recreation (observing, photographing, feeding, etc.). The participants accounted for almost 1.4 *billion* days of participation, and expended for that recreation $27.2 billion.

The trends of involvement in wildlife-associated activity for 1955 (when data were first compiled) to 1980 are equally impressive. During that time, hunter numbers increased 42.4 percent, fisherman numbers increased slightly more than 101 percent, days of hunting annually increased almost 130 percent, days of fishing annually increased 252 percent and annual expenditures increased 871 percent. Comparative figures for nonconsumptive activity are not available, but it has been suggested that the popularity of such activity has *at least* doubled in the past two decades.

Furthermore, in a comprehensive report (1980) by the U.S. Forest Service, projections for participation in hunting and fishing in the U.S. to the year 2030 (assuming opportunity available at reasonable cost) show that there will be 24 to 69 percent more hunters and 90 to 156 percent more fishermen. Continued "substantial" growth was predicted for participation in nonconsumptive wildlife activities.

Willingness to Pay

These and other surveys of the American pulse show convincingly that wildlife—game and nongame—is important to and highly valued by the public and will continue to be so into the foreseeable future. And a survey (1982) conducted by pollster Louis Harris, of the attitudes of Americans toward our water resources, revealed that a strong majority of U.S. citizens is extremely concerned about pollution of water and the destruction of wetland habitat, is dissatisfied with governmental actions to rectify the abuses of those resources, and is willing to pay the remedial costs.

Also, in 1977, the State of Colorado instituted a program whereby taxpayers could "check-off" on their 1978 State income tax forms a contribution to a nongame wildlife program. One-third of a million dollars were donated in the program's first year. Today, a total of 33 States have adopted a voluntary check-off for nongame, and approximately $9 million is being contributed annually.

Clearly, Americans want wildlife benefits, are beginning to understand and appreciate the social and ecological costs involved in the proper upkeep of

Deer killed on roadways also symbolize human-wildlife competition for space.

The encroachment of this housing development into a tidal marsh is a scene repeated countless times across the land, graphically showing one *prime reason for our nationwide loss of wetlands. Others: agriculture, logging, water projects.*

Bill Wilen, U.S. Fish and Wildlife Service

wildlife resources, and are beginning to show a willingness to share in the financial burden of management.

Another ray of hope is the citizenry who form the backbone of legislative and financial support for wildlife management programs, and who are the opponents of programs and proposals that would weaken the Nation's wildlife resources. This citizenry consists of the hunters, fishermen, trappers, bird-watchers, wildlife photographers and others for whom conservation is not a whim or fad, but instead, a largely personal obligation. These are the champions of State and Federal programs to benefit wildlife; these are the guardians of effective natural resource laws; these are the forces to be reckoned with on legislation and programs that threaten wildlife conservation; these are the primary contributors of funds for wildlife programs in the best public and resource interest.

Movers and Shakers

Individually and through private conservation organizations, these citizens are the prime movers of sound wildlife management. Collectively, they are a "special interest" group in the best sense of that now-muddied term. Their interest is wildlife, and wildlife is special because it is an important part of the wealth of the Nation and *all* citizens.

Fifty years ago, the only persons actively concerned about the welfare of wildlife were sportsmen. Despite limited organization and plenty of apathy from the rest of the public, sportsmen fueled, ignited and fanned the flames of action that the are the basis of wildlife conservation and management in this country. They were the ones to rally for the laws to protect the vestige populations of overexploited wildlife. They were the ones to encourage the education, research and on-the-ground management to restore and enhance those depleted populations. And they were the ones to provide the initial and most continuing

336

revenues, including the self-taxing mechanism of the Federal Aid in Wildlife Restoration Act, for State agency programs for game and nongame.

Broad-Based Support

Today, the support base has broadened considerably. The old guard—principally hunters—remains, as formidable, enthusiastic and generous as ever, while its hue and cry have been picked up and echoed by individuals and groups representing primarily the so-called "nonconsumptive" interests in wildlife. In addition, there are those who are concerned with other specific aspects of the environment—including water, air, soil and vegetation—and those who are concened generally with environmental quality and aesthetics. Their concern, indeed like those whose principal focus is wildlife, really is for the environment of man. Regardless of the specific focus or impetus, such concern, if accompanied by responsible action, is to the benefit of wildlife.

One measure of the "added" citizen support for wildlife and wildlife management in this country in the past 50 years is public participation in local and national wildlife-related organizations. According again to the U.S. Fish and Wildlife Service's survey, 5 percent (2.4 million) of sportsmen belonged in 1980 to local wildlife/conservation clubs and organizations and 15 percent (7.1 million) had membership in one or more national organization. Also for 1980, 3.4 percent (3.2 million) of solely nonconsumptive wildlife users were members of local wildlife-related organizations and 17.5 percent (16.3 million) had such affiliation at the national level. By this single criterion, the voice for wildlife is growing significantly in volume and intensity.

So we have reason for optimism. These and other rays of hope for the future of wildlife, despite the unwitting exploitation of the past and the pell-mell environmental and societal changes of today, lend assurance that wild animals and wild places can continue to be an important part of the American landscape and heritage.

We Have the Choice

The stresses being placed on the current populations and habitats of wildlife, *if left unchecked,* undoubtedly will alter the diversity, abundance, and distribution of most species. As in the earlier example concerning waterfowl, they also may change our notion of what constitutes America's wildlife and of our uses of that wildlife. But just as we can diminish the status of wildlife and our

traditional values of wildlife, so too can we retain and maintain them. We have the ability, the know-how, the wherewithal and still the time. Whether yesterday, today or tomorrow is the good ol' days for wildlife is entirely our choice.

In summary, no Judgment Day is foreseen for wildlife. As human population multiplies and its environmental effects spread and intensify, the status of virtually all native wildlife is bound to change. Species preferring older and more stable natural vegetative conditions, such as occurs in established wilderness, refuges, parks and similar areas, will persist in some such places. But likely not all species in all places, because most species have different seasonal habitats. The amount and suitability of other seasonal habitat outside of such reserves are expected to decrease. Therefore, on a local scale, populations of some species likely will decrease. This will be true especially for those such as the Kirtland warbler, mountain lion, spotted owl and wild sheep, requiring very specific vegetative conditions and/or relative isolation from human presence. And to a somewhat lesser, but more-manageable degree, there also will be losses within designated reserves, because increasing human activities there already are unfavorable to some species, including grizzly bears, condors, eagles, wolves, and elk with young, to name a few.

Conversely, species such as white-tailed deer, quail, mourning doves, opossums and many songbirds that favor relatively open or disturbed habitat conditions likely will prosper and expand in both number and distribution, because more habitat of that kind is created by man's occupation and exploitation of the land. This condition will particularly favor species with the ability to persist close to man and his settlements.

How Much Do We Care?

Other aspects of the man/habitat/wildlife equation are less predictable. Agriculture and forestry exert a strong influence on habitat and, inescapably, on wildlife. Tilling and harvest methods, fertilizers and pesticides already employed and yet to be devised have the potential to influence wildlife diversity, abundance, and distribution. Society's willingness to manage air, soil, and surface and ground water contaminants also will significantly affect wildlife's future. And more locally at least, man's reaction to animal depredation, noise, fouling and possible disease transmission will bear on wildlife's well-being, too.

But there are a number of positive elements in all of this, including one that essentially was absent and certainly unexpressed during America's Exploitation Era. That element—public concern—took time to arouse and focus, and at no previous time in national history was it ever so vocal and persuasive as it is now. This is attested to by the many applicable State and Federal laws, by wildlife agencies firmly in place, with dedicated and well-trained personnel, and by the large sums invested annually in wildlife and support activities, by colleges and universities offering major courses of wildlife study, by improved wildlife conservation law enforcement capability, and in many other ways.

There is no reason to suspect that the public's concern for wildlife will diminish. Rather, it will continue to grow and strengthen. If wildlife is to be short-changed by anything in the future, it will be by inadvertence, by man's alienation of wildlife habitat needs, not by the loss of professional commitment or public interest and determination.

The Federal Aid in Wildlife Restoration Act—a successful and responsive partnership of people, industry and governments—will remain a strong safeguard against the kinds of catastrophic carelessness that characterized America's treatment of wildlife and wildlife habitat in the past.

As angry and sardonic as Ding Darling's pen could be, the great cartoonist-conservationist never lost hope for the future of the land he loved and its wildlife.

339

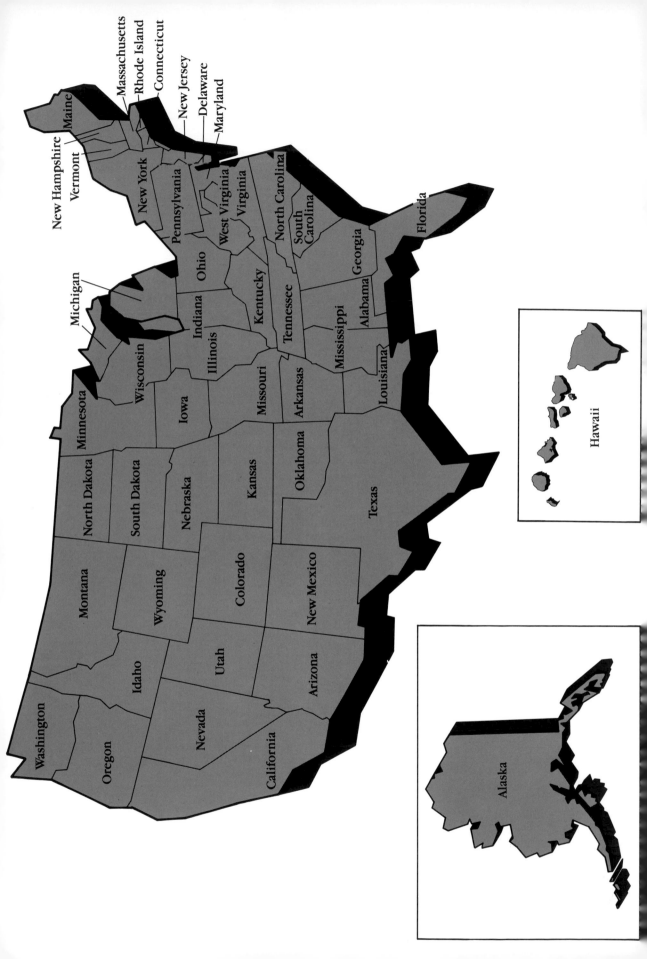

State by State

The Fish and Wildlife Service invited the wildlife agencies of every State and Territory to summarize the highlights of their 50 years of experience with the Federal Aid in Wildlife Restoration (Pittman-Robertson) Act. These are their responses, as edited by Dr. Joseph P. Linduska.

Alabama

Alabama became a state in 1819, but concern for wildlife conservation languished until 1907 when many significant laws were passed marking the first effort for organized wildlife protection. Enactment of several other laws and organizational adjustments followed and, in 1939, a major organizational change passed the Legislature which created the Department of Conservation.

The Game, Fish and Seafoods Division of the new Department was charged with administering activities of the Federal Aid in Wildlife Restoration Program. Several P-R research proposals had been approved and were underway by 1941. Alabama Polytechnic Institute (Auburn University) began awarding graduate degrees in the new field of Game Management—a direct response to the new P-R Program.

Leading the list of Alabama's many outstanding wildlife achievements with Federal Aid Funds is the early re-establishment of white-tailed deer on nearly 30 million acres of range. Concurrently, the restoration of wild turkey was implemented on approximately 20 million acres. Today, populations of 1,300,000 deer and 350,000 wild turkeys support annual harvests of about 200,000 and 35,000 respectively.

Another major outgrowth of the Pittman-Robertson Act has been the immensely popular public hunting program. Presently this system includes 32 wildife management areas, refuges and sanctuaries totaling nearly 700,000 acres. While this represents only 2 percent of the range, it provides in an average year good hunting for about 60,000 sportsmen (about 20 percent of licensed hunters). Public hunting opportunity becomes increasingly important as hunter numbers increase and many private hunting lands arc closed.

Invaluable research has been funded through P-R. The determination that age-weight ratio is a reliable measure of deer herd condition has made it practical for Alabama administrators to support one of the longest gun hunting seasons (77 days) in the United States. Bag limits of one deer per day for the buck-only season and a one buck and one doe per day during the 2-week "hunter choice" season are generous to hunting but justified by experience.

Alabama was in the forefront of mourning dove research. A hunter questionnaire mail survey has helped to clarify the effects of liberal hunting regulation on doves and other wildlife. And cooperative research on wildlife parasites and diseases, particularly of deer, has been extremely beneficial.

Investigations on wild turkeys, squirrels, raccoons, rabbits and woodcock have yielded information useful in the establishment of seasons and bag limits and produced other data useful in management. Booklets, which will be used long into the future, have been a by-product of these studies.

Land acquisition has been modest (only 32,000 acres) but the impact has been major. A 4,000 acre purchase in the late 1930's in Clarke County was developed into the Fred T. Stimpson Wildlife Sanctuary. Intensive management here and at nearby Upper State Wildlife Sanctuary provided the main reservoir of wild deer and turkeys for trapping and relocation to vacant range.

A 1980 survey of the economic impact of hunting in Alabama revealed that approximately $221 million dollars were spent in the marketplace for such items as guns, ammunition, vehicles, food, lodging, leases, taxidermy services, film and clothing. These expenditures generated at least $11 million in state and local taxes. P-R programs are largely responsible for the thriving game populations which support such an active audience of sport hunters, and therby produce economic returns which are spread widely over a large segment of the general public in Alabama.

Alaska

In 1959, its year of statehood, Alaska took over management of fish and game resources from the Federal Government. The State had a tremendous wealth of wildlife resources, a low human population, and few wildlife management problems. Human demands for wildlife were easily met and few conflicts existed between user groups. However, as oil, mining, and timber development increased, the population grew, as did the demands on the resources. The need for intensive management was at hand.

The Federal Aid in Wildlife Restoration Act was instrumental in developing one of the largest and best-staffed State wildlife management programs in the country. Habitat problems associated with exploration and development of resources in the arctic environment provided unique challenges to wildlife managers. Most of the State was, and still is, in public ownership and access for hunting and other recreation was readily available. Therefore, when the wildlife program was started, the need to secure public access was not a high priority. However, little research had been conducted and, consequently, the first task was to investigate the basic biology and needs of Alaska's wildlife species and ecosystems.

Because so little was known about the arctic environment and its wildlife, species such as moose, caribou, wolves, Dall sheep, brown/grizzly bear, and muskox were investigated in depth. Habitat requirements, reproductive biology, interrelationships with other species, and behavior all had to be studied and understood before the appropriate management strategies could be developed and implemented. Because conditions often differed greatly from other parts of the country, it was necessary to develop new research techniques for use in Alaska. The aerial survey census for caribou and moose is one example of the new methods developed.

Since Alaska maintains healthy populations of predators such as wolves, bears, and numerous furbearers, several long-term research studies have focused on predator/prey relationships. The research techniques and information from these and other studies are now being applied to habitat management and in plans that recognize the importance of relationships among people, habitats, predators and prey.

Several species, including sea otters and muskoxen, were re-established where populations had been extirpated four or five decades previously. Many Alaskan biologists have become leaders in their fields of interest and have traveled to Canada, Scandinavia, and the U.S.S.R. to lend their expertise to management of circumpolar species such as walrus, polar bear, moose, caribou, and wolf.

Additional research is needed and P-R funds will continue to play a key role in broadening our fundamental understanding of wildlife biology. The 1960's and 1970's were times of discovery about Alaska's wildlife, their populations, and their role in our ecosystems. The rapidly expanding human population, and increased demands for wildlife and other natural resources, will create the need for modern, sophisticated wildlife management, tailored to this State's unique problems. We have gained an understanding of basic wildlife ecology in an arctic environment and, with continued funding through Federal Aid in Wildlife Restoration, we will be able to bring enlightened management to wildlife as economic development continues in the years ahead.

Arizona

Coinciding with the appearance of the Pitman-Robertson program, many important but subtle changes affecting Arizona's wildlife were taking place and setting the stage for how these Federal Aid dollars ultimately would be used. The need to answer specific game management problems led to the creation of research studies in which the objectives, and the data needed to meet them, were anticipated at the outset. Such efforts then were able to qualify for Federal funds apportioned under Pittman-Robertson.

Arizona's first Federal Aid projects got underway in 1939 and were concerned with turkey, quail, beaver and pronghorn antelope. Since that time these and similar funds have paid for most of the Game and Fish Department's most important management and research projects.

One of the earlier and more significant accomplishments of the Pittman-Robertson-funded research program was the Oracle Junction Quail Study begun in 1951. This study demonstrated quite clearly that winter rainfall, not hunting, was the critical factor regulating populations of Gambel's and scaled quail. In the 1960's, Vitamin A was found to be a key to quail breeding and it was later determined that this came from green feed which followed on winter rains. Vitamin A is so important that quail do not even attempt pairing off when their diet is deficient in it.

The Three Bar Wildlife Area, bordering the west shore of Roosevelt Lake, figures in many Federal Aid studies. One project involved an extensive investigation of deer in a predator-free environment. Beginning in January 1971, a herd of deer was captured and placed in a 600-acre fenced enclosure from which all predators had been removed. Researchers observed reproduction in the area with no predation and made comparisons with reproduction in similar areas outside the enclosure, where coyotes, bears and mountain lions range. By December 1975 the total number of deer in the enclosure had grown from 11 to 37, and fawn "crops" were running 80 percent. The project, continuing over the years ever since, has consistently demonstrated that predators are a major factor influencing total deer numbers.

For years sportsmen and cattlemen had argued over the competition between deer and cattle for food. In some areas cattle are known to be heavy users of the browse species eaten by deer. Comparison studies conducted in the Chiricahua Mountains, however, showed clearly that the area's lack of browse was due to over-use by deer and was not significantly influenced by cattle.

One research tool which appeared in the early 1960's and subsequently received much publicty was the tranquilizer or "CAP-CHUR" gun, perfected by Harold C. Palmer of Georgia in cooperation with the Crossman Arms Company. Arizona Game and Fish researchers tested and experimented with this equipment for several years, and the knowledge gained has permitted using the CAP-CHUR gun for a variety of purposes, including the capture and reintroduction of native species to their former habitats in the State.

Another innovation of this period was radio-tracking equipment which has become a valuable tool in studies of deer, bear, mountain lions, elk, bighorn sheep and smaller, unhunted species as well. In one study of black bears, in which 18 had been equipped with collars, it was found that hibernation occurred irrespective of weather conditions.

The return of hunters' dollars through Pittman-Robertson has enabled Arizona Game and Fish to learn much about wildlife species that are faced with increased hunter interest and increased competition for habitat resulting from the State's enormous growth and development. This program has enabled the Department to effectively manage many species and will help it learn about the critical habitat needs of others. The benefits will accrue not only to hunters but to the entire population that values its wildlife resources.

Arkansas

The Pittman-Robertson Act has played an important part in the management of wildlife in Arkansas. Utilizing P-R funds, the State has been able to make significant strides in land acquisition, wildlife stocking and waterfowl management. There is little doubt that had it not been for the availability of funds through the P-R program, Arkansas would not have been able to achieve the success it has in the management of its wildlife resources.

The Arkansas Game and Fish Commission placed early emphasis on acquisition of land for public hunting with the result that over 300,000 acres of valuable wildlife habitat have been acquired. The availability of P-R funds for land acquisition is often the determining factor in whether or not a tract is purchased. Almost 200,000 acres of our present holdings were purchased with P-R funds at a cost of over $11 million. Had there been no P-R Act, much of this wildlife habitat would not have been purchased.

Over 120,000 acres of Arkansas' wetlands, including some of the last large remnants of the forested wetlands which were once so abundant in the eastern part of the State, have been purchased using P-R funds. Hundreds of thousands of dollars have been spent on these areas to develop seasonally-flooded impoundments for ducks. Some of the best waterfowl hunting in the Nation can be found on these State-owned management areas.

Pittman-Robertson projects provided the first extensive surveys of wildlife populations in Arkansas, laying the groundwork for much of the management that has been conducted since. These surveys revealed that many species had low, poorly distributed populations even though much suitable habitat was present. Highly successful trapping and relocation programs resulted from these findings.

The comeback of the white-tailed deer and eastern wild turkey are the most dramatic of trapping and relocation success stories. Once it was uncommon to even find a deer track in most of Arkansas, much less see a deer. The Commission embarked on a program to increase deer populations through trapping from areas of relatively high population density and relocating into sparsely populated areas that were set aside as deer refuges. Over 3,600 animals were trapped and relocated over the years, most of them being allowed to live and reproduce in the refuges under complete protection. Once their numbers approached a point of overpopulation, the refuges were opened to public hunting. The refuges provided nucleus areas from which deer populations, favored by increased harvest of timber and the lush understory growth that followed, spread throughout the State.

Today, as a result of early management efforts, deer are plentiful in most parts of the State and the population is large enough to withstand a steady increase in deer harvest each year with no adverse effect. Thanks largely to the P-R program, hunter harvest of deer in the State has risen from near zero to over 65,000 in 1984 and is still on the increase.

The comeback of the eastern wild turkey is equally impressive. In the 1930's wild turkeys were close to the vanishing point in the State. Trapping and relocation efforts, strict enforcement of protective regulations, and other management practices have resulted in a dramatic expansion in the population. Through the years more than 5,300 turkeys have been trapped and relocated. Today it is estimated that there are approximately 200,000 of these birds in the State, and the annual turkey harvest has risen from a few hundred birds per year in the 1930's to nearly 6,000 in 1984.

The commission hopes to duplicate these earlier successes with its newly implemented grouse stocking program. To date, approximately 500 ruffed grouse have been trapped in other States and relocated in Arkansas. It is hoped that this effort will result in re-establishment of this once native bird.

Efforts such as these, largely made possible through the availability of P-R funds, have benefited all who enjoy wildlife and the outdoors. Whether a person enjoys hunting, viewing wildlife, or sight-seeing he has benefited from the P-R program and will for many years to come.

California

California began participation in the Pittman-Robertson (P-R) program in 1940 with six projects. The first research projects were on beaver and mule deer in southern California, furbearers and valley quail in the semi-arid south coast; habitat improvement for sage grouse and desert game started a long series of development projects.

Thanks to P-R funding, California was able to establish one of the Nation's foremost wildlife investigation laboratories. The Department conducted 38 years of food habitat studies, making 49,500 analyses of gizzards, crops and stomachs. This dietary information helped formulate policy and management programs in the area of artificial game bird stocking, predator control, setting seasons and bag limits, and habitat manipulation. These food habitat studies, combined with nutrition studies, gave us the knowledge of how to improve chances of deer surviving in cold weather. Wildlife disease studies were instrumental in reducing the impact of fowl cholera and botulism. Pesticide investigations were responsible for restricting the use of chlorinated hydrocarbons in agriculture and the deregistration of problem chemicals over a "phase out" period. In conjunction with the lab, life history investigations were instrumental in saving the early mourning dove season and the canvasback season, opening the chukar season, and in the successful introduction of the wild turkey and white-tailed ptarmigan.

Early quail research and desert water development projects led to the development of the "Gallinaceous Guzzler", an artificial watering device for upland game and, later, to the development of the big game "guzzlers," first for deer, then for bighorn sheep. Both are of benefit to nongame as well as game species.

Nine land acquisition projects were initiated early in the program to preserve especially critical areas, primarily waterfowl habitat and deer wintering grounds. To date approximately 54,200 acres have been purchased at a cost of $427,000. Later, P-R funds were used for development and maintenance, as well as research.

One of the largest single uses of P-R has been for development and maintenance of waterfowl habitat. The State owns and maintains six major waterfowl areas under P-R comprising approximately 48,000 acres. It also manages an additional 20,000-plus acres for waterfowl and other water-associated wildlife. Annually these six areas alone provide 58,000 days of hunting, 86,000 days of fishing and 153,000 days of non-consumptive use such as bird watching or sightseeing.

Tule elk and bighorn sheep, neither of which is being hunted, are being reintroduced into historical ranges, and their populations are increasing dramatically. The growth in numbers of the bighorn is primarily due to water development. Years of research and testing have made animal immobilization or restraint an indispensable and safe tool in animal relocation and in dealing with problem animals. California's P-R program has developed a workshop to assist other States and agencies in the proper use of these techniques.

In 1968 the Nongame Wildlife Investigation Project was begun. This formalized California's nongame activities and work on such species as California condor and the San Joaquin kit fox, ultimately providing the framework for the State's current Endangered Species Program. Since 1979, P-R has been essentially the sole funding source for work on such species as golden eagles, sandhill cranes, bobcats, and spotted owls, as well as many other species of concern.

California was the second State in the Nation to start a hunter safety training program. The training is mandated for everyone prior to buying his or her first resident hunting license. Between July 1, 1954 and June 30, 1985, 1,211,488 people were trained in the use of hunting gear and wildlife management principles. The accident rate per 10,000 licensed hunters dropped from 3.10 to 0.75 during that same time period.

Colorado

In 1937, when the Federal Aid in Wildlife Restoration Act was passed, it was clear the act was intended to serve two purposes: 1) rehabilitation of wildlife population in natural habitats, and 2) wildlife research as a basis for scientific wildlife management. From the very beginning, Colorado has utilized these monies for the full range of authorized activities—land acquisition, development of hunter education, coordination, surveys, etc., and recently for comprehensive planning. But most noteworthy has been the emphasis given research.

In 1938, the Colorado Game and Fish Department created the position of Federal Aid Coordinator and appointed Arthur H. Carhart to that position. Dividends from research became immediately apparent, and during the late 1930's, Colorado's deer and elk numbers began to increase rapidly. But a protectionist attitude, forged in the early 1900's when game populations were depleted, dictated conservative antlered-only seasons. In the 1940's, Colorado used much of its P-R allocation to inventory big game and sage grouse populations, and to estimate carrying capacities of important big game winter ranges.

These efforts led to much more liberal deer and elk seasons. Colorado was a leader among Western States in initiating experimental doe hunts, followed by either-sex hunts. These innovations gave Colorado game managers the tools necessary to check overpopulations of deer and reverse trends in deteriorating winter ranges.

In 1944, thanks to intensive investigations of sage grouse, Colorado held its first sage grouse season since 1937. These efforts paved the way for continued sage grouse hunting seasons from 1953 to the present.

In 1953, Colorado held its first Rocky Mountain bighorn sheep hunting season since 1887, in large part because of P-R funded bighorn sheep studies. These seasons were aimed at reducing sheep numbers to prevent large die-offs due to the lungworm-pneumonia complex. In the late 1950's, Colorado researchers pieced together the cycle of lungworm infections in bighorn sheep and began experiments to interdict that cycle.

Resident populations of nesting Canada geese were established along Colorado's Front Range in the mid-to-late 1950's. Those efforts were so successful that some winter populations of resident geese are becoming intra-urban pests.

In 1961, Colorado established an organizationally distinct research section headquartered adjacent to the Colorado State University campus in Fort Collins. The discrete nature of the reasearch unit made possible the liberal support of P-R funds, and its affiliation with the State's land grant agricultural college helped to assure that research was innovative, diversified, and directed towards significant biological questions. This combination of location and organization has been one of the primary reasons why Colorado continues to be a national leader in wildlife research and management.

Connecticut

In Connecticut, Pittman-Robertson monies have been widely used for land acquisition, development, research and surveys, and coordination projects. Recently a technical guidance project and hunter education program have been undertaken. Early emphasis on development of State-owned lands to improve wildlife habitat has given way to technical assistance for private landowners, recommendations on state forestry operations to improve wildlife conditions and, in the last two decades, land acquisition to insure future wildlife habitat.

Connecticut has acquired 9,550 acres of land, including key parcels of tidal wetland along Long Island Sound and the Connecticut River, with P-R monies. Wetlands, though still of vital concern, are now protected by an exemplary statewide law. Purchase of prime farmland has become increasingly important and challenging in a State with rapidly dwindling open space and a declining agricultural community. The acquisition program, throughout, has been greatly aided by P-R funds which have provided flexibility and independence from the constraints of limited State funding. In other cases, State funding and gift lands have become available to the Wildlife Bureau because of the successful design and integrity of the P-R program.

Our professional staff, which now numbers 25, has grown three-fold since 1968. The activities and resulting impact of this group of general biologists, each one also a qualified specialist in his or her own field, has enhanced the status, importance, and credibility of the Wildlife Bureau, as evidenced by positive recognition received from the public. Most recently, methods of data analysis have progressed from antiquated needle sort cards to modern computerized systems, efficiently aiding sound biological management decisions. P-R funding has made all this possible.

The management of selected wildlife species has been significantly broadened in the last decade to include deer, furbearers, wild turkeys and waterfowl. Until 1975, Connecticut was not recognized as a deer hunting State. However, a growing herd, resulting from heightened forest cutting, brought agricultural damage and conflicts with other land uses, and an informed public was prepared to support an effective deer management policy. A regulated hunting program was developed to control deer numbers, and a comprehensive data collection system was established for the guidance of future management decisions. Connecticut is now in its second decade of regulated deer management.

Restoration of the wild turkey began in 1975 with the release of 22 wild-trapped birds from New York. Except for heavily-populated areas along the Connecticut River Valley and Long Island Sound, wild turkeys are now found in most of their primary and secondary habitat range in Connecticut. In May 1981, Connecticut residents hunted wild turkeys for the first time in 170 years. Subsequent fall and expanded spring seasons are continually being implemented.

Completely revised in 1981, the approved P-R Conservation Education/Firearms Safety Project now involves 300 volunteer instructors teaching nearly 200 courses to over 5,000 students per year. The CE/FS program has received a "AAA" rating from the International Association of Fish and Wildlife Agencies since 1982, its first year of full operation, and has also been recognized by the U.S. Fish and Wildlife Service as an outstanding model program for other States.

Delaware

Delaware's participation in the Federal Aid in Wildlife Restoration Program (P-R) began in 1939 when legislation was passed enabling the State to qualify. A Game Technician/Director of Education was hired who set up the State's first wildlife research and educational programs. World War II caused a 5-year lapse in participation until 1948, when a Director of Conservation was hired to establish a P-R supported wildlife conservation program.

Early efforts included educating hunters and private landowners in game management practices through demonstration projects on public lands, and research to provide the basis for management of marshes, waterfowl and a developing herd of white-tailed deer. Especially noteworthy in this early era was a management program for Canada geese, fully-funded by P-R. Working closely with private landowners, freshwater ponds were constructed near feeding areas, nucleus decoy flocks were developed and refuges were established. The result was the attraction and subsequent spread of geese to previously under-utilized areas of the State. The resultant hunting opportunities are contributing greatly to Delaware's economy.

Concurrently with these research and management activities, an extensive land acquisition program was also under way, with emphasis on coastal areas. P-R funds matched by hunting license receipts, along with other State and Federal monies, were used to acquire approximately 35,000 acres of lands and waters for public hunting and numerous forms of non-consumptive recreation. These 11 state-owned areas, in combination with two National Wildlife Refuges, have protected over 50 percent of the total Delaware River and Bay coastline.

In recent years, P-R program involvement with major land zoning and development review efforts has contributed significantly to the conservation of wildlife. Personnel funded by the P-R program maintain constant vigil over major land use programs and recommend alternative practices to protect important wildlife ecosystems from burgeoning development. Another recent project which shows early signs of succeeding is the reintroduction of wild turkeys in Delaware.

In short, the P-R program is the primary support for Delaware's statewide wildlife management system. These funds support research, land management, land acquisition, wildlife introduction, and hunter training activities that enable this State to have a viable and active wildlife program.

Florida

By creating a State Commission of Game and Fresh Water Fish on June 8, 1935, Florida made a commitment to preserve fish and wildlife communities and to provide citizens with continuing opportunities to hunt and fish. Almost simultaneously, the Federal Government launched the Federal Aid in Wildlife Restoration Act of 1937, popularly called Pittman-Robertson (P-R). It amounted to national recognition that man's conquest of nature had taken a toll on wildlife and that restorative efforts were overdue.

P-R was the backbone of Florida's wildlife management program during the Commission's early years and it formed the financial base on which its current wildlife programs are built. Between 1937 and 1960, P-R probably supported 75 percent of the wildlife work. One of the first applications for P-R funding was for the purchase of two major tracts of wildlife habitat in South Florida. In 1941, a purchase of 62,000 acres was made near Punta Gorda, followed in 1947 by 50,000 acres of Palm Beach County land, at the north end of Florida's Gold Coast, where beach frontage may now bring $1 million per linear foot. Since those initial purchases, Florida has developed a management area program second to none. Over 4.4 million acres of wild lands are available for wildlife-oriented recreation in the State. Although the Commission does not own all lands in the system, P-R continues to play a key role in operation of all the management areas.

P-R has provided funding for many research projects that contributed to the body of knowledge required for informed regulation of human activities, as well as the conservation of wildlife. In fact, P-R funds were instrumental in establishment of this State's wildlife research facility at Gainesville, in close proximity to the University of Florida.

Specific studies addressed to management needs include, for example: a study by Frank A. Winston in 1954 which allowed the Commission to set dove seasons and regulate the taking of doves based on knowledge of the birds' migratory patterns, breeding behavior and natural mortality; studies in 1958 and 1960 by Robert K. Kyde and E. B. Chamberlain, which provided similar information for both resident and migratory waterfowl; and another study, in 1960, by James A. Powell which provided a base of knowledge for management decisions on wild turkeys. Additionally, 25 years of turkey research conducted by Lovett Williams and David Austin resulted in a wealth of knowledge regarding this species.

In 1965, a major book, *The White-Tailed Deer in Florida*, was published by Richard Harlow and F. K. Jones. The book is a compendium of writings by several well-known authors from the Southeast and is a major contribution to knowledge of the life history and management of the whitetail in Florida.

Although the primary focus of P-R has been on conservation of game, some efforts have yielded significant contributions to the welfare of nongame species. For instance, Florida has a large number of endangered and threatened species, many of which have benefited directly or indirectly from P-R projects. The purchase of Judges Bat Cave in northwest Florida and an eastern brown pelican restocking program are examples. The bat cave is one of very few known to be suitable for winter hibernation of the endangered gray bat, a friendly Florida native that can consume up to 1,000 insects per night. Since the bats may live up to 30 years, they can provide free insect control for a long time.

Finally, P-R has made a major contribution by providing funding for wildlife management planning. In Florida, that planning concept has evolved into a strategic planning approach for operating all nine programs of the Commission. Such plans now guide the activities of all divisions and offices.

The P-R program has allowed States to respond to a complex set of problems and issues with a scientific approach to managing the man/environment relationship. The State's sportsmen realize that the 11 percent tax levied on their equipment has been put to good use as an investment in the future of sport hunting and the natural environment. More importantly, it has been a way for citizens who love the outdoors to contribute to the welfare of wildlife and habitats, assuring their presence for future generations.

Georgia

Georgia received its first Pittman-Robertson funds in 1944, at which time five projects were funded. Since then, these funds have provided the backbone of wildlife management in the State. The following is a brief review of some of the major accomplishments under this program.

In 1944, the Cedar Creek and Coastal Flatwood Wildlife Management Areas (WMA) became the first Federally-funded wildlife management areas in Georgia. Today (1985), the State operates 58 WMA's on over 1.2 million acres of land. Over 6 million man-days of outdoor recreation occurred on these areas in 1984. Outdoor recreational use of these WMA's includes not only hunting and fishing but also field trials, hiking, camping, photography, nature walks, canoeing, spelunking and other activities.

In addition to managing wildlife lands, Georgia has had significant success in the restoration of wildlife through P-R funded projects. A particularly noteworthy development arising out of one project has found application throughout the world. This was the development of the prototype dart gun by Jack Crockford, James Jenkins, and Frank Hayes which has since been refined into a sophisticated instrument for administering drugs to wild animals. Without this tool for capturing wildlife, restoration and research programs would be infinitely more difficult.

The Georgia Game and Fish Division used this new capture technique to further deer restoration in the State. In the 1940's, deer occurred only in isolated river swamps in Georgia. In 1944, a project for capturing deer was begun which resulted in the release of 3,741 deer in the State. The herd subsequently expanded from 33,000 in 1950 to approximately 900,000 in 1985. Deer now occur, and hunting is allowed, in all counties in the State. The harvest in 1985 was in excess of 170,000 compared to 4,000 in 1950. This one wildlife resource, currently valued at $94 million annually, represents one of the great success stories of the P-R program in Georgia.

In 1972, Georgia Game and Fish initiated a wild turkey restoration project funded by P-R. At that time, the State had approximately 17,000 of the birds; today there are turkeys in 141 counties with a population exceeding 150,000 birds. Due to this effort, the number of counties open for turkey hunting has expanded from 38 in 1972 to 101 in 1985, and over 31,000 turkey hunters in Georgia expend nearly 200,000 man-days in pursuit of the sport.

Migratory flights of Canada geese into Georgia have dwindled to only a few thousand annually and hunting them is not allowed. However, resident flocks have been established throughout the State with a current minimum population of 10,000. We are now looking forward to having a goose season in the near future, due to this restorative effort made possible by P-R.

Through P-R, approximately twenty survey and ten research projects are funded annually on game and non-game species. Much of the information is used in the establishment of hunting seasons and in monitoring non-game species. Additional to the good purpose of restoring and maintaining wildlife populations in Georgia, P-R funds have also provided for a great deal of public recreation related to the wildlife resource.

Hawaii

Hawaii first participated in the Pittman-Robertson program in 1945. At that time, hunting was primarily a "gentlemen's" sport on private lands or a mechanism for eradication of feral animals in government forest reserves and watersheds. Virtually nothing was known of the life history, distribution, or population dynamics of game birds or mammals on the Islands. The first significant use of the grant-in-aid funds was the employment of Drs. Charles and Elizabeth Schwartz to conduct a reconnaissance of game birds. Their resulting classic, *Game Birds in Hawaii,* laid the foundation for a professional wildlife management program which continues to this day.

With P-R support, hunter access roads, water control devices, hunter checking stations, boundary signs, food crop plantings, and noxious plant controls were instituted on public hunting areas on the Islands of Hawaii, Maui, Molokai, Lanai, Oahu, and Kauai. Additionally, inducements to private landowners resulted in more recreational hunting opportunities for the public under cooperative agreements. Public hunting acreage increased from 25,832 acres in 1950 to 1,029,000 acres in 1985, partly as a result of this P-R program. As a reflection of hunter interest, license sales increased from a low of 2,917 in 1945 to a high of 12,107 in 1984.

Staffing with professional wildlife biologists made possible surveys, inventories, and research essential to sound management. New big game species, including the European bighorn sheep (mouflon), pronghorn, and black-tailed deer, were introduced in suitable habitats. Monographs on the axis deer, feral sheep, mouflon, and feral pigs resulted in significant program changes in terms of bag limits, hunting seasons, and range management.

Under the Foreign Game Introduction Program, nine species of game birds were brought from India, Africa, Asia, and North and South America for attempted establishment on the major islands. Of these, the grey, black and Erckel's francolin, Rio Grande turkey, and Gambel's quail now figure prominently in the hunter's bag.

Although P-R funding initially focused on game species, it has since included projects for such endangered species as Hawaiian goose (nene), Hawaiian duck (koloa), waterbirds (stilt, coot, gallinule), and the Hawaiian crow (alala). This effort included inventories, habitat management, life history research, and captive propagation. Wildlife sanctuaries, established on State lands, or under cooperative agreements with private landowners, provided secure habitats for the release of captive stock. Over 80,000 acres of refuges for seabirds, waterbirds, forest birds, and the endangered monk seal are now under management.

Federal Aid in Wildlife Restoration has provided Hawaii with a means for land acquisition, habitat management, stocking, research, and inventories, all of which have been crucial in keeping pace with the demand for hunter recreation and the preservaton of many endangered species.

Idaho

The Idaho Fish and Game Department began participating in the Federal Aid program in 1939 with a modest allotment of less than $20,000. It has since expanded to a million-dollar-plus program in 1986. Most Federal Aid projects conducted in the late 1930's and 40's were surveys designed to determine the location and status of big game in winter.

The Department developed 5-year species management plans in 1980 and, in 1985, updated them for the period 1986-1990. These documents are all inclusive of management work and suffice as P-R project documents to secure funding.

In 1973, a wildlife laboratory was constructed in Boise where all lab work, including determining the age of mammals, food habits work, blood work on turkeys, studies of lead shot contamination of waterfowl, and many miscellaneous tests are conducted.

With the aid of P-R funds, the Department has acquired 55,893 acres of land in 24 of the 44 counties in the State. Major purchases have been made in eastern Idaho that provide 15,770 acres of big game winter range and a migration corridor in Freemont County and 10,725 acres of waterfowl areas in Jefferson County. Following World War II, several small ranches in the Middle Fork of the Salmon River and other "back country" areas were purchased with P-R funds as a means of withdrawing livestock grazing on critical big game winter range used by deer, elk, and bighorn sheep. These ranches are still administered by the Department. P-R continues to fund the operations of 14 major Wildlife Management Areas in Idaho along with administering and maintaining numerous small tracts and hunter access areas.

In the 1950's, several research projects were initiated using Federal Aid monies. These included the first research efforts on individual species or groups of species. Most notable were projects on bighorn sheep, mountain goats, waterfowl, beaver, and antelope. Intensive surveys of big game habitat were also initiated during this time in the Clearwater drainage (elk) and in the Cassia area (mule deer). During the 1960's, research efforts on mule deer ecology were started in southwestern Idaho, along with the first sage grouse research project. The 1970's saw a major increase in funding available through Federal Aid and studies on antelope, mountain goat, Rocky Mountain elk, and bighorn sheep ecology were added. The first studies using satellite imagery, as well as the first studies of moose and black bear ecology also occurred in this period.

The mountain goat study deserves special note because it was the first to document a lack of compensatory response in reproduction for a stagnant population. Data from this research had significant impacts on the management philosophy for goats in several other States and provinces as well as in Idaho.

The black bear research project resulted in one of the largest data bases on this species in North America. Over 1,200 black bears were captured and data were collected on population size, sex and age structure, movement and activity patterns, reproductive biology, denning activities and den characteristics, and food habits of hunted and unhunted populations.

Clearly, the Federal Aid program has contributed significantly to Idaho's wildlife management program and has greatly increased our knowledge of species biology and habitat requirements.

Illinois

Recent studies indicate that the public spends more than $1 billion annually in Illinois on activities associated with wildlife, such as hunting, fishing, bird-watching, and nature photography. Pittman-Robertson funds may be the biggest reason much of that revenue-attracting wildlife exists here.

Since its first involvement with the program in 1939, Illinois has received nearly $39 million to fund more than 100 projects ranging from land acquisition and research and development to conservation education, facility construction and maintenance, and work under cooperative agreements.

Illinois, in the middle of the Mississippi Flyway, has become one of the Nation's major duck- and goose-hunting areas, as well as a wintering ground and a rest-stop for birds in migration. More than 300,000 ducks and geese winter here annually. Before the advent of P-R, the birds were only occasional visitors.

In 1928, for example, Horseshoe Lake Conservation Area in southern Illinois hosted only 1,000 Canada geese. Expanded from 49 to 3,787 acres with P-R funds, and further enlarged with other funding, Horseshoe Lake now covers 7,901 acres and has a wintering population in excess of 150,000 Canadas annually. It is the State's largest goose management area and a tourist attraction of national and international scope for birders and other wildlife enthusiasts.

Mermet Lake Conservation Area and Union County Refuge, two other components in southern Illinois' network of waterfowl management sites, were created largely with P-R money which bought 2,009 of Mermet's 2,580 acres and 4,792 of Union County's 6,202 acres.

Between 1939 and 1975, the P-R program also enabled the Department of Conservation to acquire and develop all or a greater part of the following sites for waterfowl management and hunting: Rice Lake, Anderson Lake, Sanganois, Spring Branch and Sam Dale Conservation Areas; Stephen Forbes and Chain O' Lakes State Parks; and the Marshall County and Baldwin Lake Fish and Wildlife Areas.

But waterfowl, its hunters and observers are not the only beneficiaries of P-R in Illinois. These funds also bought half of the 2,330-acre Green River and the 2,300-acre Turkey Bluffs Conservation Areas, 2,111 privately-owned acres lying within the 262,000-acre Shawnee National Forest, and 353 acres of the 1,301-acre Sam Dale Conservation Area, and approximately half of Beaver Dam State Park's 734 acres. All but Beaver Dam are important hunting sites for upland game, deer and other species.

Well over 150,000 additional acres have been set aside and/or developed as wildlife habitat across the State through "Acres for Wildlife," a statewide public lands development project, and through cooperative agreements with Federal, State, and local agencies, and private landowners. P-R funding has been vital to all of these programs. In a State considered habitat-poor (95 percent of the land is privately-owned and most of it intensively cultivated) the importance of this "bonus" habitat to wildlife cannot be overstated.

Illinois wildlife success stories for which P-R can take much credit include: wood ducks—sparse before P-R and now in huntable numbers following programs of research, and habitat acquisition and development; white-tailed deer—numbering a few thousand before 1937, and now providing an annual harvest that in 1985 totaled a record 31,900 animals; turkeys—a once extirpated species that was re-introduced into two counties during the 1960's, reached hunting numbers in the 1970's, and now may be taken in 20 counties and viewed in many more; and giant Canada geese—brought to sporting status through stocking, management, and range expansion. Additionally, many of the 72 animals and 364 plants on State endangered or threatened species lists, as well as many other non-game creatures, have been beneficiaries of game-oriented programs and land acquisitions funded by Pittman-Robertson.

Indiana

Indiana's participation in the Pittman-Robertson program started in 1939, at a time when the Division of Fish and Wildlife had no college-trained employees, and the major activities were raising and stocking quail, pheasant and fish. There is no doubt that the division eventually would have expanded its operation to include more constructive work, but with the infusion of Pittman-Robertson funds and its attendant requirements, wildlife management was able to advance further and faster.

Initially, a significant change was made in response to a Federal requirement that P-R project leaders meet certain minimum employment qualifications and that they be reasonably free of political involvement. This resulted in the hiring of career-oriented employees and the implementation of effective and continuing wildlife restoration programs, as evidenced by the fact that four of the seven original biologists associated with the Federal Aid program, since its inception in 1940, remained with the division until retirement.

White-tailed deer were extinct in Indiana when a project in 1941 started the restoration efforts by releasing 200 deer purchased from Wisconsin. By 1984, there were deer in every county and the estimated deer population had reached 150,000. More than 195,000 deer hunting licenses were sold in that year, and almost 28,000 deer were harvested. And the herd is still expanding. Similar successes can be claimed for ruffed grouse and wild turkeys. In the early 1940's, grouse were present only as remnant populations, and turkeys had vanished entirely. But with a gradual return of suitable habitat and an extensive Federal Aid trapping and restocking program, grouse have been restored to most of their original haunts, and turkeys are making a strong comeback. Grouse can now be hunted in 17 counties and turkeys in 24.

Wildlife research and survey work have been other important Federal Aid activities providing vital information for management. Without Federal funds, Indiana would not have been able to do the research to provide information on population dynamics and harvest analysis, necessary to establish harvest regulations. Equal in importance to finding out the "right things to do," is finding out the "wrong things to do." For example, one research study in Indiana clearly disproved the widely held belief that stocking pen-reared birds was the way to replenish wild game populations. Statistics showed that only 6 percent of stocked bobwhite quail and 10 percent of stocked cock pheasants were harvested the ensuing hunting season, proving that artificial stocking was a waste of the hunter's dollar. This research not only stopped an unproductive existing program, but also prevented many stocking schemes from getting past legislative committee meetings.

In Indiana, more P-R funds have been spent on land acquisition than for any other purpose. So far, we have acquired more than 55,000 acres; the 75 percent reimbursement feature of P-R is an excellent justification to a legislative budget committee for obtaining State matching funds. Federal monies have also been used extensively to improve and maintain wetlands, and to develop and maintain upland game habitat on State fish and wildlife areas, as well as State and Federal forests. For a State such as Indiana, where public hunting areas were scarce, P-R has provided a tremendous boost. Sixteen fish and wildlife areas around the State now provide for hunter access. It is doubtful that this would have been accomplished in the absence of the Pittman-Robertson program.

Iowa

The most significant contribution of the Pittman-Robertson program in Iowa was to enable the State to purchase and protect several thousand acres of wetland, forestland and natural areas. Prior to P-R, the only public lands available to hunters and outdoor enthusiasts were sovereign lands and portions of Stephens and Shimek Forest totaling about 49,070 acres. Since 1937, 42,146 acres have been purchased through the program and, additionally, funds are used to manage and maintain approximately 290,000 acres of public wildlife lands.

During the 1940's, the acquisition of wetlands was the primary use of P-R funds with several major wetland complexes and marshes purchased for between $10 and $60 per acre. Acquisition continued during the 1950's but, additionally, some wetland development and upland habitat work was done on private lands. From 1950 through 1958, the Conservation Commission conducted a farm-game habitat development program funded mostly from Pittman-Robertson. This resulted in the establishment of several thousand acres of wildlife habitat on private land. Unfortunately, an intensive agricultural movement throughout the State put an end to this effort as marginal lands and former wildlife habitats were converted to row crops. Needless to say, the farm-game habitat program was reduced in size and more money was directed toward acquisition and development.

In the early 1950's, four wildlife management units were started and the number has since grown to 20. These units were established in order to manage public hunting areas more effectively, and to provide better facilities for hunters. Also, wildlife biologists were assigned to give technical assistance to landowners with the result that much-needed wildlife habitat has been created on private lands over recent years.

From the 1980's through today, P-R funds have been used primarily for land acquisition, wildlife research and the development and management of public areas.

Pittman-Robertson has had a significant positive impact on wildlife management in Iowa. Through its assistance, major accomplishments were achieved not only in acquiring many areas but also in developing them. These developments have included such things as the building and repair of water control structures for wetlands, providing access areas and parking lots, the construction of boat launching sites, and the delineation of boundaries through fencing and signs.

Two noteworthy accomplishments in wildlife research and management in Iowa have involved the wild turkey and Canada goose. Through trades with other States and eventual transplanting, turkey populations have skyrocketed. Iowa's first turkey hunting season in 1974 produced some 115 harvested birds; 10 years later approximately 4,200 were taken. And a Canada goose restoration program which began in 1967, also under P-R, is now producing some 10,000 young annually. Other research conducted through P-R funding has involved red fox, coyote and raccoon with improved management of these furbearers being one result. A nongame program in the State is just getting underway with funding provided by a "checkoff" from State income taxes. It is anticipated that P-R funds will be applied to the program as it grows in scope.

Iowa's future program will continue to emphasize land acquisitions for wildlife management areas. The Commission plans to acquire large blocks that can be effectively managed for a variety of wildlife species and a variety of uses by the public. But the continuing challenge in Iowa will be the future of wildlife and its relation to agriculture. The Conservation Commission must concentrate its studies and management to benefit certain species of wildlife while being in tune with agricultural practices of our State.

Kansas

From game protection and land acquisition to habitat management on private lands, Pittman-Robertson and the Kansas Fish and Game commission have evolved together during the past 50 years. In 1937, when the Pittman-Robertson Act was passed, the Kansas Forestry, Fish and Game Commission had been in the game protection business for 32 years. At the time, Kansas had no significant big game populations, and wildlife in the State was recovering from several years of severe drought.

Two of the first projects funded through P-R were the Meade County Pheasant Farm and the 19,800-acre Cheyenne Bottoms Wildlife Area, a large wetland in the center of the State. These projects represented a new direction for the agency, away from simply enforcing game laws, toward conserving and managing game populations.

In 1950, the Commission embarked on a major land acquisition program, buying more land at Cheyenne Bottoms as well as waterfowl habitat at the Marais des Cygnes and Neosho Wildlife Areas. Today, the Kansas Fish and Game Commission (as it is now called) holds title to nearly 57,000 acres, purchased and managed through

P-R. An additional 175,000 acres of lands and waters associated with Federal projects are also managed with P-R assistance.

In the 1960's the agency used P-R funds to expand its wildlife research programs and to introduce standardized methods for surveying upland game populations. Better information led to better management and today Kansas boasts some of the best pheasant and quail hunting in the country. In fact, Kansas is one of only a few States with huntable populations of both lesser and greater prairie-chickens, with an annual harvest larger than the total populations of these birds in most other prairie States!

Big game also benefited from the program. In 1965, with Kansas' deer herd growing steadily, the State held its first deer season in modern times. The year before, pronghorn and wild turkey re-introductions were begun with P-R funds. Now Kansas has nearly 2,000 antelope and 45,000 wild turkeys and limited hunting has been conducted on these species since 1974.

In the early 1970's, KF&G brought wildlife management to private lands. P-R moneys were used to help fund district wildlife biologist positions, allowing more direct contact with landowners. In 1973, the agency began a Wildlife Habitat Improvement Program (WHIP) for private lands, providing advice and direct assistance to landowners. Today, more than 2,600 landowners have over a million acres enrolled.

In 1977, Kansas became one of the first States under the P-R program to develop a comprehensive statewide wildlife plan with the U.S. Fish and Wildlife Service. Comprehensive planning has allowed KF&G to establish a clear direction for wildlife and to more effectively administer long-term projects.

KF&G is now re-introducing giant Canada geese to the State. In 1985 alone, over 1,000 goslings were released in prime pond habitat in eastern Kansas, and the outlook for resident breeding populations is bright. River otters, ruffed grouse, and sharp-tailed grouse are also being re-introduced into selected areas of the State.

Kansans can be proud of the accomplishments made possible through the Pittman-Robertson program. Without these funds, Kansas Fish and Game would find it difficult to meet the increasingly complex challenges of natural resource management: demands for more wildlife, species diversity, and harvestable surpluses—all on fewer acres of habitat. Just as P-R funds enabled us to conserve wildlands initially, they must now help us manage them ever more intensively.

Kentucky

The Federal Aid in Wildlife Restoration legislation (Pittman-Robertson Act) gave birth to one of the great success stories in wildlife management. By applying a sound funding base and rigorous scientific scrutiny to wildlife management, it took us from the Dark Ages and gave us a glimpse at the Renaissance and what the future could offer for wildlife and its human caretakers.

Kentucky became a participant in the program in 1938, but only a few minor projects were implemented before the end of World War II. In 1946, some of the first wildlife school graduates were employed to lead the initial development and research projects. In the years that followed, Kentucky undertook deer and turkey restoration, forest wildlife range improvement and an evaluation of pen-reared quail stocking. Research studies were implemented on turkeys, deer, ruffed grouse, squirrels, and waterfowl. Soon thereafter, studies on rabbits, doves, and exotic birds were underway, as was work on farm game and techniques for the improvement of waterfowl habitat. Acquisition of wildlife management areas was begun in an effort to preserve habitats and provide public hunting grounds.

The interval 1954-64 brought a change in objectives. The once-ambitious research program was sharply curtailed in favor of enlarging upon land acquisition and development.

The period from the 1960's to the present has been one of dramatic changes in the Kentucky landscape. "Clean" farming became the order of the day, and large-scale development of Kentucky's abundant timber and mineral resources was pervasive. It was no longer practical to depend upon private farms and woodlands as a primary source of game. Habitat types that remained in spite of competing land uses seemed to offer better prospects for managing game and making it available to hunters.

Having adopted this new management strategy, Kentucky today has a large and increasing deer herd, and a renewed turkey restoration effort has been extremely successful. Waterfowl management efforts are strategically placed to take advantage of annual migrations; and renewed attention is being given to restoring ruffed grouse to their historic ranges across the State.

Recent research efforts range from analyses of lead shot toxicity in waterfowl to the mathematical modeling of deer, raccoon, fox, and bobcat populations. Newer technologies utilizing Landsat photography for habitat analysis have also proven useful.

Renewed efforts at habitat restoration on reclaimed surface mines, and on lands retired from farming, give promise of making these areas more supportive of wildlife. The maturation of Kentucky's abundant forest lands should ensure the well-being of forest wildlife for the immediate future, at least.

Kentucky's nongame wildlife program is funded through a tax checkoff and P-R. Restoration of the osprey and assessing the status of all of our abundant wildlife resources are among the program's major objectives.

Over the years, Kentucky has acquired over 60,000 acres of wildlife lands, and an additional 200,000 acres are managed for wildlife under lease or license from other public agencies.

The Kentucky Department of Fish and Wildlife Resources acknowledges the important role that the Federal Aid program has played in the restoration of wildlife in the Bluegrass State and the satisfaction of its citizens and visitors.

Louisiana

The Louisiana Department of Wildlife and Fisheries, through the Federal Aid (P-R) program, has been very successful in meeting the research, development, and management needs of the wildlife resources of this "Sportsman's Paradise." Federal Aid funds provided the impetus for dove research in the southeastern States beginning in the early 1950's. This early effort demonstrated that dove hunting could be increased substantially without affecting the size of the dove population. Presently, the size of the dove breeding population is monitored by an annual call-count survey financed by Federal Aid funds.

Waterfowl populations have been closely monitored in the coastal marsh with the aid of P-R funds. In additional to aerial waterfowl surveys, this agency has gathered information and conducted extensive banding studies to help develop appropriate hunting regulation including the September teal season. Other work has demonstrated that a lead poisoning problem exists in certain areas.

The return of the wild turkey in Louisiana must certainly be considered one of the most successful wildlife management activities undertaken by the Department. Brought back from the brink, the wild turkey numbered only about 1,500 birds in the late 1940's. Through an aggressive trapping and restocking program, populations now are estimated to be more than 16,000. A survey conducted in 1984 indicated that approximately 15,600 hunters went afield in quest of this trophy bird. The growth rate of this sport has been astounding in recent years as the population of wild turkeys continues to expand.

Pittman-Robertson funds made available after World War II became the essential component of the State's highly successful deer restoration program. Research and management needs that followed have been met almost entirely through the contributions of Federal Aid and have included almost every aspect of the biology of the white-tailed deer and the ranges they occupy. In summary, Federal Aid made possible the extensive deer herds our State enjoys today and it continues to ensure their existence by providing essential support for research, management, and development programs.

The Louisiana Department of Wildlife and Fisheries presently manages 28 Wildlife Management Areas (WMA's) of which 22 are State-owned. Thirty-four are under the direct supervision of the Game Division and it is on these WMA's that Pittman-Robertson funds are utilized for development, maintenance, and management. The total, all open for public recreation, is 1,080,915 acres.

Maine

The need for wildlife research and development work in Maine was recognized in the early 1930's by the then Commissioner of the Department of Inland Fisheries and Wildlife, George J. Stobie. He was, in fact, instrumental in the passage of the Congressional Act creating Federal Aid in Wildlife Restoration. In 1938, the Maine Legislature and Governor Lewis O. Barrows assented to the provisions of the newly enacted Federal law, making Maine one of the first States to enter into the program. While Maine still had an abundance of habitat and a high wildlife potential, the State was not adequately producing many wildlife species. P-R funding provided the original monies needed to initiate scientifically oriented wildlife projects. The Department soon established a Wildlife Research Division and hired its first game biologists. Within a short time the first wildlife research project was under way.

Maine's first P-R project, entitled "Waterfowl Restoration and Research," was undertaken to determine what areas had the most potential for waterfowl. Waterfowl were live-trapped and banded in order to learn more of migration routes and age and sex ratios; and inventories were made of the local nesting species. This project, completed in 1943, identified many of the ecological requirements of the black and ring-necked ducks and other principal Atlantic Flyway species. This was followed by a restoration project involving plantings of aquatics for the improvement of waterfowl habitat.

During the ensuing years, Federal Aid in Wildlife Restoration played a key role in the continued development of Maine's wildlife management programs. These funds provided the resources needed to acquire and enhance important wildlife habitat, rebuild wood duck populations, and establish nesting populations of Canada geese. P-R funding supported numerous land acquisition projects, as well as the implementation of wildlife management practices on over 500,000 acres of publicly owned land. These include a variety of upland and wetland habitats, and over 200 seabird nesting islands. Information about the location of sensitive wildlife habitats, such as deer wintering areas, eagle nests, and colonial nesting bird colonies, has been routinely collected and incorporated into State, municipal and private land-use planning and control programs. Forest management practices which provide for the needs of wildlife have been formulated and integrated into the management of public and private lands throughout the State.

P-R projects have provided the information needed to assess the status of the black bear and adequately regulate harvest levels; to rebuild depleted beaver populations, and re-establish wild turkeys. White-tailed deer and moose population trends have been closely monitored, as have furbearer populations, making it possible to maintain these highly valued resources while still providing for their use. Inherent in the scientific approach is basic investigation into the status and needs of most Maine game species through hunter surveys and questionnaires, environmental impact investigations, habitat inventories; and habitat acquisition, protection and enhancement.

Since 1968, P-R funding has been instrumental in the development of species management plans, long-term operational programs, and associated program management systems. The planning process provides for the systematic evaluation of the wildlife resources of the State and their use, the establishment of species management goals and objectives, identification of problems, and the formulation of sound and efficient programs to address major areas of concern. As a result, wildlife management in Maine today comprises a mix of research and management activities designed to ensure that the Department's long-term management goals and objectives are achieved.

Maryland

No single act of man has benefited Maryland's wildlife resources more than the passage in 1937 of the Pittman-Robertson Act. In the 50 years since that historic legislation was signed into law, Maryland's wildlife management efforts have risen from virtual obscurity to their proper place of distinction among Maryland's many governmental programs.

While Maryland's accomplishments under P-R are many, few compare with the swift and thorough restoration of the white-tailed deer. After deer had been nearly eliminated from the State at the turn of the century, the deer season was reopened in 1929 and 5 were killed. In 1931, just 32 deer were taken from Maryland's two westernmost counties. With a boost in funds from the Pittman-Robertson Act, restocking efforts were begun in the late 1930's and by 1960, 22 of Maryland's 23 counties had a deer season. The full fruition of this management effort was reached in the hunting season just ended (1985) when 18,749 were killed. And, in believe-it-or-not fashion, this season also recorded the first in which a resident, hunting in all the special seasons and by all permissible means, could have legally taken 25 deer—sika and whitetails, combined. Today, P-R funds continue to support management efforts for deer in the form of habitat analysis, browse cutting and damage control.

The wild turkey has also benefited tremendously from P-R funding. In fact, without Federal funding, it's doubtful if Maryland would have a viable wild turkey population. Habitat loss during the early 1900's was a major factor in the decline of the birds and, by 1919, they were declared "absent from Maryland" by the State game warden, except for a very few local populations in the western mountains.

Refinements in trapping techniques made it possible to obtain adequate numbers of wild birds and re-introductions were begun in 1965. By that date, numerous forest areas had recovered from earlier abuses and were capable of supporting wild populations.

Today, the wild turkey's occupied range totals more than 1,200 square miles and covers most areas of the State including the lower Eastern Shore, where a spring season was scheduled for 1987 in Worcester County. Pittman-Robertson funds continue to finance trap-and-transplant efforts, as well as habitat manipulation projects.

Maryland's portion of the Chesapeake Bay is an important wintering area for some two dozen species of waterfowl, many of which underwent serious decline during the half-century-long era of market hunting. While remedial legislation, mainly in the form of the Migratory Bird Treaty Act, did much to reduce this slaughter, other events appeared to jeopardize this great migratory resource. Industrial growth, urban sprawl, and farming all led to dredging, filling, and drainage projects which rapidly destroyed substantial acreages of emergent and submergent habitats.

Supported by funds from the Pittman-Robertson Act, and the Migratory Bird Hunting and Conservation Stamp (Duck Stamp) Act, surveys of Maryland's most besieged wetlands were conducted in the 1950's and updated and broadened in the 1960's. These helped to point out the changes, losses and degradation occurring in Maryland's wetlands. Following on these inventories, the Maryland Forest, Park and Wildlife Service implemented a waterfowl habitat management program on State wetlands which includes impoundments, dugout ponds, blasted potholes, green-tree reservoirs, and level ditchings. Private landowners are given technical assistance in implementing their own waterfowl habitat improvements.

Continuing studies and surveys on waterfowl have been funded in whole or in part by Federal funds. These include: annual breeding ground and pond index inventories, periodic transect surveys over public areas during the fall and winter months, special counts of canvasbacks, brant, and snow geese during the fall and winter, participation in the national winter waterfowl inventory, hunter harvest estimates, waterfowl parts collections, and banding on breeding and wintering grounds.

Today, Marylanders enjoy more than 80,000 acres of public land designated as Wildlife Management Areas. Many land parcels have been acquired with Federal funds, and today the Pittman-Robertson Act provides funding for dozens of ongoing research projects, restoration and recovery efforts, and habitat development projects. Virtually every species of wildlife within the borders of the State has benefited directly or indirectly.

The past 50 years have provided a firm foundation upon which Maryland's wildlife management program has built a lasting legacy for future generations. With few exceptions, the future of Maryland's varied and valuable wildlife resources appears secure.

Massachusetts

The passage of the Federal Aid in Wildlife Restoration Act (Pittman-Robertson Act) in 1937 may well be seen as the birth of professional wildlife management in Massachusetts. Programs of research and restoration, and increasingly professional cooperative land management efforts, have led to a resurgence of wildlife in the Commonwealth.

The results are apparent in many areas. Both hunters and viewers of white-tailed deer, the State's number-one big game animal, recall the lean years of the late 1960's when the herd was estimated at 6,000. Under careful management, based on research, controlled harvests were implemented and the herd has since grown to an estimated 38,000. Indications are that this level can be sustained. Both the abundance and the obvious health of these animals stand as testimony to success in maintaining the herd in balance with available habitat.

Wild turkeys, extirpated from the State since 1851, were re-introduced through a Pittman-Robertson program in 1972. From the original 27 birds, the flock grew and expanded its range, allowing the Division of Fisheries and Wildlife to open a limited hunting season in 1980. Since that time, turkey populations have continued to increase and now may be found throughout most of the State.

Once scarce, black bears have responded to protection and have re-colonized many rural portions of the Commonwealth. Research continues to provide new information on these animals and has assisted in establishing regulated hunting seasons which have allowed the bear population to grow while minimizing damage to human enterprise.

Coordinated land use and planning, conducted under P-R, have promoted the growth of furbearer populations and even restored the fisher, a species once thought to have been eradicated. The eastern coyote, not previously recorded in the State, is now present and growing in numbers. Biologists continue to monitor the harvest of furbearers to assure that thrifty populations are maintained—within the limits of the land's capacity to support them.

P-R research has enabled biologists to investigate the increasing population of mallards and the decreasing population of black ducks, and to learn about resident geese and their interrelationship with urban mallards as well as with mallards in natural habitats. Findings from surveys have led to the development of multiple hunting zones for waterfowl in ways to increase hunter satisfaction while meeting harvest reduction goals for black ducks.

Other species, as well, have repopulated State-owned and -managed lands made attractive through P-R funded habitat management programs. Wood ducks, ospreys and loons are increasing as a result of installing supplemental nesting structures. Bald eagles and peregrine falcons have been reared and released, and natural nesting of these species is anticipated in the near future.

In 1972, Massachusetts first provided P-R funds for hunter safety education, which has gone far toward promoting safety and sportsmanship and ensuring that young hunters have a sound understanding of their equipment. Nearly 300 volunteers annually donate time to train 3,500-4,000 students in proficiency and safe handling of bows and firearms.

Over the years, wildlife professionals have advised legislators, mediated public controversies, served on local regulatory committees, and worked in a variety of ways to mitigate environmental pressures and pollution. The results have been an increased interest in, and awareness of, environmental matters. Looking ahead, we hope that introduction of wildlife-related concepts in school curricula will extend that awareness and aid in developing a citizenry fully appreciative of the importance of wildlife, and committed to responsible action.

Michigan

After the Pittman-Robertson Act (P-R) was passed in 1937, Michigan initiated its Federal Aid program with a research project titled, "Coordination of Game Management and Farm Practices." The next two Federal Aid projects involved land acquisition; one to expand the existing Rose Lake Wildlife Experiment Station (now the Rose Lake Wildlife Research Center), and the other to acquire hunting lands. In the 1930's, large amounts of farmland in southern Michigan were idled because of the economic depression. The Department of Conservation made the most of this opportunity; it developed an acquisition program to provide public lands for hunting.

Over the past 50 years, the State has acquired over 300,000 acres of land with Pittman-Robertson participation, and Federal Aid-funded research has produced over 1,500 publications. Habitat improvements have been implemented on P-R acquired land as well as on thousands of acres of other State-owned and private lands.

Land acquisition and management priorities have shifted to accommodate wildlife needs. The initial emphasis was on the acquisition of marginal farmland in southern Michigan. Only lands unproductive as farms were bought and much of this land was purchased for five to ten dollars an acre. Most of the land had been either over-farmed or over-grazed and the objective during the 1938-1970 period was to establish as much permanent vegetative cover as possible. Since open, blowing sand was a common condition, revegetation was also done as a soil conservation measure.

By the early 1970's, the combination of plant succession, and management for woody cover, had converted these once poor lands to a mixed forest, brush, and small-scale, food plot matrix. A P-R research study showed that this management strategy was successful for wildlife. Southern Michigan game areas comprise less than 3 percent of the land area; yet they make up 10 percent of the region's forested area, provide for 25 percent of the hunting effort, and 25 percent of the total wildlife harvested in the southern third of the State.

While southern Michigan farmland and northern Michigan forest areas continue to be acquired and managed, wetlands (especially Great Lakes marshes) have been the high priority during the past 15 years. Management of wetlands has been shifting from creation of intensely manipulated waterfowl harvest areas to more natural marsh habitats. This management approach still necessitates careful water control through diking, ditching, and pumping.

Michigan's research program has expanded from species investigations and habitat manipulation evaluations to intensive work on animal physiology and people's perception of the resource. The physiology work has been centered at the two northern research stations, Houghton Lake and Cusino. This work progressed from simple deer feeding trials to determining weight changes and reproductive success on different diets. Recent work includes studies of complex endocrine, physiological, and social changes in deer herds under different regimes of nutrients, density, and social structure.

Michigan has made great strides in maintaining and building its wildlife populations, and in providing for their use and enjoyment by a rapidly increasing populace. The P-R program has been of immeasurable assistance in fulfilling this sizable task.

Minnesota

More than $30 million worth of wildlife restoration; that's how much the Pittman-Robertson program has provided to the State of Minnesota.

The first allocation of $26,352 which became available on July 1, 1938 reimbursed the State for lands purchased for our first public hunting grounds, now part of the Carlos Avery and the Thief Lake Wildlife

Management Areas, and for habitat improvement and boundary posting in these and other Wildlife Management Areas (WMA's).

That first Federal Aid grant was extremely important as it provided a great impetus for developing Minnesota's current wildlife research and management programs. Although by present-day standards the money was a small amount, the value of that first allocation is illustrated by the fact that a 440-acre tract in Carlos Avery purchased for $9,700 in 1938 is now worth probably $250,000.

Impressed with the need for habitat preservation, Richard J. Dorer, Federal Aid Coordinator from 1942 to 1954, led a drive to establish the "Save Minnesota's Wetlands Fund." Voluntary contributions fell short and, in 1957, the State Legislature added a $1 surcharge (since raised to $4) to the hunting license fee, specifically for land acquisition and development.

P-R funds have paid for a large share of the land in our 997 wildlife management areas, where more than 528,000 acres (825 square miles!) are now owned by the State and preserved for hunting, trapping, and related outdoor activities. Substantial economic benefits to local people—cafes, motels, sporting goods stores, land-owners who rent hunting blinds, etc.—have become evident in the vicinity of our larger WMA's.

Due partly, we believe, to the good showing of P-R, several conservation organizations have been encouraged to assist in the preservation and management of our WMA's. The Nature Conservancy has donated land or bought choice tracts to preserve them until State acquisition funds became available. The Minnesota Waterfowl Association and Ducks Unlimited have provided funds for development.

Under P-R projects, our Fish and Wildlife personnel exert broad influence on the management of the fish and wildlife habitat through technical advice to a wide range of government and private land developers, and by reviewing State and Federal permit applications which sometimes contain potentially harmful aspects.

Two P-R projects that have received enthusiastic support from the outdoor community are the re-establishment of the giant Canada goose and the establishment of the wild turkey.

Giant Canadas raised at the Carlos Avery WMA were used to start flocks in our larger wildlife areas, and elsewhere in the State, in cooperation with local sportsmen's clubs. From a handful of breeders in Minnesota in the 1950's these geese have increased to perhaps 3,000 breeding pairs and a summer population of 20,000 to 30,000 birds in our wildlife areas. In addition, as many as 25,000 giant Canadas are found in Rochester, Minnesota during the winter, many of which find their ancestry in the DNR's stocking program.

A shortage of suitable habitat has prevented wild turkeys from attaining the same degree of success as the giant Canada geese, but a peak fall population of 6,000 birds occurred in 1981 in the two southeastern Minnesota counties where live-trapped birds from other States had been released in prior years. An average of about 2,000 turkey permits are issued for the spring hunting season.

All Minnesotans who value our wildlife heritage owe a debt of gratitude to the program, not only for the direct contribution it has made to this once-dwindling resource, but for the inspiration it has brought to other conservation groups who have joined in this massive restoration effort.

Mississippi

Conservation of wildlife resources and enforcement of conservation laws in Mississippi were almost unheard of before the close of World War I. In 1926, the Mississippi Legislature passed laws to regulate hunting, fishing and trapping. Each county was required to appoint a game warden to enforce these laws.

In 1932, the Legislature created the Mississippi Game and Fish Commission, the predecessor of today's Mississippi Department of Wildlife Conservation (DWC). Early objectives of the agency were to eliminate market hunting and to undertake a game survey to determine the density and distribution of game species.

Deer populations were estimated at 7,357 and turkeys at 5,000, with huntable populations of both species only in a very few of the 82 counties. In 1934, a game release program was started with deer obtained from Texas and somewhat inferior pen-reared wild turkeys. Today's annual harvest figures, by contrast, are 250,000 deer and near 50,000 wild turkeys.

The stage had been set for what later proved to be the turning point in wildlife restoration. In the July 1938 issue of Mississippi Game and Fish, the State's official conservation magazine, there appeared this headline: "Federal State Wildlife Funds Available Now." ... "Under the new Federal-State Cooperative plan for wildlife restoration which went into effect July 1, Mississippi is expected to receive $45,000 annually for the $15,000 it will put up as matching funds ...," the article stated.

A total of 40 game refuges, comprising approximately 241,000 acres, were leased. These areas were release sites for all types of wildlife, especially deer and turkeys. As populations increased, the refuge system became a source for stocking other desirable locations across the State. Wherever local people supported the program, lands adjacent to the refuges developed viable game populations.

We estimate the white-tailed deer population in Mississippi today to be in excess of 1.5 million animals, and there are probably more than a half million eastern wild turkeys.

The refuge system gradually has developed into 32 wildlife management areas (WMA) encompassing 900,000-plus acres, most of them leased from the U.S. Forest Service, the Army Corps of Engineers, and private land owners like forest products companies. Six of them are State-owned and total 77,063 acres. Federal Aid funds were used to purchase 36,427 of the State-owned acres.

Mississippi's deer restoration program evolved into one of population management by the 1961-62 hunting season, when the first antlerless deer season was prescribed for Bolivar County in the Mississippi Delta. The State now supports either-sex hunting on a statewide basis.

Today, technical guidance to landowners and organized hunting clubs is provided by the Mississippi Cooperative Deer Management Assistance Program (DMAP) begun in 1977. By being involved in the data-keeping process, State sportsmen help the biological staff of the Department make management decisions specifically for their area. In 1984-85, 405 landowners or clubs were involved in collecting data from 16,356 deer.

In addition to working with the Cooperative Wildlife Research Unit, the agency has cooperative ties with research scientists at Mississippi State University (MSU). P-R funds enable the university workers to seek answers to wildlife problems identified by the Department.

This unique relationship between managers and researchers has led to the development of Mississippi's deer management system on both public (WMA's) and private (DMAP) lands. The entire focus of the 1976-80 period was the white- tailed deer. Since then, however, DWC biologists and MSU researchers have expanded this work to include furbearers, turkeys, bobcats, doves, squirrels and waterfowl.

In 50 years of Federal Aid in Mississippi, both game and nongame populations have responded to improved management. Good habitat, sportsman coorperation, guidance of the scientific community, and assured funding of P-R—all have helped make a better future for Mississippi's wildlife and the citizens who enjoy it.

Missouri

Perhaps nowhere in the country is this 50th anniversary of the Pittman-Robertson Act more appropriately acknowledged than in Missouri. For it was also in 1937 that a non-political Missouri Department of Conservation was formed by an amendment to the State Constitution.

At that time our wildlife resource was at rock-bottom. During the preceding 100 years of settlement and development, the landscape had changed drastically because of destructive logging, intensive agricultural activity, industrial growth and a rapidly expanding human population.

The simultaneous advent of non-political wildlife administration and enactment of the Pittman-Robertson Act provided the means to meet an awesome challenge. One of the first actions of the new Missouri Conservation Commission was approval of a program which would apply its share of the funds to a single project—wildlife research.

Over the past 50 years, this effort led to the successful restoration and continuing management of several native game species—notably the white-tailed deer and the eastern wild turkey. Results are most easily demonstrated by a review of harvests. Hunting of deer was prohibited after the 1937 season produced a harvest of only 108 whitetails. Seven years later, the season was opened to the first "bucks-only" hunt of 1944 which produced a harvest of 583. The first "any-deer" season of 1951 gave hunters 5,519. Since 1944, 950,000 whitetails have been harvested. That's more than 40 times the total estimated deer population before P-R, bringing recreational pleasure to more than 5.3 million licensed hunters.

P-R funded wild turkey research and subsequent restoration of this majestic game bird is in some ways even more dramatic. Research on the use of game farm birds was evaluated, and it was concluded that release of over 14,000 had resulted in no long-term benefit. It was clear that restoration of wild turkeys in Missouri, if it were ever to become a reality, would have to depend upon live-trapped native wild birds. The season was closed in 1938, and refuges were established to protect remnant wild flocks. Techniques of habitat improvement were implemented to greatly increase turkey populations on refuges. The cannon net trap (originally designed for use on waterfowl) was successfully adapted for turkey trapping and led to a full-scale trapping and restocking program by 1957. Results during the following years were almost immediate and highly successful.

As in the case of deer, hunting seasons best show the overall success of this work. The first "gobbler-only" season of 1960 (after a 22-year closed season) resulted in a harvest of 94 birds during a three-day season in 14 counties. Presently, all of Missouri's 114 counties have a 14-day, two-gobbler spring season, and additionally 86 counties are open during a 14-day, "any-sex" fall season. Over 250,000 wild turkeys have been harvested by slightly more than 934,000 licensed hunters during the past 25 years.

Turkey restocking in Missouri has been completed, but trapping continues for purposes of trading with other States, wherein we receive pheasants, ruffed grouse, river otters, etc. P-R supported research has also greatly benefited virtually all species of small game, nongame and endangered species, providing basic life history data and management guidance for most wildlife indigenous to Missouri.

In addition to research, P-R funds have been used primarily for acquisition of public recreational lands. During the period 1940 through 1985, more than 105,000 acres of prairies, wetlands, and forest areas were acquired. Another 25 upland wildlife areas have been acquired which also provide hunting opportunity as well as serving as demonstration areas for wildlife management techniques and soil erosion control practices.

Without P-R funding, many of these successes might have eventually come about, but they would have been longer in coming and serious losses would have undoubtedly occurred during the interim. P-R funding, totaling more than $38 million, has provided an important financial means for the implementation of a scientifically-based wildlife management program mandated by a vote of the people.

Montana

Prior to 1940, game management in Montana consisted primarily of restricting harvests, establishing preserves and paying bounties on predators. Assenting legislation in 1941 authorized Montana's use of P-R funds and prohibited diversion of hunting license fees for purposes other than wildlife restoration.

Three major game management objectives have been adopted since the advent of P-R in 1941:
1) to develop and sustain maximum game populations consistent with available habitats and other land uses,
2) to assure maximum production and utilization of annual game surpluses, and
3) to provide maximum recreational opportunities for sportsmen.

Accomplishing these objectives has also generated a broad diversity of hunting and viewing opportunities.

Technically trained biologists began inventorying game populations and initiating land development projects in 1941. Management practices changed as reliable data accumulated; most of the old concepts were abandoned. Specific hunting districts, more responsive to the big game and habitat resources, were delineated. Seasonal surveys of populations, annual harvests and big game winter ranges were developed and implemented.

Land acquisition and development, supported by P-R, have significantly enhanced key habitats for game and non-game animals. Approximately 192,307 acres have been purchased or leased with P-R funds: 165,285 acres for big game habitat and 27,022 acres for waterfowl management purposes. The Sun River and Beartooth big game winter ranges and Freezout Lake Waterfowl Management Area rank among the most outstanding in the Nation.

Trapping and transplanting re-established many herds of bighorn sheep, mountain goats, antelope, elk and deer. Similar techniques resulted in huntable populations of Merriam's turkeys. The fisher was re-established in parts of western Montana.

Wildlife research since 1941 has addressed many of Montana's game, furbearer and predator species. Research on nongame species, begun on an intermittent basis in 1950, became a fulltime effort in 1977.

Major ecological projects included studies of deer (statewide) and gray partridge; effects of logging practices on elk, and effects of altering sagebrush communities on antelope, sage grouse, and other wildlife. Various effects of harvest regulations, pesticides and fossil fuel exploration on wildlife have also been assessed. Computer programs were developed to analyze population parameters, allowable rates of harvest, movements and habitat factors.

A wildlife laboratory, initiated in 1955, has provided information on food habits, sex, age, reproduction and disease-parasite identifications. It has also monitored known mortalities of grizzly bears and mountain lions, and coordinated the use of wildlife immoblizing drugs.

Montana's participation in P-R has yielded countless benefits to wildlife, hunters, and nonhunters.
- Deer harvests (bucks only) during 1945-51 did not exceed 40,000 annually; harvests since then (including does) averaged 101,000 annually, with a record of 169,000 in 1984.
- Statewide antelope populations, reduced to about 3,000 by 1924, recovered to about 100,000 by 1965. Annual harvest have exceeded 18,000 since 1952, with a record of 33,000 in 1984.
- Moose, mountain goats and bighorn sheep have recovered from a few remnant herds to huntable populations in many areas.

People spent more than 2 million days hunting in Montana in 1982. That recreational demand is expected to increase by 50 percent by 1990. While accurate estimates of days spent viewing or photographing wildlife are unavailable for Montana, data from other States suggest they may surpass those for hunting. Without the support of hunters' license fees and P-R funds, it is unlikely that these levels of wildlife recreation would exist in Montana today, or could continue in the future.

Nebraska

Since 1939, when Nebraska received its first apportionment for $20,448.51, the Federal Aid in Wildlife Restoration program (P-R) has supported some of the State's most ambitious and successful wildlife enhancement projects. P-R funding has fueled projects to acquire critical wildlife habitat, introduce or re-establish game species, and carry on research and management programs essential to fulfilling the Commission's role as steward of the State's wildlife resource.

P-R funds have been used in the acquisition, maintenance and enhancement of 73 Wildlife Management Areas—33,400 acres of crucial habitat in a State having relatively little public land. Also wetlands in the Rainwater Basin area of Nebraska, where only 10 percent of the original marshes have survived the inroads of agriculture, have been acquired.

If a single success story from this cooperative program were to be singled out, it would be the re-introduction of the wild turkey. Extirpated from the State by the early 1900's, wild turkeys were first released in the Pine Ridge country of northwest Nebraska in 1959. The transplanted birds established and proliferated beyond expectation, and 500 permits were issued for a fall hunt in 1962. Since that time turkeys have spread or been transplanted to most of the State's suitable habitat. By the end of 1985, wild turkeys had provided 332,000 man-days of hunting and uncounted hours of pleasure to wildlife enthusiasts.

Less dramatically, other species have benefited from P-R. During the early 1900's, only remnant herds of pronghorn remained in Nebraska. Under complete protection, pronghorns eventually returned to western Nebraska, and during the late 1950's and early 1960's, 1,077 pronghorns were trapped and reintroduced to the Sandhills region, an 18,000-square-mile expanse of native grassland in north-central Nebraska.

During the 1970's Canada geese were reestablished in their native breeding grounds in the Sandhills and mule deer and whitetails were restored from less than 100 at the turn of the century to an estimated 100,000 to 125,000 in 1985.

These are some of the conspicuous success stories, but for each of the big stories there are dozens of less spectacular successes, many involving nongame wildlife species that benefit equally when habitat is preserved and improved for game.

The role of P-R in Nebraska has been one of the unsung hero or anonymous philanthropist. Since its inception, these funds have supported many management and research projects with significant, long-term benefits. Beginning with the study of the Great Plains muskrat during the late 1940's and early 1950's, and continuing in recent years with a 10-year study of the ring-necked pheasant and sharp-tailed grouse, P-R has been behind nearly every advance in the management of Nebraska's wildlife. Funds have been used to study mallards and Canada geese, in forensic law enforcement to identify species by blood or tissue samples, and to provide technical assistance for the enhancement of wildlife habitat on lands managed by State and Federal agencies. Funds have been used to pump water into dry marshes critical to waterfowl and other migratory birds on their annual journey north to mate and nest. The whole story of the contribution of the Pittman-Robertson program to the preservation of our priceless natural heritage could fill many volumes, but the best proof of its good work is in the gabble of wild geese as they "butterfly" down to a Rainwater Basin marsh, the dancing of courting sharptails on a Sandhill meadow, or the yelp of a Merriam's turkey drifting down a Pine Ridge canyon.

Nevada

Nevada's Senator Key Pittman co-sponsored the Federal Aid in Wildlife Restoration Act of 1937, but his home State was not eligible to receive funds until 1947 when the Fish and Game Commission was reorganized as a statewide wildlife agency. Although Nevada's P-R programs had a belated start, they focused on some of the most important problems of the time.

Early on, it was recognized by a few farsighted individuals that Nevada's wetlands were extremely valuable, if for no other reason than their relative scarcity. The loss of many of these areas, through water diversions and competing uses, alerted wildlife biologists to the need to protect and manage the remaining habitats.

By 1950, the Department gained control, by lease, withdrawal, or purchase, of some 267,874 acres of wetland habitat to be protected and managed for the primary benefit of wildlife, specifically waterfowl. Of this total, 39,774 acres were purchased in fee title through the P-R program, currently comprising eight State-owned and -operated wildlife management areas. These areas provide a secure place for all kinds of wildlife and thousands of recreational use-days annually for hunters and non-hunters alike.

One of the first management efforts in Nevada concerned mule deer. Individual herds were delineated through trapping and marking and their paths and times of migration were established. Additionally, important habitats on their seasonal-use areas were identified. This same procedure of herd management has been applied to every major big game species in the State.

Another early P-R program focused on the establishment or re-establishment of wildlife in the State, particularly upland game birds. As a result, huntable populations of chukar and gray partridges, scaled quail, ring-necked pheasant, white-winged pheasant and Himalayan snow cock have been added to the list of native species, which is limited to sage grouse, blue grouse, mountain quail, Gambel's quail, valley quail and mourning dove. The Himalayan snow cock, imported from Pakistan in 1962, is now firmly established in parts of Elko County and provides the only known hunting of this bird in the Western Hemisphere.

Big game trapping and transplants have been conducted for pronghorn antelope, Rocky Mountain elk, bighorn sheep, and the Rocky Mountain goat, which is not native to Nevada. From a nucleus of 23 animals obtained from the State of Washington, a self-sustaining population was established. The first hunting season was held in Elko County in 1978 with all three hunters recording success.

All three subspecies of bighorn sheep—desert, California and Rocky Mountain—once occupied the State. The latter two were extirpated about 1920 or 1930 and, although the desert race survived, it was severely reduced in numbers and distribution. The return of the California bighorn in 1967 marked the beginning reintroduction effort in the State. This was soon followed by the reintroduction of desert and Rocky Mountain sheep. Through 1985, a total of 539 bighorn have been transplanted onto 24 different sites.

During the 1970's, mule deer management underwent major changes, mainly to improve the accuracy of census and harvest data. In place of ground counts of the deer herds, aerial surveys by helicopter provided better and more accurate information, and a measure of the harvest, throught mandatory return of post-season questionnaires, improved the accuracy of kill data. As a result, Nevada's mule deer harvest was changed to a statewide quota system that has greatly improved efficiency while safeguarding the herds.

In the 1970's, a growing awareness of environmental values swept the Nation. In Nevada, this was partly reflected through an increased concern for nongame wildlife.

To this end, a program was begun in 1973 with one man assigned the task of nongame management throughout the State. Today, four biologists are monitoring priority species, helping make land use decisions involving wildlife, and working to increase public awareness of the values of nongame wildlife and the essential nature of nongame habitat.

This brief summary is suggestive, at best, of the great good that the P-R program has brought to Nevada. More than being instrumental in restoring our native fauna to a healthful condition, it has provided the means for adding interesting exotics, thereby giving further appeal to this desert State.

New Hampshire

In a State that is 87 percent forested, Fish and Game personnel have called upon the beaver and its inherent engineering ability to provide and maintain many thousands of acres of habitat for waterfowl and furbearers. Under a P-R project initiated in 1947, "Statewide Game and Furbearer Habitat Improvement Program," a beaver management program was implemented to the benefit of wildlife and enjoyment by the public.

A general policy of the Department is to perpetuate beaver wherever their presence is beneficial locally. A liberal trapping season is based on harvest information obtained under another P-R funded project, and surplus animals are removed annually. However, managing a beaver population at or near carrying capacity of the locality also entails the responsibility of dealing with problem or nuisance beaver.

Control measures are employed on nuisance colonies to meet special problems. Beaver are removed from areas where they are causing excessive damage but, in areas where they can be tolerated, hundreds of acres of beaver-created impoundments are preserved, resulting in favorable beaver population levels and stabilization of water levels.

If unmanaged, beavers' dam building frequently interferes with human enterprises. P-R funding in New Hampshire contributed to the development of the "beaver pipe," a water level stabilizing device which can be used to alleviate the hazards to highways caused when beavers dam culverts, or the flooding of valuable timber, fields or roadways. A "beaver pipe" is a 24-foot-long, 12-inch-square wooden sluice box with one closed end and a bottom of 2-by-4-inch wire mesh. When pushed through, or set on top of a beaver dam (wire side down with the solid end extending out into the pond) and secured by steel fence posts, water flows freely through the bottom of the box out over the dam. The pipe can be set at almost any level and the beavers' efforts to stop the flow are usually futile.

In the case of a plugged culvert, the dam is removed and a heavy wire mesh fence is installed around the mouth of the culvert and secured with steel posts. If the beavers rebuild the dam on the fence, a "beaver pipe" can then be placed through the fence to keep the water at a desired level.

The "beaver pipe program" has been a relatively small part of New Hampshire's wildlife management program ($8,000 per year). But in terms of waterfowl habitat enhancement, the approximately 375 acres of beaver marsh preserved annually by this means is of considerable value. The benefits to wildlife, as well as to our sporting and non-sporting constituency who use these areas, is incalculable and a clear example of the value of the Pittman-Robertson program to New Hampshire.

New Jersey

The New Jersey Division of Fish, Game and Wildlife has participated in the P-R program since its inception 50 years ago. Initial work centered on the development of State wildlife management areas. These activities included the construction of roads, parking lots, culverts, bridges, the clearing of new fields, planting of food plots and hedgerows, and the management of new forests. All these activities were directed at creating habitat diversity for all wildlife species and developing access for the public to enjoy it. In addition, dikes were constructed to create both freshwater and saltwater impoundments.

From 1947 to 1976, approximately 21,685 acres of wetland, upland, and marsh type habitats were acquired with P-R funds.

The Division has carried out a wide range of Federally funded research and monitoring activities; however, two particularly successful endeavors stand out.

The first involves the management of New Jersey's deer herd. By 1900, New Jersey's white-tailed deer had been reduced to a few remnant wild populations and one or two small, confined, private herds. The reported hunter harvest was only 20 deer in 1901. Through the enactment and enforcement of protective laws, and restocking efforts, the deer increased rapidly and damage to agricultural crops soon became a problem. It was not surprising that the first P-R funded research (1940) was concerned primarily with the identification and control of agricultural damage by deer. By the early 1950's, research on deer had intensified and expanded. Data on age, condition and reproduction was also collected and analyzed.

As a result, New Jersey has adopted a number of new management programs which have resulted in maximizing the economic and recreational benefits of deer while maintaining their densities at a level to minimize negative impacts. These programs include a mandatory check station system (1972), a deer management zone system (1974), a winter archery season (1975), a muzzleloader rifle season (1978), a second deer tag program for the fall archery and shotgun seasons (1980), and extensions of a second tag program to the muzzleloader and winter archery seasons(1984).

Due to these Federal Aid projects, New Jersey has come a long way in deer management. From a reported harvest of 2,173 in 1937, the annual reported harvest now exceeds 25,000 (25,619 in the 1984-85 season). New Jersey deer hunters are now offered over 90 deer hunting days and the opportunity to take eight deer each year.

After an absence of nearly a century, wild turkeys were re-introduced to New Jersey in 1977 under a Federal Aid project. Wild trapped stock obtained from Vermont and New York was released into suitable habitat in the northwestern portion of the State. The original flock dispersed and increased rapidly, and by 1979 the live-trapping and transfer of birds from the original flocks was begun.

The first spring gobbler hunt was held in 1981 and produced a harvest of 71. Since this initial season, 705 gobblers have been taken in the annual spring season, including 217 in 1985.

Wild turkeys have now expanded their range into 15 of New Jersey's counties and occupy 2,000 of an estimated 2,300 square miles of available turkey range. The 1985 fall population was estimated at between 5,500 and 5,800. The restoration of the wild turkey has been one of the outstanding success stories of New Jersey's wildlife management efforts.

New Mexico

With the help of early P-R allotments, key areas of lesser prairie chicken habitat in eastern New Mexico were purchased or leased, protected and improved. The response of prairie chicken populations allowed re-opening of hunting seasons, which continue to the present. The restoration work won for the State's Department of Game and Fish a Citation for Conservation Achievement from the National Wildlife Federation and the National Committee on the Prairie Chicken.

P-R funds contributed to restoration of antelope, elk and bighorn sheep to huntable numbers through transplants within the State and acquisitions from outside. New Mexico pioneered in techniques for moving antelope from areas of surplus to areas of low antelope numbers.

More recently, acquisitions of certain large tracts in northern New Mexico have facilitated management of these lands for the benefit of big game and the hunting public. For at least three decades, other tracts of big game habitat have been improved and protected, increasing hunting opportunity for the public and providing benefits for both big game and other wildlife. For many years, payment of an annual lease fee for hunting and fishing rights on lands managed by the State Land Office ensured those rights for sportsmen while enhancing the value of wildlife as one of the competing uses of those lands.

Lands have also been acquired along the major north-south river valleys used by migrating waterfowl. Protection, water development and provision of food crops on these areas have benefitted waterfowl, and hunters and birdwatchers both enjoy the birds' longer presence in the State.

Central to good wildlife management are collection and analysis of data on harvests, habitat conditions, population dynamics and relationships of survival and productivity to quality and quantity of nutrition, disease, hunting, predation, and other factors. P-R funds have supported such research. Research on claeophorosis in elk and deer and on various parasites in bighorns has produced new understanding of causes and progress of these diseases, as well as innovative approaches to treatment. Deer research has produced other innovations, including capture by helicopter-hazing into large nets for attachment or insertion of transmitters for studies by telemetry. A recently developed population-environmental computer model for mule deer should produce new insights helpful to better deer management.

In New Mexico, P-R funds have also been used in:

- Developing a comprehensive wildlife plan. Incorported into Federal agencies' commitments, the plan helps assure protection and improvement of habitat on millions of acres of Federally-owned land in New Mexico.
- Monitoring actions and proposals affecting the wildlife environment, encouraging those beneficial to wildlife, and proposing mitigation of those causing loss of wildlife habitat.
- Providing stability to New Mexico's nongame and endangered species programs when funds from other sources were lacking.
- Producing publications reporting management and research efforts. A report on the economic values of hunting and fishing in the State was important to the status of wildlife management in New Mexico. Another, *New Mexico Wildlife Management,* was awarded The Wildlife Society's Conservation Education Award.
- Introducing oryx, ibex, and Barbary sheep to New Mexico's ranges, providing unique opportunities for hunters in the United States.

New York

The Pittman-Robertson Act provided the means to carry out wildlife management practices in New York which otherwise might never have been accomplished; or at best, conducted in a very limited fashion. Certainly, both hunting and non-hunting opportunity to enjoy wildlife on public and private lands would be far less than it is today.

Early use of P-R funds in New York concentrated on acquiring basic information. Comprehensive wetland surveys produced documentary benchmark reports on five major wetland sections of the State. Intensive pheasant research studied the factors limiting abundance and the value of game farm liberated stock. Critically needed techniques for capturing, marking and handling wildlife and measuring habitat quantity and quality were devised. Pathology studies looked at disease impacts on wildlife. Early management began with a project in which over 48 million evergreen trees were planted on private land and approximately 2000 water impoundments were constructed across the State to create waterfowl habitat.

The period was marked by a rapid growth in human populations, and dramatic impacts on the environment demanded a critical look at the needs of both wildlife and the people who used it. Projects that failed to meet broad new goals were eliminated; new programs evolved that were aimed at habitat protection, wildlife enhancement and utilization. A few key accomplishments resulting from this more focused approach are presented as follows:

- The acquisition of 32,807 acres of wetland and public access lands either added to existing State Wildlife Management Areas or created entirely new ones. Extensive maintenance, habitat management and public use developments were carried out on 56 such areas, totalling 150,000 acres.
- A research-directed big game management program produces a harvest of 150,000 deer annually, on a sustained yield basis, while maintaining high deer visibility for non-hunters' benefit.
- A wild turkey restoration and management program now boasts a fall hunting season across the entire southern tier of counties and a one-month spring season over several counties of the Adirondack periphery.
- A waterfowl zoning system, based on a 30-year research effort, has permitted the creation of five hunting zones, each reflecting peak abundance in time and location of species migrating through New York.
- Wildlife Management Units have been established for small game and furbearers which permit more sophisticated harvest regulations through recognition of specific ecological zones.
- Inventories monitor critical habitats (including wetlands), and surveys assay hunter effort and harvests of all major game species.
- An endangered species program, 35 percent P-R funded, includes restoration efforts for the bald eagle and peregrine falcon and investigation of several other endangered species.

In summary, projects funded by the P-R Act have made it possible to sort out and understand key segments of complex ecological systems and thereby confidently manage wildlife for the combined benefit of both wildlife and humanity. Moreover, this great fund of scientific knowledge will serve as a solid foundation for still further enlightened management to come. It is significant that almost all game and fur species are harvested today at much higher levels than in 1937. Yet, even in the face of ever-increasing destruction and degradation of habitats through industrial pollution, urban sprawl, wetlands drainage, etc., no managed species has dropped to a "threatened" category—nor is there any likely prospect that it will.

North Carolina

In the past 50 years, the Federal Aid in Wildlife Restoration program has provided funding vital to managing the wildlife resources of North Carolina. These funds have been used by the North Carolina Wildlife Resources Commission to acquire habitat, manage public lands, restock depleted populations of animals, and carry out research. The P-R funds are indispensable in providing for both the welfare of wildlife species and the opportunity for the public to enjoy them in the Nation's tenth most populous State.

Approximately 50,000 acres of land have come under title to the Commission through the P-R program. These purchases have been used to protect unique and critical habitats and to provide opportunity for the public to participate in wildlife-oriented recreation.

At present, P-R funds contribute to managing approximately 2 million acres of lands in the Commission's Game Lands Program. This acreage includes approximately 180,000 acres of Commission-owned lands and 500,000 acres of corporate- and other privately-owned lands which are leased for the benefit of the public. Approximately 1,300,000 acres of Federal lands are managed for wildlife under cooperative agreement with the U.S. Forest Service and other Federal agencies. Funds are used for developing and maintaining habitat improvements, public use facilities, and boundaries. The equipment and facilities necessary for carrying out management activities are also funded under the P-R program, and although lands are managed primarily for game, many nongame and endangered species and unique habitats also benefit.

The restocking of animals in North Carolina has primarily concerned deer and wild turkeys in areas where they had been extirpated. Management of the white-tailed deer has been especially successful, due in part to restocking efforts over the years. From remnant populations, primarily in the mountains and coastal plain, deer have increased to the point that, in 1985, every county in the State had an open hunting season. There is no longer a need for restocking, and management emphasis now mainly concerns the manipulation of seasons and deer numbers to provide maximum recreational opportunity. A restocking program for wild turkeys continues and is beginning to show benefits, as indicated by an increase in the annual harvest over the past several years.

P-R funded research has been conducted on practically every game species in the State, and a great deal of information as been gained which contributes to biologically sound management. Studies have also aided in assessing the attitudes and preferences of the public, determining harvest rates of many species, and estimating recreational and other benefits of management activities.

The P-R program has been, and will continue to be, essential in funding wildlife conservation activities in North Carolina. A continuation of these activities will help assure the future of the wildlife resources while providing maximum recreational opportunity for the citizens of the State.

North Dakota

The passage of the Pittman-Robertson Federal Aid in Wildlife Restoration Act in 1937 marked the start of scientific management of wildlife in North Dakota. Previously, game and fish activities consisted mainly of establishment and enforcement of laws, pheasant and fish stocking and establishment of game reserves. Funds, and experience in wildlife management, were in short supply. The much needed P-R funding enabled the North Dakota Game and Fish Department to start statewide surveys of game populations, wildlife research, land acquisition, and habitat development.

Since then, wildlife population data have been available to aid in management decisions. Wildlife research has provided valuable information concerning fox/coyote/game bird relationships, big game and waterfowl populations, epizootic hemorrhagic disease, plus other topics.

In 1955, North Dakota had approximately 500 free-flying Canada geese, nearly all on Federal refuges. A P-R funded restoration program has produced a huntable population of about 1,500 breeding pairs ranging over a large portion of the State. A small population of California bighorn sheep has been established in North Dakota's badlands to replace the Audubon Mountain sheep, now extinct.

Over 45,000 acres of wetlands, uplands and forest lands have been purchased with P-R funds as wildlife management areas. A major accomplishment has been the preservation of numerous forest land tracts, many which would have been cleared if not purchased.

North Dakota's wildlife management areas (150 units totaling 150,484 acres) have been developed and maintained through these programs. From 1949 to 1966, 13,000,000 trees were planted for wildlife throughout the State, benefiting numerous species.

The value and accomplishments of the Pittman-Robertson Federal Aid in Wildlife Restoration program are obvious to North Dakotans. The past activities have been rewarding, and many challenges remain for the future.

Ohio

Hunters of today often dream of the "good old days" when game abounded and there were plenty of places to hunt. But back in the "good old days" of 1937, when the P-R Program began, the real story in Ohio was quite different. Hunting seasons were closed for bobwhite quail and ruffed grouse—Ohio's only native game birds. Turkeys had been extirpated and sightings of deer were rare. Waterfowl were at low levels, due to drought in the Canadian nesting grounds, and the State was becoming urbanized and intensively farmed, placing further burdens on wildlife.

P-R monies have been used by Ohio's Division of Wildlife in three areas: land acquisition, habitat management and development, and research and surveys. Land acquisition was paramount in the early years when the Division purchased valuable wetlands and upland sites to guard against their disappearance under the plow. The area most recently purchased is the 5,306-acre Killbuck Marsh, the largest remaining inland marsh outside of Lake Erie. To date, 57,820 acres have been purchased with P-R funds on 34 wildlife areas and Shawnee State Forest. These lands account for 66 percent of the Division's holdings, and include the largest tallgrass prairie and some of the largest unbroken wetlands and bottomland hardwoods remaining in Ohio. Hunters, birdwatchers, fishermen, trappers, sightseers, and many others enjoy the benefits of these areas.

P-R monies have been used since the inception of the program to fund both surveys and research on the many factors that affect the numbers and health of game populations. Hunting seasons for many small game species were lengthened when research showed that regulated hunting had little effect on wild populations. Research and surveys helped set the stage for the successful return of Canada geese, wild turkey, white-tailed deer, wood ducks, and beaver in the State.

Habitat management and development is now the central focus in the use of P-R monies. Management practices include tree, shrub, food plot, and grass/legume plantings, nesting structure placement, water level management, and technical assistance to private landowners. The goal is to provide wildlife with adequate places to feed, rest, and raise their young.

Wildlife areas are also managed to provide quality hunting and access for sportsmen. A good example is the controlled waterfowl hunting on Magee Marsh Wildlife Areas near Lake Erie. The managed marsh has well-spaced blinds and hunters enjoy some of the best duck hunting in the Mississippi Flyway. Parking lots, access roads, and trails make wildlife areas accessible to everyone.

The benefits of healthy wildlife populations reach beyond hunters and watchers of wildlife. Economic gain to Ohio from deer hunting alone amounts to about $100 million each year—a great economic boost to rural areas. That includes what the hunters spend on food, lodging, gasoline, clothes, guns, and ammunition.

In some respects the "good old days" are here today because of P-R funding. Sportsmen enjoy hunting turkey, deer, Canada geese, ruffed grouse, and other species in abundance. Non-hunters also enjoy the plentiful wildlife that sportsmen have helped make possible through excise taxes paid into the P-R program. With its dependable funding and skilled administration by USFWS biologists, P-R has been an important contribution to the stability, continuity, and success of wildlife management in Ohio during the last 50 years.

Oklahoma

As in many other States, near the turn of the century, deer in Oklahoma had been nearly eliminated by unrestricted market hunting and habitat destruction. In 1916, the entire deer population was estimated at only 500, found only in four isolated areas. Although deer were protected at this time, the population grew slowly until a Pittman-Robertson funded restoration program was initiated in the mid-1940's. Six tracts were purchased as deer refuges and a vigorous restocking program was begun. Between 1947 and 1972, more than 8,500 deer were trapped and transplanted to unoccupied habitat. Today's deer population is estimated at over 150,000. Annually, it provides over one million man-days of recreation to deer hunters of the State who spend more than 42 million dollars in hunting-related purchases and activities.

Numbering only a few hundred birds in 1940, the wild turkey is another important game species which was almost lost. As with deer, under P-R funding, wild turkeys were trapped and transplanted to vacant habitat. The establishment of the Rio Grande subspecies in western and central regions was begun in 1954, and the eastern wild turkey in eastern counties in 1971. With a current population of more than 80,000, the wild turkey is again secure in the State and annually provides more than 160,000 days of recreation for hunters. By the late 1980's, every county in the State will be open during a month-long spring turkey season with several counties permitting a bag of three toms.

Land acquisition began in 1944 with all areas being managed under the "multiple use" concept and permitting a variety of activities, such as hunting, fishing, hiking, backpacking, sightseeing, nature photography and outdoor education. However, protection and propagation of wildlife continue as the primary objectives. A total of 720,000 acres in 45 tracts are managed by the Department of Wildlife Conservation. Of this total, 74,250 acres were purchased with P-R funds, the remainder being either owned by the State of Oklahoma or managed by the State through cooperative agreements or licensed from entities such as the U.S. Army Corps of Engineers, Bureau of Reclamation, National Park Service or U.S. Forest Service. The operation and maintenance of these areas, including such items as fencing, planting of food and cover plots, vegetation control, development of roads and fire trails and posting, are all P-R funded.

Beginning in 1980, Oklahoma required the purchase of a State duck stamp for hunting waterfowl. Revenues from these sales have been used to match P-R funds in creating an intensive waterfowl management program, statewide. Numerous wetlands have been improved or created and maintained. Over 3,000 acres provided with diking are flooded each fall to attract and hold migrating waterfowl, and aerial seeding of mudflats around major reservoirs has helped make these places more attractive.

Improved hunter access has been gained through cooperative ties with State parks, industrial cooling reservoirs and private landowners. Additionally, some 4,500 giant Canada geese from Northern States have been released in Oklahoma in hopes of establishing a resident nesting population. The chances for success look good.

Oregon

Oregon, the original Beaver State, became so-known for the importance of this animal in the exploration of the area. Trappers from across the continent swarmed west in search of their furs. As a result, beaver populations were trapped to such a low point that the animals were given full protection around the turn of the century.

The availability of P-R funds in 1937 made research and management possible and the first approved project was directed at the beaver. The valuable animals now inhabit all suitable habitat in the State and provide an annual income of more than $100,000 to trappers. Since this original project, P-R funds have financed a wide variety of studies and management programs that have benefited wildlife.

Some earlier studies concerned game damage to private croplands, while later work was done to expand the range of such animals as the bighorn sheep, antelope and elk. Native to the State, the bighorn disappeared about the turn of the century and it was through P-R funds that a nucleus herd was re-established. At this 50th anniversary of the P-R program, bighorns are well established and hunters have been allowed to take a limited number of mature rams from the widespread herds.

The many projects on individual species in Oregon have been as varied as the habitats which support them. Sea otter were brought back to the ocean waters of the State, and the problems of survival of the ring-necked pheasant in the Willamette Valley have been studied. More basic studies on bobcats and raccoons have been designed to obtain basic life history and habitat information on these furbearers.

Like many States, Oregon has used large sums of P-R money to obtain critical habitat and to provide public access. Since the inception of the program, more than $8 million have been expended to acquire some 114,000 acres outright. Additional areas have been made available to hunters through the purchase of easements and access agreements.

One of the most spectacular areas acquired for waterfowl has been the Sauvie Island area, 20 minutes from downtown Portland. A traditional wintering ground for waterfowl, this 8,000-acre area was in danger of being completely changed into agricultural lands and, later, housing developments. Sauvie Island not only provides some of the best waterfowl hunting in the State, but is a prime area for a great variety of nongame birds and other wildlife. Bird-watchers and other lovers of wildlife find it an intriguing place the year around.

Several marsh areas, acquired in the eastern part of the State, also have been developed with food plantings and water control structures for the benefit of waterfowl. But myriad shore birds and other species are in no way excluded. They, too, are attracted by a right combination of food, water and shelter and flock to these managed areas. As at Sauvie Island, a great following of bird-watchers share the grounds with waterfowl hunters.

Elsewhere in Oregon, P-R funds have been used to acquire and improve large tracts of big game habitat. Additionally, habitat work has been done on privately- and Federally-owned lands, both to improve big game ranges, and to provide alternative areas that help to keep big game off private properties.

All told, the P-R program has done a great deal to preserve and enlarge upon the wildlife resources of Oregon. In doing so, it has helped gain for the State a reputation for being a good place to live.

Pennsylvania

Pennsylvania is among the smaller States (33rd in land area) but it ranks number one in hunting license sales. That entitles it to receive a higher proportion of P-R funds than any of the other States except Alaska and Texas. Over the years, these funds have been used for land acquisition, wildlife research, habitat development and hunter education.

P-R funds have made possible the acquisition of 176,934 acres of State Game Lands at a total cost of $3,928,565. Three-quarters of that, $2,946,424, was paid with P-R funds. Research projects on wild turkeys, white-tailed deer, woodcock, snow-shoe hares, ring-necked pheasants and eastern cottontails were supported with P-R funds, and much of the agency's overall philosophies are based on information gleaned from these studies. Other P-R-funded research projects included evaluations of wildlife management practices on pipelines and mining operations, and inventories of soil and cover conditions on State Game lands. Mammal surveys conducted in the 1950's using P-R funds represent the most authoritative accounts of mammal distribution in the State. Some of the Commonwealth's most attractive spots for wildlife and people were developed with P-R funds. Conneaut Marsh, a 555-acre impoundment in northwestern Pennsylvania, is one such example.

Today, the State's entire P-R allotment is used for habitat development on State Game Lands and on properties enrolled in the Pennsylvania Game Commission's public access programs. This habitat development project, initiated over 30 years ago, has since become our sole P-R program and covers such diverse activities as: management practices on State Game Lands (including the construction of roads, bridges, gates and parking lots) and administration of the agency's cooperative access programs; forest inventories, timber stand improvements, preservation of mast (nut and acorn) and den trees, and the preparation of cutting sites; construction, erection and maintenance of wildlife nesting devices; operation of the commission's Howard Nursery (in part) and the planting of trees and shrubs produced there; and, the creation and management of herbaceous openings and wetlands areas.

Finally, the cost of leasing, mapping, and posting associated with Farm-Game, Safety Zone and Forest-Game Cooperative projects are covered under this umbrella program, as are seedlings, seed packets, border cuttings and technical assistance provided cooperating landowners. As a result of this statewide, cooperative program, sportsmen enjoy access to over 4.4 million acres of private land in addition to that owned by the State.

Thanks to P-R support, the Game Commission has been able to carry out ambitious programs of land acquisition, habitat development, wildlife research, and hunter education, and to upgrade wildlife management from an art to a refined science.

The end result has been to make secure the rich array of wildlife in the Keystone State, while greatly enlarging upon the public's enjoyment of it.

Rhode Island

In 1937, Rhode Island sold 8,683 hunting licenses and owned 7,430 acres of recreational reservations, mostly in parks or monument areas. The largest contiguous unit was 3,000 acres. Activities of the then Division of Fish and Game consisted of the liberation of pheasants, quail and rabbits, control of vermin, and enforcement of fish and game laws.

The first Pittman-Robertson project in Rhode Island was initiated in 1939. Its objective was "the development of a wildlife demonstration area, typical of the submarginal areas of the State, in order that methods of holding and increasing the upland game of such areas may be worked out."

Since then, numerous research and survey projects have been initiated, including routine studies of population density and distribution; management plans for State-owned lands; life history studies of white-tailed deer and an intensive management plan for deer on Prudence Island in Narragansett Bay; life history studies of the mute swan and Canada goose; an intensive mammal study which resulted in the highly popular publication "The Mammals of Rhode Island"; successful introduction of wild turkeys and subsequent managed hunting; evaluation of environmental pollution, including lead shot on waterfowl; furbearer studies, including diseases, distribution, and economic importance; and evaluation of tick fauna, and their relationship to Lyme disease and other tick-borne diseases.

While research and management programs have contributed greatly to wildlife in Rhode Island, the lands acquired under P-R have been of even greater benefit. The first purchase, in 1949, bore this note in the Department's annual report for that year: "Great Swamp, famous in Colonial history, as the site of the last stand of the Narragansett Indians and once noted for its wildlife, is our first land acquisition project under the Pittman-Robertson Act. Negotiations are underway to purchase some 2,600 acres of this area and the actual purchase should soon be completed. This will be a State-owned wildlife management area, devoted entirely to the restoration of wildlife." Today, the Great Swamp Management Area consists of over 3,050 acres, and the total acquired in Rhode Island under the Pittman-Robertson program exceeds 8,300 acres, at a total cost in excess of $2,200,000. In addition, several hundred acres of private land and nearly 30,000 acres of additional State recreational land are now influenced by various P-R activities. This is nearly 5 times the acreage owned or controlled by the Department in 1937 when P-R was enacted.

In the meantime, hunting license sales, which peaked in 1969 at 19,551, have since leveled at approximately 13,500. With the continued loss of private land to development, the increased public holdings take on added significance.

South Carolina

The Pittman-Robertson (P-R) Act of 1937 signaled a new beginning for wildlife in South Carolina. At this time, certain game animals, such as deer, wild turkeys and wood ducks, were at low population levels. Also, the public's knowledge of wildlife management and its importance was almost nonexistent.

During the 1940's and early 1950's, deer and turkey populations were small across much of South Carolina. This soon changed due to the restocking, management, and research efforts funded through the P-R Act.

From 1952 through 1957, 72 deer were stocked in the State's Western Piedmont region. The first public hunt in this area, in 1957, resulted in the harvest of one deer. Soon afterwards, from 1957 through 1962, 192 deer were stocked in the Central Piedmont. The first public hunt on this land was in 1962; again, one deer was harvested. Since the seasons originally opened, the deer harvest for both regions has risen substantially each year, reaching a high of 17,263 deer in 1984-85. Due to these restocking efforts, and technical assistance provided to landowners by Wildlife Department biologists, the statewide deer population has flourished as well. In 1985, a minimum of 60,182 deer were harvested.

Wild turkey restoration efforts have been equally successful. From 318 turkeys originally stocked in the Piedmont area of South Carolina, the harvest has risen annually on public hunting lands to a high of 3,576 in 1985. A research project funded by P-R since 1970 has ensured the future of this valuable trophy bird for the hunter and non-hunter alike.

Of course, many of the restoration efforts would not have been possible without the large expanse (over one million acres) of Game Management Area (GMA) lands provided by the U.S. Forest Service, private timber companies and private landowners. The operation of the GMA program, including posting boundary lines, check stations operations, development and maintenance of wildlife openings, and hunt camp operations, all is made possible through P-R funding.

Funds from the Pittman-Robertson Act have provided for the acquisition and operation of the Webb Wildlife Center and Bear Island, Santee-Delta and Samworth management areas. These lands provide quality hunting for deer, turkey, quail, waterfowl and other species. In addition, bird-watchers, hikers, campers, fishermen, photographers and other groups enjoy the bountiful wildlife populations present on these lands.

P-R also funds management activities in 12 waterfowl impoundments, which provide prime overwintering habitat. In addition, P-R projects involving wood ducks and Canada geese have led to expanded populations of these species.

One of the most popular Wildlife Department projects is the Public Dove Field Program. P-R funding allows for intensive management of more than 30 dove fields throughout the State. These fields encompass over 2,000 acres of quality habitat and provide excellent hunting opportunities for this popular game bird.

These are but a few of the accomplishments made possible by P-R funding. Through the restoration of our wildlife resources, this program has helped improve and maintain the quality of outdoors which our citizens have come to enjoy and expect.

South Dakota

The Pittman-Robertson program has been the cornerstone of wildlife management in South Dakota since its passage in 1937. At that time the State was beginning to recover from a severe drought and harsh winters that had devastated wildlife populations. The Game Department employed no trained wildlife biologists. Game wardens, primarily involved in law enforcement, generally lacked the skill and interest needed for modern wildlife management.

The P-R program provided the necessary funding to help restore the struggling wildlife populations and to bring the State into the era of modern, scientific wildlife management through structured research and surveys. South Dakota today boasts some of the best hunting in the United States, due in large part to the stable financial assistance provided by P-R during the last 50 years.

Early efforts to restore game were partly funded by P-R. Following on the drought years, a massive statewide pheasant restocking program helped rebuild the pheasant population to its present level of a $35 million annual industry in South Dakota.

Exceptional wild turkey hunting in the Black Hills is also a direct result of the P-R program. Wild turkeys were introduced into the Black Hills for the first time in 1948. Today sportsmen from all over the Nation come here to enjoy outstanding wild turkey hunting. In 1984, 6,607 hunters harvested 2,067 turkeys—a success rate of 31 percent.

P-R also contributed to the success of an ongoing statewide project to restore the giant Canada goose. The geese have been successfully reintroduced into 16 counties and the program is still expanding to other suitable areas of the State. In 1985, 1,970 permits were issued to harvest 4,570 giant Canada geese.

Prior to the P-R Act, South Dakota had only 16 Public Shooting Areas. Since 1939, 354 tracts have been acquired using these funds. These tracts, managed for wildlife and open to public hunting, also include some of the best nongame wildlife habitat in the State. The areas are scattered throughout the State and provide a wide variety of habitats and hunting opportunity. Also, they are open to other recreational uses as long as those activities do not interfere with their primary purpose.

In keeping with its long-time commitment to wildlife habitat restoration on private land, the Game, Fish and Parks Department, in cooperation with the South Dakota Pheasant Congress, began a nationally recognized Pheasant Restoration Program in 1976. Participating landowners are paid to plant and maintain up to 40 acres of retired cropland as prime dense nesting cover for a minimum of five years. Since 1979, incentive payments totaling $3.6 million have been made to 1,537 landowners for developing and maintaining 37,300 acres of nesting cover.

Over the past 50 years, P-R has been the major source of revenue to fund the statewide land management and development program. About $1 million of P-R funds are used annually to manage for wildlife 154,000 acres of State-owned or leased land in more than 600 management units.

Much of the early research on pheasant biology and management was conducted using P-R funds, as are 13 current game research projects.

Annual game regulations and subsequent analyses of harvest depend on wildlife surveys and inventories. During the past 40 years P-R funds have been used to finance this vital process. The department annually conducts 38 surveys of small game, big game and nongame species.

Tennessee

The legendary Davy Crockett and other heroes of Tennessee's rugged backwoods past contributed to a picture that lingers today, one of tall mountains and wide valleys filled with strong men and hardy women living off the land's bounty—bear and deer and turkey and grouse, quail, and rabbit.

But as Tennessee and america came of age, the true picture changed. No longer was wildlife abundant. By the late 1800's, Tennessee's deer were nearly wiped out by year-round hunting; turkey were almost extirpated from the State. The black bear retreated into the most inaccessible parts of the mountains.

Tennessee's Game and Fish Department was created in 1913 with one employee. The agency grew, laws were passed but the State's wildlife populations, especially big game, continued to dwindle. The long, uphill struggle to correct the problems began to gain speed in 1938—the year Pittman-Robertson money first began flowing.

By the mid-1980s, Tennessee had received $27,222,510.08 in apportionments. In the fiscal year 1985-86, its share of the P-R pie totalled slightly over $1.4 million.

In 1938, Tennessee received $10,685, which today wouldn't buy most new cars on the market. In 1938, however, that money was used as the first payment for 18,108 acres that now make up part of the 20,000-acre Cheatham Wildlife Management Area owned entirely by the Tennessee Wildlife Resources Agency.

In 1942, the state's apportionment of slightly over $14,000 was applied toward the purchase of 69,000 acres of land and 2,000 acres of mineral rights. The State added $6,000 of its own money to the first year's purchase price of what is now called Catoosa WMA, another of Tennessee's most popular and heavily used public hunting areas.

Through the years, P-R has helped purchase slightly over 169,000 acres in Tennessee. These acres will continue to increase in value if the pattern of closed access to private lands continues.

Of equal importance has been P-R's funding of wildlife research and management. The two most important and successful wildlife projects ever undertaken in Tennessee were the white-tailed deer and wild turkey restoration programs. Both have relied heavily on P-R funds.

Tennessee's deer were still virtually non-existent in the 1940's and 50's. Using P-R money, along with hunting license fees, the State embarked on a restoration effort. Seventeen whitetails were trapped in North Carolina's Pisgah National Forest and relocated on Chuck Swan WMA. Between 1946 and 1950 several hundred deer were transplanted to Tennessee from Wisconsin. Four whitetails relocated to Fort Campbell from Texas provided "seed stock" for much of the State. The progeny of these deer now number an estimated 400,000 and they are still increasing! Hunters will harvest somewhere around 65,000 this year.

The wild turkey restoration program, started in the late 1930's, also depended heavily on P-R for funding. There was not a huntable population of the birds from the early 1920's through the late 1940's. In 1951, hunters harvested only 14 birds in two counties. In 1985, Tennesseans harvested turkeys in 48 of the 95 counties with a record 1,142 killed.

Other significant projects that have depended on Pittman-Robertson for funding are the Tri-state Bear Study, European Hog Study and research projects on raccoon, coyote, grouse and small game.

Tennesseans can be proud of their wildlife heritage and the role they have played in ensuring the future of wildlife. It is the sportsmen's dollars, spent for hunting licenses and permits, as well as the taxes on sporting equipment, which go into the Pittman-Robertson funds, that have made the difference.

Texas

Since the initial project in 1938, over 100 projects, involving several thousand individual wildlife investigations, have been funded under the Pittman-Robertson program.

At the beginning of P-R in Texas there were approximately 225,000 white-tailed deer, 100,000 Rio Grande turkeys, and 8,000 pronghorn antelope. Eastern turkeys had been extirpated from the State.

By 1985, these numbers had grown to approximately 3.5 million white-tailed deer, 500,000 turkeys, and 16,000 pronghorns, and the 1984 deer harvest exceeded the total number of deer present in the State in 1938. Turkey harvests fluctuate between 306,000 and 650,000 annually. Eastern turkeys are being restored, with four counties in eastern Texas now having hunting seasons. The P-R program has been an immense success in restoration of game populations to record levels in Texas.

Another major achievement has been the preservation of wildlife habitat through land acquisition. A total of 180,127 acres had been acquired in fee title and some 201,466 leased or licensed under the P-R program by 1985. These lands provide outdoor laboratories for research, opportunities for wildlife observation and study, refuges for migratory species, broodstock for restocking, and public hunting opportunities.

Research has been an important aspect of the Texas P-R program, with studies conducted by Parks and Wildlife Department personnel and through interagency agreements with State universities and agencies. These investigations have addressed the life requirements of major game species and factors affecting their well-being—information which is required for sound management. Research has not been limited to game species but has included work on such species as peregrine falcons, southern bald eagles, red-cockaded woodpeckers, interior least terns, Mexican ducks, whooping cranes, Pecos River muskrats, river otters, golden cheeked warblers, golden eagles, and bobcats.

Personnel assigned to P-R projects have responded to thousands of requests for technical information, prepared hundreds of information publications and presented thousands of programs on wildlife resource management. The inventory and mapping of wildlife habitats on a statewide basis, using space age technology, has been another major accomplishment. Built into this system is the ability to measure habitat changes over time.

In brief, the P-R program has provided a means by which numerous species have been returned to a healthy status in Texas and a promise that the future of wildlife resources in this State will continue to be secure.

Utah

Utah is proud to join in commemorating the first 50 years of progress in wildlife restoration achieved under the Pittman-Robertson Act. In 1937, almost before the ink on President Roosevelt's signature was dry, the Nation's first P-R project was underway in Utah. The Ogden Bay Waterfowl Management Area had modest beginnings but has since matured into a nearly 17,000-acre management area that annually provides more than 30,000 hunter days of recreation and upwards of 65,000 ducks, geese and swans in the bag. Added to this are thousands of visitor days devoted to educational and other nonconsumptive uses. Ogden Bay, however, was merely a beginning. In the ensuing 50 years, P-R funds helped preserve additional areas of critical wetland habitat throughout the State. These areas not only provide important "resting habitat" for migratory birds, but also offer a permanent home to many resident species.

Beyond preserving wetland habitat, Utah has also been a leader in acquiring and protecting from development, critical habitat for mule deer, elk and other big game species. In the West, big game winter range had always been scarce, even before settlement. In modern times, urbanization, agricultural development and a constantly expanding human population have accentuated the problem. The need for preservation and wise management of the remaining acres is acute. The State of Utah has therefore set a goal to acquire or control approximately 600,000 acres of strategically located winter habitat, the minimum acreage considered necessary to maintain reasonable big game populations into the foreseeable future. With Pittman-Robertson assistance, substantial progress toward this goal has been achieved. To date, slightly more than 250,000 acres have been acquired.

Federal Aid, although essential for acquiring critical habitats, also funds other important activities. Among these are research projects aimed at improving the condition of big game ranges. Utah is proud of its pioneering role in developing many widely accepted range rehabilitation techniques. Mechanical, chemical and biological methods, such as innovative use of livestock grazing for vegetation and habitat management, are now used effectively throughout the West.

The Pittman-Robertson program also has played an important role in the restoration of a variety of wildlife species to historic or unoccupied habitat. The wild turkey, desert and Rocky Mountain bighorn sheep, Rocky Mountain goat, white-tailed ptarmigan and elk now inhabit many areas that, prior to 1937, contained few wildlife species. Trapping and transplanting of wildlife has enriched the quality of life for all citizens, hunters and nonhunters alike. Perhaps less dramatic but equally important is the role Federal Aid plays in day-to-day management of wildlife resources. Wise management is directly dependent on collection of accurate and timely habitat and population data. Without Federal assistance, it would be very difficult for Utah to fund such an effort and, consequently, the quality of management decisions would suffer.

For 50 years, the Pittman-Robertson Act has played a central role in research, habitat acquisition, development and management of Utah's wildlife resources and our wildlife heritage has been enriched accordingly. It is with gratitude that we commend the framers of the Act for their foresight and look forward to the next 50 years.

Vermont

Vermont's first 50 years of involvement with the Pittman-Robertson programs has been extremely productive. In fact, the thriving wildlife populations found throughout Vermont today would not be here if it were not for the Federal Aid funds for surveys, research, land acquisition and habitat inventories.

On September 27, 1938, the Vermont Wildlife Survey became the first Pittman-Robertson project in the State. The survey, conducted by all 18 of the Vermont Fish and Game Service's wardens, was designed to determine the status and distribution of game populations. The rudimentary nature of this first project highlights the fact that the Fish and Game agencies of the day were grossly understaffed and lacked the resources to collect even the simplest information needed to manage wildlife.

Most of the early biological surveys were of game species, but as early as 1946, Vermont's first P-R Coordinator, Leonard E. Foote, recognized that "... songbirds, although usually small creatures, appear in such numbers and are such a welcome addition to our total wildlife fauna that their management should not be neglected ..."

Foote, as well as others of his day, realized that even though funding for wildlife management came solely from hunting-related revenues, wildlife managers were charged with the management of all wildlife, not just game species. This responsibility is still shouldered without complaint by Vermont's sportsmen.

Many game populations in Vermont had been badly depleted before the Pittman-Robertson program began, but have since been restored to healthy levels. A few species, such as the wild turkey, had been extirpated and needed to be reintroduced.

In 1969 and 1970, using P-R funds, 31 wild turkeys were live-trapped in New York State and released in the southwestern Vermont towns of Pawlet and Hubbardton. Today, following trap and transport efforts, wild turkeys are found in all the suitable habitat in Vermont, making its Wild Turkey Restoration project one of the State's best examples of productive use of Pittman-Robertson funds.

All Vermonters benefit from the contributions sportsmen make to the State's economy. Hunting, fishing, and trapping had a total economic impact of over $179 million in 1980, with hunting and trapping accounting for 60 percent of that figure.

While this 50th anniversary of Pittman-Robertson is a proper time to reflect on achievements of the past, it is not a time for complacency. Vermont is faced with escalating pressures on its land and wildlife resources. Pittman-Robertson funds will be crucial in meeting these demands. Protection of important wildlife habitat requires facts upon which to base impact assessments when development projects are proposed. Vermont's 92,000 acres of Waterfowl Refuges and Wildlife Management Areas, most of which were purchased with P-R funds, will have to be managed more intensively. Populations of all wildlife species must be monitored more closely.

If the successes of the last 50 years are any indication, these challenges will be met in Vermont through the continuance of the cooperative efforts afforded by the Pittman-Robertson program.

Virginia

In 1937, Virginia Congressman A. Willis Robertson, then Chairman of the House Select Committee on Conservation of Wildlife Resources, co-sponsored the Pittman-Robertson Act. As a former Chairman of the Virginia Game Commission, he understood the needs of wildlife, the concerns of sportsmen and, above all, the safeguards necessary to ensure that excise tax dollars for wildlife did indeed end up with the responsible State fish and wildlife agency. He wisely included in the legislation an assent provision, whereby the States must agree to enact laws prohibiting the use of hunting license fees for any purpose other than the administration of their fish and game agency. The passage of this legislation has proved to be a milestone for wildlife conservation work, as virtually every facet of wildlife management in Virginia has in some way been enhanced or influenced by this program.

In the early years, much of the assistance from P-R was utilized, along with receipts from the sale of National Forest Stamps and Game Commission monies, to purchase deer for restoration throughout the State. Between 1930 and 1950, whitetails from North Carolina, Pennsylvania, Michigan, Wisconsin and Alabama were released into areas of suitable habitat in Virginia. These releases, together with the support of sportsmen and landowners, and suitable habitat conditions, have resulted in a statewide deer herd which sustains a harvest approaching 100,000 animals per year.

A similar success was realized with the wild turkey. Since the mid-50's when a technique for trapping native wild turkeys was developed, over 800 turkeys have been released in suitable but unoccupied ranges statewide. Today, Virginia turkey hunters enjoy some form of hunting (fall and/or spring seasons) in every county, and the annual harvest has risen from 2,149 birds in 1951 to a record harvest of 18,475 in 1982.

P-R has also supported the acquisition and management of wildlife management areas. Fifty-four State-owned and cooperatively managed areas offer 2.3 million acres of public hunting and wildlife management lands. While accounting for only about 9 percent of the total land in the Commonwealth, these areas produce approximately 50 percent of the black bears harvested and 25 percent of the deer and turkeys. Of the 178,865 acres which the Game Commission owns, 103,193 or 58 percent were purchased with Pittman-Robertson dollars. The P-R funded habitat development project also provides for manipulation practices (timber harvest, prescribed burning, planting of food and cover, construction of waterholes, etc.) and the development and maintenance of equipment storage buildings, workshops and manager residences, roads and trails, parking lots, boat ramps and other public use facilities for both the hunting and non-hunting public.

The P-R program has likewise supported the commission's research program which, in addition to many game species, has given attention to nongame and endangered species such as the bald eagle, peregrine falcon, Delmarva fox squirrel and red-cockaded woodpecker. P-R is also helping to fund a computerized data base which contains information on the distribution, life history and habitat requirements of all wildlife in Virginia. Additionally, State fish and game agencies have access to a P-R funded reference service of the U.S. Fish and Wildlife Service through a computer program called Dialog. This covers a wide range of literature in the wildlife field and, among other things, helps individual States to avoid duplication of research which has already been done or is in progress.

In summary, by insuring against the diversion of funds, the Pittman-Robertson program has served to shelter from the political arena a much-needed ingredient for wildlife management—money. And, in so doing, it has provided the stability and continuity necessary for professional wildlife resource management. Without question, the provisions and requirements of the P-R Act have contributed greatly to the re-enforcement of wildlife management along sound biological lines everywhere.

Washington

Pittman-Robertson funds have been instrumental in acquiring, operating and maintaining wildlife areas throughout Washington for nearly half a century. These lands provide vital wildlife habitat and important outdoor recreation in a State that is the smallest of the 11 Western States but which has the second-highest human population and second-highest population density. Of the Western States, Washington has the most hunting and fishing license holders per square mile, but the least Federally-owned land to provide hunting, fishing or other outdoor recreation. With only 12 million acres of Federal land, Washington is well behind such States as Nevada (60 million acres) and Idaho (34 million acres). However, an aggressive program of land acquisition under P-R has helped put Washington near the forefront with reference to State-owned lands which serve the same purposes for wildlife and outdoor recreationists.

Eight wildlife areas, managed primarily for waterfowl and waterfowl hunting and totaling over 13,000 acres, were purchased by the Department of Game in the 1930's and 1940's. P-R funds accounted for over $376,000 of the $500,000 total purchase price. These areas, including western Washington's Lake Terrell and Skagit Wildlife Areas and the Stratford Wildlife Area on the east side of the State, provide some of Washington's best public duck and goose hunting.

The department also used P-R funds to pay part of the cost for about 400 acres of small game habitat, including the very popular Scatter Creek Wildlife Area in western Washington, a 1,269-acre mecca for pheasant hunters, field trialers and bird watchers.

Perhaps the most important land purchases of the last 50 years were those areas managed as big game habitat and big game hunting areas. Pittman-Robertson monies totaling over $1.2 million were used to help buy those areas, and they provide some of the State's most important big game winter range. The Colockum, Oak Creek, Methow, Sinlahekin, Wooten, Olympic, Grouse Flats and LeClerc Creek Wildlife Areas total over 140,000 acres. Scattered throughout the State, these areas provide habitat for Rocky Mountain and Roosevelt elk, black-tailed, mule and white-tailed deer, cougar, bobcat and black bear, as well as small game, waterfowl, furbearers and nongame species. Additionally, as a result of preemption by man of the elk's natural winter range, the Oak Creek Wildlife Area is the scene of one of the country's largest elk-feeding operations in winter.

Pittman-Robertson funds were used, not only to purchase these public lands that provide over 2 million user-days per year, but also for operation and management. Nearly $1.6 million in P-R funds were used for this purpose in fiscal 1985.

The Department of Game's Habitat Development/Hunter Access Program (partly funded through P-R) is one of the Department's oldest ongoing programs. Originally established in 1947, it provides for the development of wildlife habitat on private lands and also establishes, through negotiated agreement, public hunting access to privately owned property.

In recent years, P-R funding has helped make possible in-depth studies of Washington's mountain goats, mountain sheep and big cats. Also, in 1984, a study of deer populations in western Okanogan County, the state's most important mule deer area, was begun. This last-mentioned study is of special relevance since a major ski-resort complex will soon have a considerable impact on the area. Such research is important to the welfare of Washington's wildlife and to its citizens as well, who look upon wildlife as an important part of the quality of life in the Pacific Northwest.

West Virginia

Before passage of the Pittman-Robertson Act, wildlife management in West Virginia was limited almost exclusively to regulating hunting seasons and bag limits. Population estimates of 1,000 deer (1910) and 6,000 turkeys (as late as 1944) showed clearly that more needed to be done. The West Virginia Conservation Commission by the 1920's had recognized the need to purchase and develop "wild lands", but with the only revenue for wildlife coming from the sale of hunting and fishing licenses, the Commission was limited in what it could do.

P-R provided matching funds for approved projects including land acquisition, development, wildlife research, and restocking. The Commission put this funding to work immediately, with the purchase of Nathaniel Mountain in 1938 as the first "wildlife management" project. In 1946, Project W-17-D-1 funded wildlife management on national forests. In cooperation with the U.S. Forest Service, national forest land was divided into management areas and a resident manager was assigned to each area. A later project divided the State into conservation districts with a wildlife biologist in charge of each district. Work done under these and similar projects included the construction and/or maintenance of clearings, waterholes, fire lines, area headquarters buildings, nesting structures, and public use facilities. Other work included: tree and shrub plantings, stocking wildlife, collecting harvest data, conducting population surveys, assisting in research projects, predator control, and additional land purchases.

Presently, the Department of Natural Resources is operating a single wildlife management project which funds work on 41 public hunting areas and other State-controlled land totaling approximately 248,000 acres (much of it purchased entirely or in part with P-R money) and approximately 1,000,000 acres of national forest lands. Transplanting of wild turkeys, deer, wild boar, Canada geese, and other wildlife has been accomplished under this project.

By the 1960's, game populations began to flourish. This trend continues in the 1980's as new harvest and distribution records for species such as deer, bear, and wild turkey offer conclusive evidence that P-R funds are paying an excellent return to the hunters who, in turn, make the P-R program possible.

Pittman-Robertson monies have been a vital part of West Virginia's game research program and have enabled biologists to obtain information on numerous wildlife species. In 1940, a survey was designed to gather wildlife population data in various counties and on State forests. The results were used to initiate studies of various game species, in particular the white-tailed deer, black bear, and wild turkey. As information on these species became available, it was applied to management. Hunting seasons and regulations were adjusted to promote population growth which has resulted in record harvests of these species in recent years.

During the 1940's, studies on beavers, rabbits, squirrels, and quail yielded information useful in management. Migratory bird inquiries, started in 1958, showed the importance of preserving wetland habitat, and a more recent study of translocated raccoons has helped demonstrate that stocking can be a waste of sportsmen's dollars.

In 1969, P-R funds were used in a successful fisher introduction effort, and, currently, costs of a river otter re-introduction program are partially underwritten by P-R revenues. These re-introductions have restored valuable furbearers once native to the State.

Dissemination of research findings to the public has helped promote an understanding of the role and rewards of wildlife research. Numerous bulletins and semi-technical publications have been written and distributed with the help of hunting license monies and P-R funds.

The P-R Act has funded a combined research/management effort which has resulted in many recreational opportunities for both the hunter and the nonhunter, while ensuring the future of sport hunting in West Virginia.

Wisconsin

The Federal Aid in Wildlife Restoration Act has meant many things to the natural resources and people of Wisconsin. Perhaps of greatest importance has been OPPORTUNITY—opportunity to acquire land for wildlife management, and opportunity to hire biologists to develop techniques that facilitate the management of habitat and wildlife. Wisconsin is a rural State with millions of acres of woods, marsh, fields and other types of wildlife habitat. This land base plus P-R funding has provided the opportunity for acquisition and development for over 200 Wildlife Management Areas throughout the State which total over 450,000 acres. The system, in its entirely, affords several million recreation days annually to hunters and others.

One of the first areas acquired and developed with P-R funds was the Horicon Marsh State Wildlife Area. Cooperative efforts with the U.S. Fish and Wildlife Service at the adjoining Horicon National Wildlife Refuge resulted in a management program to provide habitat attractive to migrating Canada geese. Flowages were constructed, water control structures installed, food crops planted and regulations to protect the flock implemented. To learn more about the dynamics of this flock, research studies were conducted on the breeding grounds in Canada, on migratory stopovers in the spring and fall, and on harvest trends. The net result has been a series of wildlife restoration projects which, combined with cooperation from the U.S. Fish and Wildlife Service, Canadian agencies and several other States, has provided an estimated 250,000 Canada geese for the autumn enjoyment of both the hunter and casual viewer each year.

While hunters contribute most of the funds used in the P-R program, Wisconsin has always attempted to provide benefits to a wide range of wildlife species (game and nongame, alike) and to the non-hunting public. In the 1950's, P-R funds were used to help acquire one of the major "hawk alleys" in east central Wisconsin. This area, commonly used as a resting area by hawks in migration, is extremely popular with bird watchers and a valuable site for banding as well. In the Crex Meadows and Sandhill Wildlife Areas, two large properties with intensive habitat developments, are visited by well over 150,000 people annually, 80 percent of whom come for non-hunting-related enjoyment. A long-term habitat development and research project for prairie chickens, a State-listed threatened species, has provided guidelines to help insure a future for these birds in Wisconsin.

An oft-mentioned success story under the P-R program is white-tailed deer management. In the 1950's, Wisconsin began studies to learn more about population dynamics, habitat requirements and harvest of deer. These endeavors have since produced guidelines for forest- and deer-management, and harvest regulations including an acceptable season for antlerless deer. This highly successful program has led to a harvest by riflemen and archers of approximately 325,000 whitetails in 1985 compared with 36,000 in 1955.

Wyoming

Pittman-Robertson funds have played an important role in Wyoming's wildlife research and in habitat acquisition and improvement.

Over 100,000 acres of prime winter habitat have been acquired to the benefit of a variety of big game, upland birds and waterfowl. An equal acreage has been made available by the Bureau of Reclamation and other Federal land management agencies for joint management with the Wyoming Game and Fish Department.

Antelope have benefited from P-R funded research, and stand as one of the major success stories. Around the turn of the century, the estimated population in Wyoming was fewer than 5,000 animals and many thought the antelope was a doomed species. Since that time, pronghorns have increased to more than 300,000 after the hunting season. During the last five years, hunters have harvested an average of 75,000 yearly.

Other species of big game have benefited as well. In the 1950's a P-R funded study on the Jackson Hole elk herd established guidelines for the future management and welfare of the herd. The resulting publication, *The Elk of Jackson Hole,* is still regarded as the most comprehensive work on this population of elk.

P-R funds also provided for a much-needed study on the bighorn sheep of Whiskey Mountain near Dubois. Purposes of the research were to determine year-round mortality causes and evaluate the influence of possible management changes. As a result of research-directed management, the sheep populations of Whiskey Mountain have been very successful and are among the largest and most visible populations in North America. Over the years, approximately 850 have been removed from Whiskey Mountain by trapping, and transplanted to other areas. In this way, bighorns have been reestablished in former habitats and small existing herds have been enhanced in Wyoming and neighboring States. A key ingredient to the success of the herd has been the acquisition of the Whiskey Basin Habitat Unit, which provides important winter range.

Pittman-Robertson funds have also played an important role in the development of a disease laboratory at the University of Wyoming campus and the Sybille Wildlife Research Unit west of Wheatland. The laboratory has been in operation for over 30 years in cooperation with the University, and the Sybille Wildlife Research Unit, in operation since the 1950's, was the first of its kind in the Nation. The Sybille Unit has served as a model for wildlife agencies in the United states and foreign countries in the development of similar facilities.

Other notable P-R funded efforts at the research laboratory include the brucellosis study in the Jackson Hole elk herd, and the identification of wild game and animal body tissues for improving law enforcement investigations.

But there have been many notable P-R accomplishments outside research also. Foremost among these is the development of a comprehensive fish and wildlife plan. This management plan now serves as a blueprint for the entire agency operation.

Both sportsmen and wildlife of Wyoming have benefitted tremendously from P-R funded programs. Important studies have served to improve management of a number of species which has led to more animals and better opportunities for hunters. Other funds have made possible the purchase of key wildlife habitats which have enhanced wildlife populations while assuring permanent access for the general public to observe wildlife in their natural habitat.

Guam

Guam has participated in the Pittman-Robertson Federal Aid program since 1957, when this U.S. territory in the western Pacific first became eligible for funding. Since that time, the P-R program has been the backbone of the wildlife management and conservation efforts of the Division of Aquatic and Wildlife Resources, Guam Department of Agriculture.

Guam is the southernmost and largest of the fifteen Mariana Islands, an archipelago located halfway between Japan and New Guinea and approximately 1,000 miles east of the Philippines. It is approximately 28 miles long and 3.7 to 8 miles wide, with a land area of approximately 341 square miles. It has been an unincorporated territory of the United States since 1898, and the residents were granted U.S. citizenship with the passage of the Organic Act in 1950. Guam has a resident population of about 106,000, based on the 1980 census, and a transient military population of approximately 20,000.

The Pittman-Robertson program on Guam began as a study of the feasibility of licensed hunting and has developed into dynamic game management and endangered species recovery programs.

P-R provided the impetus for development of legislation granting the authority to manage and regulate wildlife resources on Guam. Under P-R, the necessary survey and inventory work was done to allow the establishment of regulations requiring hunting licenses and setting hunting seasons and bag limits for selected game species.

Most of Guam's game species were introduced by the Spanish when they colonized the island several hundreds years ago. Wild pigs, descended from domestic stock, are ubiquitous and are popular game animals. Guam's most prized big game animal, however, is a form of sambar deer that was introduced from the Philippines in 1771. Another Spanish introduction is the Philippine turtle dove, a popular game bird. These introduced game species have been managed with P-R funds since the program began on Guam.

Not all game species were introduced by the Spanish; one of the first major P-R funded projects was the introduction of black francolin from India in 1961, in conjunction with the foreign game bird introduction program of the U.S. Fish and Wildlife Service. Although several other species were also tried, only the black francolin succeeded. This species is now firmly established throughout the southern half of the island, is expanding its range northward, and is an increasingly popular game bird.

Guam's native fauna have not been ignored. Initially, several native birds, including two species of dove and the endemic Guam rail, and the Marianas fruit bat, were managed as game species; but continuing population declines resulted in total protection being extended to the native fauna. P-R funded activities resulted in the passage of local endangered species legislation, and the eventual Federal listing of seven species of birds and two species of fruit bats as endangered.

The native fauna has declined drastically over the last 20 to 30 years and several species of birds have become extinct within the last five years. Extinction is imminent for several others. P-R funded research has documented this decline and, more recently, determined its cause. After evaluating numerous possible causes of this widespread decline, predation by the introduced brown tree snake has been determined to be the major cause of the decline of native birds and a possible factor in the decline of fruit bats.

A captive breeding program for the Guam rail and Micronesian kingfisher was begun using P-R funds. Although too late for some species, captive breeding is thought to have a good chance at saving the rail and kingfisher from extinction, as the initial efforts with both species have been successful.

Guam has received several indirect benefits from P-R funded wildlife management programs. The presence of a highly qualified biological staff has provided guidance and technical expertise that has helped direct the course of development and reduce the adverse effects of a growing economy. The presence of sound wildlife management programs to protect and preserve the native wildlife has helped to raise the public consciousness and done much to develop a conservation ethic in the people.

P-R has been the mainstay of wildlife management and conservation for nearly 30 years; the only local funding that has been regularly provided has been for law enforcement. Guam has received some funding under Section 6 of the Endangered Species Act of 1973, but funds through this program have been minimal and sporadic. Were it not for the P-R program, it can safely be said that there would probably be no wildlife management and conservation program on Guam, little or no recreational hunting, and virtually no hope for survival of the native wildlife species.

Northern Mariana Islands

The P-R program in the Commonwealth of the Northern Mariana Islands (CNMI) was initiated in 1981, and the first wildlife biologists were hired by the Division of Fish and Wildlife on Saipan in 1983. The CNMI is a chain of 14 Pacific islands located north of Guam, 3,800 miles west of Hawaii and 1500 miles southeast of Japan. Like many small island ecosystems, the Marianas have been adversely affected by exotic species and large scale human distrubance. Several islands were devastated by heavy fighting during World War II.

In a few years, the P-R program has gathered a significant amount of biological data on game and nongame wildlife. The Division has proceeded with 13 high priority job projects, including 3 studies of game mammals, 1 investigation involving game birds, 4 projects dealing with endangered species, 3 nongame bird studies, 1 project devoted to review and comment on land use and development, and 1 project dealing with wildlife management areas and habitat improvement.

Major accomplishments include the addition of basic scientific data on the distribution, status, and breeding biology of many important wildlife species which have been used in setting hunting seasons, bag limits, and general regulations. The goal is to encourage recreational use of wildlife, while managing the land and the animals for long term sustainable harvests. The P-R program has also supported projects for setting aside sizable areas of public land and even entire islands as wildlife sanctuaries. On small islands, where land is always in high demand, saving habitat for wildlife is extremely important.

Information gathered in the first years has been instrumental in removing one species of bird, the Tinian monarch, from the endangered species list and has led to a petition to place two native bat species on the endangered species list. Division surveys have also verified the extinction of an endemic duck, the Marianas mallard. One ongoing project is developing ways to improve for wildlife the monocultures of Tangantangan, an exotic tree introduced after World War II to control erosion. Another wildlife problem being addressed through P-R funding is the impact of feral goats and pigs on native plants and animals. Certain islands are in need of measures to control feral animals.

Most importantly, P-R funding has allowed the Division of Fish and Wildlife to take a leading role in Commonwealth government as the chief advocate for wildlife resources. The Division acts as a liaison and coordinates activities with the U.S. Fish and Wildlife Service, Army Corps of Engineers, Soil Conservation Service, Department of the Navy, National Park Service, and other Federal agencies. At the local level, the Division responds to wildlife-related land development issues and permit applications that may potentially affect wildlife. With P-R support, the Commonwealth Division of Fish and Wildlife is off to an excellent professional and political beginning. An appropriate and positive course for the future has been charted.

The U.S. Virgin Islands

The United States Virgin Islands, a U.S. territory since its purchase from Denmark in 1917, has been fortunate to be included as a beneficiary of the Federal Aid in Wildlife Restoration Act since P-R's inception in 1937. With a small annual allotment (about $10,000 annually for all expenses), territorial wildlife restoration activities were, of necessity, restricted during the first three decades of funding. All project work was done by one person and an occasional part-time helper. Amendments to the law, and a partial reorganization of the territorial government allowed the Pittman-Robertson activities and staff to expand in 1971. There are presently five full-time P-R biologists, and numerous other support personnel partly paid by P-R funds.

Certain game birds have been historically present in the territory, including several species of ducks but, most notably, doves and pigeons. The Zenaida dove has long been the chief game bird in the Virgin Islands, and as such has been a significant focus of wildlife studies. Particular emphasis has been given to stock assessment, breeding biology, movements, parasites, and other relevant factors. When it was more abundant, the white-crowned pigeon also received considerable attention, especially in banding studies.

Most other game species have been introduced. Game bird introductions, including northern and crested bobwhite, California valley quail, chachalaca, and the ring-necked pheasant, have been notably unsuccessful. These transplants seemed to have failed at least in part due to predation by the small Indian mongoose, which was itself introduced to the territory in the late 19th Century to control rats then plaguing the important local sugar cane industry. The ground-dwelling mongoose (diurnal) did not solve the (nocturnal) rat problem. However, it did prey on other ground-dwelling or ground-nesting wildlife and, additionally, was found to be an alternate host-carrier of several species of ticks as well as a potential carrier of rabies. Several eradication studies were made. Ironically, the sugar cane industry was phased out 20 years ago, but the mongoose remains.

Introduced from the continental States about 1790, the white-tailed deer was also implicated as a host-carrier of ticks, and became the subject of intensive studies in this regard, as well in its own right as the only game mammal in the territory.

Shortly after the Federal Endangered Species Act of 1973 was enacted, P-R funding enabled the territory to determine what species in the Virgin Islands were endangered or threatened. More recent studies have been directed towards a better understanding of the biology, distribution, and seasonality of—and threats to—the thousands of seabirds which use the Virgin Islands offshore cays as colonial nesting sites.

The direction of all our efforts is to develop a unified management plan for wildlife in the Virgin Islands, an objective which can only be realized with the full support of the P-R program.

Statistical Tables Concerning Pittman-Robertson Program

Pittman-Robertson Fund Receipts 1939-1985

YEAR	FIREARMS, SHELLS & CARTRIDGES	PISTOLS AND REVOLVERS	BOWS, ARROWS AND RELATED EQUIPMENT	TOTAL
1939	$2,976,020	—	—	$2,976,020
1940	3,707,844	—	—	3,707,844
1941	5,535,773	—	—	5,535,773
1942	5,072,588	—	—	5,072,588
1943	1,149,333	—	—	1,149,333
1944	1,061,045	—	—	1,061,045
1945	3,132,402	—	—	3,132,402
1946	5,232,465	—	—	5,232,465
1947	9,031,274	—	—	9,031,274
1948	11,276,687	—	—	11,276,687
1949	10,378,538	—	—	10,378,538
1950	9,351,614	—	—	9,351,614
1951	17,846,424	—	—	17,846,424
1952	10,679,059	—	—	10,679,059
1953	12,147,554	—	—	12,147,554
1954	10,266,258	—	—	10,266,258
1955	12,400,508	—	—	12,400,508
1956	14,302,000	—	—	14,302,000
1957	15,149,179	—	—	15,149,179
1958	14,617,361	—	—	14,617,361
1959	13,908,699	—	—	13,908,699
1960	15,589,708	—	—	15,589,708
1961	14,985,093	—	—	14,985,093
1962	14,911,717	—	—	14,911,717
1963	16,237,887	—	—	16,237,887
1964	17,454,941	—	—	17,454,941
1965	20,200,720	—	—	20,200,720
1966	24,343,804	—	—	24,343,804
1967	27,805,901	—	—	27,805,901
1968	31,371,605	—	—	31,371,605
1969	33,081,322	—	—	33,081,322
1970	32,805,725	—	—	32,805,725
1971	29,483,850	7,220,240[1]	—	36,704,089
1972	35,770,401	7,563,132	—	43,333,533
1973	41,468,209	8,332,059	—	49,800,268
1974	47,754,104	9,100,568	—	56,854,672
1975	51,169,700	11,330,809	546,137[2]	63,046,646
1976[3]	68,598,467	14,413,574	6,675,113	89,687,154
1977	50,179,173	13,215,377	4,394,766	67,789,316
1978	63,664,716	16,327,005	6,026,912	86,018,633
1979	71,398,120	17,536,941	5,039,041	93,974,102
1980	62,299,206	22,255,369	6,160,076	90,714,651
1981	87,925,368	26,689,244	7,273,387	121,887,999
1982	73,812,342	30,063,804	7,577,883	111,454,029
1983	62,799,518	24,104,308	6,802,876	93,706,702
1984	57,492,106	21,069,109	7,311,039	85,872,254
1985	89,207,881	23,221,396	8,399,239	120,828,516
TOTAL	$1,331,034,203	$252,442,934	$66,206,469	$1,649,683,606

[1]Receipts from the 10% excise tax on pistols and revolvers was added to the P-R program by the amendment to the Act of 1970, (P.L. 91-503), Oct. 23, 1970.

[2]An 11% excise tax on certain archery equipment was imposed by Public Law 92-558, Oct. 25, 1972, adding the receipts to the P-R program. The Act of June 8, 1974, (P.L. 93-313), deferred the effective date of the tax on archery equipment until January 1, 1975. The receipts are for the period Jan. 1-June 30, 1975.

[3]Includes receipts during the Fiscal Year Transition Quarter, July 1-Sept. 30, 1976.

Pittman-Robertson Apportionments, 1939-1986

FISCAL YEAR	APPROPRIATION	ADMINISTRATIVE DEDUCTIONS	APPORTIONMENTS WILDLIFE	HUNTER EDUCATION	TOTAL
1939	$1,000,000	$110,000	$890,000	—	$890,000
1940	2,976,020	100,000	1,400,000	—	1,400,000
1941	3,707,844	200,000	2,300,000	—	2,300,000
1942	5,535,773	179,400	2,570,600	—	2,570,600
1943	5,072,588	100,000	1,150,000	—	1,150,000
1944	1,149,333	80,000	920,000	—	920,000
1945	1,061,045	82,500	817,500	—	817,500
1946	3,132,402	100,000	900,000	—	900,000
1947	5,232,465	200,000	2,300,000	—	2,300,000
1948	9,031,274	722,502	8,308,772	—	8,308,772
1949	11,276,687	451,067	10,825,620	—	10,825,620
1950	10,378,538	415,142	9,963,397	—	9,963,397
1951	9,351,614[1]	561,097	8,790,517	—	8,790,517
1952	17,846,424	535,393	17,311,031	—	17,311,031
1953	10,679,059	533,953	10,145,106	—	10,145,106
1954	12,147,554	242,651	11,904,903	—	11,904,903
1955	10,266,258	359,458	9,906,800	—	9,906,800
1956	12,400,508[2]	670,008	14,423,994	—	14,423,994
1957	14,302,000[2]	615,494	16,380,000	—	16,380,000
1958	15,149,179[2]	742,672	17,100,000	—	17,100,000
1959	14,617,361[2]	784,854	16,526,000	—	16,526,000
1960	13,908,699[2]	766,193	15,318,778	—	15,318,778
1961	15,589,708	857,708	14,239,298	—	14,239,298
1962	14,985,093	985,093	14,250,666	—	14,250,666
1963	14,911,717	979,717	13,676,573	—	13,676,573
1964	16,237,887	580,000	16,673,077	—	16,673,077
1965	17,454,941	719,941	16,735,000	—	16,735,000
1966	20,200,720	964,720	19,236,000	—	19,236,000
1967	24,343,804	810,804	23,533,000	—	23,533,000
1968	27,805,901	1,485,901	26,320,000	—	26,320,000
1969	31,371,605	1,051,605	30,320,000	—	30,320,000
1970	33,081,322	1,406,322	31,675,000	—	31,675,000
1971	32,805,725	2,005,725	30,800,000	—	30,800,000
1972	36,704,089	2,249,089	30,844,900	3,610,100	34,455,000
1973	43,333,533	2,288,533	37,263,500	3,781,500	41,045,000
1974	49,800,268	2,415,268	43,219,000	4,166,000	47,385,000
1975	56,854,672	3,384,672	48,920,000	4,550,000	53,470,000
1976	63,046,646	4,446,646	52,670,000	5,930,000	58,600,000
1977	89,687,154	5,287,154	73,900,000	10,500,000	84,400,000
1978	67,789,316	4,889,316	54,100,000	8,800,000	62,900,000
1979	86,018,633	3,818,633	71,024,000	11,176,000	82,200,000
1980	93,974,102	4,974,102	77,712,000	11,288,000	89,000,000
1981	90,714,651	7,250,651	69,194,000	14,200,000	83,394,000
1982	121,887,999	4,927,999	99,980,000	16,980,000	116,960,000
1983	111,454,029	4,394,029	88,240,000	18,820,000	107,060,000
1984	93,706,702	5,256,702	73,000,000	15,450,000	88,450,000
1985	85,872,254	6,772,254	64,910,000	14,190,000	79,100,000
1986	120,828,516	8,528,516	92,340,900	15,130,000	107,471,100
TOTAL	$1,650,683,612	$91,283,481	$1,394,929,931	$158,571,800	$1,553,501,731

[1]In fiscal year 1951 and thereafter the excise tax receipts were appropriated under permanent-indefinite appropriations as provided by the Department of the Interior Appropriations Act, Fiscal Year 1951, Sept. 6, 1950 (64 stat. 693).

[2]Includes $2,693,493.73 of the unappropriated excise tax receipts collected during fiscal years 1939-1946. This "backlog," totaling $13,467,468.61, was appropriated 20% in each of the five fiscal years 1956-1960, as authorized by the Act of August 12, 1955 (69 stat. 698).

Pittman-Robertson Funds Obligated for Selected Types of Projects, 1967-1985[1]

STATE	SURVEY AND INVESTIGATIONS	LAND ACQUISITION	DEVELOPMENT	COORDINATION[2]	HUNTER EDUCATION	PLANNING[3]	TECHNICAL GUIDANCE[4]
ALABAMA	3,239,500.00	1,488,968.00	13,918,783.00	1,672,707.00	742,833.00	0.00	0.00
ALASKA	51,314,523.00	168,750.00	603,768.00	12,942,665.00	1,133,187.00	613,358.00	0.00
ARIZONA	14,088,124.00	18,845.00	6,727,171.00	881,947.00	787,247.00	1,091,722.00	0.00
ARKANSAS	1,480,116.00	7,379,079.00	13,084,507.00	449,998.00	1,456,881.00	0.00	535,594.00
CALIFORNIA	13,092,095.00	351,819.00	30,302,428.00	963,613.00	2,413,963.00	972,139.00	0.00
COLORADO	17,151,417.73	1,079,941.39	8,383,033.64	733,732.14	2,329,898.22	596,846.87	187,223.00
CONNECTICUT	1,860,471.68	3,884,405.90	555,410.13	145,720.38	582,792.25	0.00	367,922.84
DELAWARE	941,661.76	679,989.10	3,772,739.87	412,969.12	302,292.23	0.00	108,716.38
FLORIDA	4,135,187.00	813,203.00	18,684,143.00	807,854.00	4,036,129.00	0.00	561,275.00
GEORGIA	3,471,915.00	1,788,229.00	20,756,740.00	1,207,944.00	1,355,707.00	0.00	575,014.00
HAWAII	1,575,763.00	0.00	2,184,026.00	412,592.00	224,766.00	0.00	153,654.00
IDAHO	9,162,230.00	843,756.00	8,106,173.00	174,100.00	1,042,039.00	95,011.00	0.00
ILLINOIS	6,466,494.12	1,032,660.73	16,984,852.68	372,525.94	983,110.01	120,177.15	0.00
INDIANA	1,884,689.23	5,127,779.94	14,941,225.18	272,450.15	786,985.34	0.00	0.00
IOWA	2,594,825.12	4,851,133.73	13,341,606.55	79,804.22	784,478.55	0.00	0.00
KANSAS	2,976,679.77	1,935,381.75	16,233,602.06	744,518.95	1,600,425.85	864,852.06	195,743.00
KENTUCKY	2,956,585.00	4,863,795.00	7,878,759.00	890,265.00	3,494,020.00	0.00	273,985.00
LOUISIANA	4,241,617.00	0.00	15,361,002.00	969,750.00	2,422,000.00	0.00	611,273.00
MAINE	4,723,535.84	300,494.78	4,822,694.83	834,361.70	1,067,271.31	1,735,114.14	321,503.10
MARYLAND	2,047,026.64	179,676.30	5,731,434.41	413,628.60	1,376,557.45	283,203.13	174,683.43
MASSACHUSETTS	2,437,441.36	1,061,150.79	2,629,596.00	236,169.23	1,174,326.03	117,631.25	99,558.71
MICHIGAN	7,723,153.50	8,819,134.94	20,633,873.43	(506.49)	3,507,108.05	0.00	0.00
MINNESOTA	417,220.36	14,877,517.49	14,516,361.06	522,788.31	1,235,009.86	0.00	0.00
MISSISSIPPI	2,469,867.00	3,856,896.00	14,916,297.00	709,397.00	2,235,450.00	0.00	565,622.00
MISSOURI	7,967,615.96	15,750,315.84	4,490,567.64	0.00	554,705.80	0.00	0.00
MONTANA	19,797,697.32	3,815,152.82	5,904,136.06	1,180,041.63	872,872.92	129,502.75	331,746.00
NEBRASKA	5,310,664.79	4,543,615.05	8,852,681.91	589,230.00	1,149,470.50	0.00	606,510.00
NEVADA	8,981,897.00	321,411.00	6,601,047.00	823,807.00	697,972.00	515,591.00	544,059.00
NEW HAMPSHIRE	1,970,948.33	1,066,673.75	1,169,242.85	488,039.71	1,050,946.11	0.00	99,308.72
NEW JERSEY	2,917,041.25	777,220.66	3,754,938.94	250,950.97	1,766,420.76	62,899.98	97,775.29
NEX MEXICO	12,481,386.00	3,366,194.00	5,132,832.00	901,140.00	1,235,908.00	348,537.00	0.00
NEW YORK	10,042,486.51	2,791,956.85	10,433,507.69	1,676,077.48	3,916,445.63	0.00	2,590,970.73

PR Funds Obligated for Selected Types of Projects, 1967-1985[1] (continued)

STATE	SURVEY AND INVESTIGATIONS	LAND ACQUISITION	DEVELOPMENT	COORDINATION[2]	HUNTER EDUCATION	PLANNING[3]	TECHNICAL GUIDANCE[4]
NORTH CAROLINA	3,395,998.00	1,128,170.00	17,231,187.00	1,197,588.00	1,554,665.00	0.00	1,139,131.00
NORTH DAKOTA	6,269,104.75	1,506,925.76	6,178,664.17	606,450.00	893,250.00	336,360.00	338,750.00
OHIO	3,666,236.48	5,299,261.12	14,690,174.44	321,232.95	2,431,540.61	0.00	0.00
OKLAHOMA	5,417,723.00	590,175.00	12,554,669.00	1,708,434.00	482,582.00	7,602.00	0.00
OREGON	4,442,298.00	1,724,513.00	17,603,489.00	1,141,962.00	702,927.00	308,539.00	350,880.00
PENNSYLVANIA	1,108,271.64	2,257,316.77	41,594,889.84	0.00	0.00	69,834.20	0.00
RHODE ISLAND	1,105,884.17	2,713,853.87	2,321,724.93	325,582.51	345,715.72	0.00	0.00
SOUTH CAROLINA	1,515,357.00	54,597.00	14,238,870.00	1,191,324.00	1,929,443.00	0.00	555,914.00
SOUTH DAKOTA	5,250,099.49	1,133,191.91	11,818,268.07	486,481.43	733,478.12	216,118.78	1,556,382.75
TENNESSEE	4,312,170.00	380,010.00	16,191,583.00	1,386,256.00	3,556,117.00	319,098.00	368,643.00
TEXAS	29,101,523.00	1,083,893.00	8,991,603.00	7,463,814.00	1,577,893.00	1,374,200.00	0.00
UTAH	11,262,573.03	6,815,530.70	4,017,893.53	494,578.00	1,279,464.99	0.00	0.00
VERMONT	2,460,270.74	1,180,444.58	1,675,319.66	351,602.75	898,962.02	0.00	160,977.27
VIRGINIA	3,548,906.15	6,248,174.75	9,746,668.70	923,508.06	1,821,372.98	0.00	0.00
WASHINGTON	3,526,979.00	878,443.00	14,252,448.00	1,976,201.00	2,014,378.00	287,900.00	846,593.00
WEST VIRGINIA	1,738,653.33	0.00	7,866,068.39	1,150,123.01	1,407,465.49	449,301.21	1,719,044.67
WISCONSIN	5,108,224.86	16,948,841.22	8,210,406.68	(417.58)	2,801,558.46	358,944.01	174,373.76
WYOMING	8,819,213.30	3,681,210.50	10,407,222.88	705,685.04	601,741.00 [5]	120,000.00	44,000.00
PUERTO RICO	2,523,696.00	0.00	1,707,791.00	595,613.00	[5]	114,676.00	263,726.00
GUAM	919,953.00	0.00	134,307.00	320,151.00	[5]	0.00	0.00
VIRGIN ISLANDS	1,638,639.00	0.00	4,000.00	71,993.00	[5]	0.00	11,400.00
AMERICAN SAMOA[6]	—	—					—
MARIANA ISLANDS	177,668.00	0.00	0.00	56,107.00		0.00	0.00
ALL STATES	339,231,318.21	151,459,698.99	542,846,429.22	55,234,550.21	73,351,747.26	11,509,158.53	16,531,952.65

[1] Detailed breakdown prior to 1967 not available.
[2] Covers project planning, administration and supervision by the States.
[3] Covers preparation and maintenance of comprehensive and modular conservation plans.
[4] Covers advice provided to improve, protect, or create environments or to manage fish and wildlife populations, areas, or habitats for increased production or for public utilization of fish and wildlife.
[5] Activity not approvable.
[6] Participation first authorized for 1985. No funds obligated until 1986.

Pittman-Robertson Funds Apportioned to States
for Fiscal Year 1986

	WILDLIFE RESTORATION	HUNTER EDUCATION*	TOTAL
ALABAMA	$1,527,125	$366,355	$1,893,480
ALASKA	4,617,045	151,302	4,768,347
ARIZONA	2,183,337	255,961	2,439,298
ARKANSAS	1,586,734	215,243	1,801,977
CALIFORNIA	3,685,721	453,906	4,139,627
COLORADO	2,353,549	272,063	2,625,612
CONNECTICUT	461,705	292,663	754,368
DELAWARE	461,705	151,302	613,007
FLORIDA	1,543,051	453,906	1,996,957
GEORGIA	1,862,302	453,906	2,316,208
HAWAII	461,705	151,302	613,007
IDAHO	1,877,516	151,302	2,028,818
ILLINOIS	1,721,109	453,906	2,175,015
INDIANA	1,395,809	453,906	1,849,715
IOWA	1,542,516	274,375	1,816,891
KANSAS	1,869,943	222,561	2,092,504
KENTUCKY	1,421,162	344,824	1,765,986
LOUISIANA	1,757,345	395,919	2,153,264
MAINE	1,077,677	151,302	1,228,979
MARYLAND	616,709	397,094	1,013,803
MASSACHUSETTS	461,705	453,906	915,611
MICHIGAN	3,323,700	453,906	3,777,606
MINNESOTA	2,482,390	383,975	2,866,365
MISSISSIPPI	1,489,701	237,387	1,727,088
MISSOURI	2,324,431	453,906	2,778,337
MONTANA	2,809,413	151,302	2,960,715
NEBRASKA	1,594,390	151,302	1,745,692
NEVADA	1,760,655	151,302	1,911,957
NEW HAMPSHIRE	461,705	151,302	613,007
NEW JERSEY	480,977	453,906	934,883
NEX MEXICO	2,139,231	151,302	2,290,533
NEW YORK	2,903,287	453,906	3,357,193
NORTH CAROLINA	1,668,107	453,906	2,122,013
NORTH DAKOTA	1,284,850	151,302	1,436,152
OHIO	1,860,758	453,906	2,314,664
OKLAHOMA	2,039,352	284,911	2,324,263
OREGON	2,377,856	247,937	2,625,793
PENNSYLVANIA	4,106,710	453,906	4,560,616
RHODE ISLAND	461,705	151,302	613,007
SOUTH CAROLINA	995,287	293,759	1,289,046
SOUTH DAKOTA	1,593,381	151,302	1,744,683
TENNESSEE	2,108,816	432,345	2,541,161
TEXAS	4,617,045	453,906	5,070,951
UTAH	1,863,724	151,302	2,015,026
VERMONT	503,010	151,302	654,312
VIRGINIA	1,831,907	453,906	2,285,813
WASHINGTON	1,824,120	388,968	2,213,088
WEST VIRGINIA	1,242,634	151,302	1,393,936
WISCONSIN	2,743,749	443,136	3,186,885
WYOMING	1,885,230	151,302	2,036,532
PUERTO RICO	461,705	—	461,705
GUAM	153,901	—	153,901
VIRGIN ISLANDS	153,901	—	153,901
AMERICAN SAMOA	153,901	—	153,901
MARIANA ISLANDS	153,901	—	153,901
TOTAL	$92,340,900	$15,130,200	$107,471,100

* State may use for either hunter education or wildlife restoration.

Index